OCR DESIGN & TECHNOLOGY FOR GCSE

ELECTRONICS & CONTROL SYSTEMS

TERRY BREAM

JOHN DRURY

EDITOR: BOB WHITE

HODDER
EDUCATION
AN HACHETTE UK COMPANY

Orders: please contact Bookpoint Ltd, 130 Milton Park, Abingdon, Oxon
OX14 4SB. Telephone: +44 (0)1235 8 27720. Fax: +44 (0)1235 400454.
Lines are open from 9.00am to 5.00pm, Monday to Saturday, with a
24-hour message-answering service. You can also order through our
website www.hoddereducation.co.uk

If you have any comments to make about this, or any of our other titles,
please send them to educationenquiries@hodder.co.uk

British Library Cataloguing in Publication Data
A catalogue record for this title is available from the British Library

ISBN: 978 0 340 98201 3

First Edition Published 2009
Impression number 10 9 8 7 6 5 4 3 2 1
Year   2012 2011 2010 2009

Copyright © 2009 Terry Bream and John Drury

Illustrations by Art Construction

Hachette UK's policy is to use papers that are natural, renewable and
recyclable products and made from wood grown in sustainable forests.
The logging and manufacturing processes are expected to conform to the
environmental regulations of the country of origin.

Cover photo from Don Farrall/Photodisc
Typeset by Fakenham Photosetting Ltd, Fakenham, Norfolk
Printed in Italy for Hodder Education, an Hachette UK Company,
338 Euston Road, London NW1 3BH

CONTENTS

HOW TO GET THE MOST OUT OF THIS BOOK

Welcome to OCR Design and Technology for GCSE Electronics & Control Systems (specification numbers J301 and J041).

The book has been designed to support you throughout your GCSE course. It provides clear and precise guidance for each of the four units that make up the full course qualification, along with detailed information about the subject content of the course. It will be an extremely effective resource in helping you prepare for both controlled assessment and examined units.

The book has been written and developed by a team of writers who all have considerable specialist knowledge of the subject area and are all very experienced teachers.

The book:
- *is student focused. The aim of the book is to help you achieve the best possible results from your study of GCSE Electronics & Control Systems*
- *gives clear guidance of exactly what is expected of you in both controlled assessment and examined units*
- *contains examiner tips and guidance to help improve your performance in both controlled assessment and examined units*
- *provides detailed information relating to the subject content and designing*
- *is designed to help you locate information quickly*
- *is focused on the OCR specification for GCSE Electronics & Control Systems*
- *has relevance and value to other GCSE Electronics & Control Systems courses.*

The book outlines the knowledge, skills and understanding required to be successful within GCSE Electronics & Control Systems. It is designed to give you a 'body of knowledge' which can be used to develop your own knowledge and understanding during the course and support you when undertaking both controlled assessment and examined units.

Chapters 1–9 form the 'body of knowledge'. Chapters 10–13 give specific guidance about each of the units that make up the GCSE course.

Unit A511 Introduction to Designing and Making

Chapter 10 gives detailed information about the structure of the controlled assessment unit and the rules relating to the controlled assessment task you will undertake. It clearly explains what you need to do section by section and includes examiner tips to help improve your performance. Specific reference is made to the assessment criteria and an explanation is provided as to how the criteria will be applied to your product. Examples of students' work are used within the text to reinforce the requirements of each section.

Unit A512 Sustainable Design

Chapter 11 provides detailed information relating to this unit. It gives a clear explanation of the structure of the examination and gives further information relating to the key aspects of sustainability in relation to GCSE Electronics & Control Systems. The chapter examines:

- The 6Rs in relation to Electronics & Control Systems
- The social and moral issues linked to the manufacture, use and disposal of products manufactured using Electronics & Control Systems
- The impact of cultural issues on the design of new products
- How to select materials that are both suitable and sustainable
- Current issues affecting the design of new products.

Unit A513 Making Quality Products

Chapter 12 follows a similar format to Chapter 10. It explains the requirements of the unit section by section and includes examiner tips to guide you through the controlled assessment task.

Unit A514 Technical Aspects of Designing and Making

Chapter 13 is designed to help you prepare for the written examination. It clearly describes the format of the examination paper and gives examples of questions. Examiner tips are given to help you identify the type of question and the approach you should take in completing your answer.

Icons used in this book

Introduction boxes provide a short overview of the topics under discussion in the section.

KEY POINTS

- Key Points boxes list key aspects of a topic.

KEY TERMS

Key Terms boxes provide definitions of the technical terms used in the section.

EXAMINER'S TIPS

Examiner's Tips boxes give tips on how to improve performance in both the controlled assessment and examined units.

LEARNING OUTCOMES

Learning Outcomes boxes highlight the knowledge and understanding you should have developed by the end of the section.

ACTIVITY

Activity boxes suggest interesting tasks to support, enhance and extend learning opportunities.

CASE STUDY

Case study boxes provide examples of how real-life businesses use the knowledge and skills discussed.

QUESTIONS

Questions boxes provide practice questions to test key areas of the content of the specification.

All examples of student work included in this book are available in larger format on the OCR Design & Technology for GCSE: Electronics & Control Systems Teacher's Resource DVD-ROM (ISBN 978 0 340 91190).

ACKNOWLEDGEMENTS

The authors would like to thank the following:

Sam Richardson, The West Somerset Community College; Joseph Bryant, The West Somerset Community College; Dale Christian, Eastbourne College; Jack Marshall; Ross Culbertson, Radley College; Luke Ingram, The Chase, Malvern; Shajeen Shailendra, Haberdashers' Aske's Boys' School; Philip Plumbley, De La Salle, St Helens; Jackson Dimiglio-Wood, The West Somerset Community College; Rowan Snell, The West Somerset Community College; Ace Gearboxes, Northampton (machine photos); Campion School, Northampton (machine photos and projects); Caroline Chisholm School, Northampton (machine photos and projects); Harting Integrated Solutions Ltd (Surface mount technology); Matthew Clarke Northants County Council (Solar and wind powered signs); Revolution Education (PIC equipment); Susan Bream (proofreading and help with photography).

The authors and publishers would like to thank the following for use of photographs and illustrations in this volume:

Figure 1.2a © Steven Allan/ iStockphoto.com; Figure 1.2b © Stockbyte/Getty Images; Figure 1.2c © Imagestate Media; Figure 1.2d © Valerie Loiseleux/ iStockphoto.com; Figure 1.6 with kind permission by Roy Beardmore; Figure 1.15 fischertechnik; Figure 1.19 © Revolution Education Ltd (www.picaxe.co.uk); Figure 1.20 reproduced with kind permission by Crocodile Clips; Figure 1.21 reproduced with kind permission by New Wave Concepts; Figure 1.22 reproduced with kind permission by New Wave Concepts; Figure 1.23 © Andrey Prokhorov/iStockphoto.com; Figure 1.24 Emmanuel LATTES/Alamy; Figure 2.2 © Dominique Sarraute/The Image Bank/Getty Images; Figure 2.3 © Amanda Smith/ iStockphoto.com; Figure 2.7 reproduced with kind permission by Peratech Ltd; Figure 2.9 reproduced with kind permission by TEP; Figure 2.10 © sergey shlyaev/iStockphoto.com; Figure 2.11 reproduced with kind permission by Cornerstone Research Group, Inc; Figure 2.12 reproduced with kind permission by Teaching Resources Ltd, Middlesex University; Figure 2.13 George Disario/courtesy of Konarka Technologies; Figure 2.14 © Stockbyte/Getty Images; Figure 2.16 reproduced with kind permission by Rapid Electronics; Figure 2.17 reproduced with kind permission by Rapid Electronics; Figure 2.18 PAUL RAPSON / SCIENCE PHOTO LIBRARY; Figure 2.19 © 1996 FSC A.C; Figure 2.20 ra photography/ iStockphoto.com; Figure 2.22 Rapid Ltd; Figure 2.23 Rapid Ltd; Figure 2.24 Rapid Ltd; Figure 2.25 Rapid Ltd; Figure 2.27 ©Revolution Education Ltd (www.picaxe.co.uk); Figure 2.28 Low Power Radio Solutions Ltd.; Figure 4.49 © Dan Driedger/ iStockphoto.com; Figure 9.1 reproduced with kind permission by BSI; Figure 9.4 © Paul Mckeown/ iStockphoto.com; Figure 9.5 reproduced with kind permission by WD-40; Figure 11.1 © Andrey Prokhorov/ iStockphoto.com; Figure 11.3 © Achim Prill/ iStockphoto.com; Figure 11.4 © Marcus Clackson/ iStockphoto.com; Figure 11.5 © Olivier Blondeau/ iStockphoto.com; Figure 11.6 © Gary Unwin - Fotolia.com; Figure 11.7 Image from The OLPC wiki (http://wiki.laptop.org/go/Image:Khairat_School_-_XOctoPlug.JPG/) Released under Creative Commons Attribution 2.5 license; Figure 11.8 © Dawn Hudson - Fotolia.com; Figure 11.9 Fairtrade Foundation; Figure 11.10 © Andrey Prokhorov/iStockphoto.com; Figure 11.12 reproduced with kind permission by European Ecolabel

Text on pages 223 and 224 on Control of Substances Harzardous to Health Regulations 2002 reproduced under the terms of the Click-Use Licence.

Every effort has been made to trace and acknowledge copyright. The publishers will be glad to make suitable arrangements with any copyright holders whom it has not been possible to contact.

CHAPTER 1

DESIGNING AND PRODUCTION PLANNING

1.1 IDENTIFICATION OF A DESIGN NEED

LEARNING OUTCOMES

By the end of this section you should have developed a knowledge and understanding of:

- contexts and user groups
- design briefs.

You will have to produce work for two controlled assessment units as part of this GCSE qualification. Both of these projects will be based around themes that will be provided by OCR, the examination board. You will need to explore these themes in order to identify both a design problem that needs to be solved and the target users for the product. Additionally, as part of your course, you will undertake other design projects which will develop your knowledge and understanding of design.

The context

The context is a description of a situation in which a design problem may exist. An example of a context could be:

A rise in cycle theft and vandalism has been noticed at a local rail station.

In order to identify a potential user group and design brief, it is necessary to explore the context further. The most common starting point for developing a context is to use a **mind map** (thought shower). Using a mind

map will allow you to explore many different elements of a context and will identify connections and threads which will lead to a specific problem area.

For the controlled assessment units, you will need to consider the themes provided by the examination board. A mind map can be used to identify a design problem or, in the case of unit A511, a product for analysis and development.

A sample mind map is shown in Fig. 1.1. This is based on security.

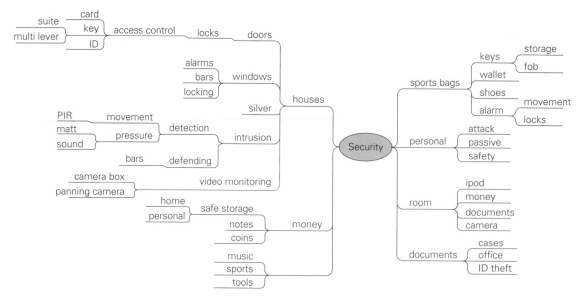

Figure 1.1 A mind map of security

A number of possible project problems are suggested from this diagram: electronic locks, window alarms, intrusion alarms, control of security cameras, safe storage of money, sports equipment, sports bags, personal safety alarms, room security or document security.

More threads can be expanded upon, as your interests and enquiry develop; only when you have made three or four branches can you get to a specific problem area.

The target user group

Who will actually use the products? What image do you have of these customers? Is it a group you know or do you have to carry out some research into this group of people?

The use of pictures, images and text is a good way to establish who your target users will be and what they would expect from your product. By using images of people, products and lifestyles, you can quickly focus

on the design possibilities and have a clearer image of the customer

The design brief

This is a short clear statement of what you intend to design and make. The brief may contain details of the context and user group you have identified. It is important that the design brief is worded in such a way that you do not make assumptions about what the product will look like or any other details about the product you might eventually make. From the sports lifestyle mood board, it is possible to identify customers who use training gyms, locker rooms, sports bags and associated equipment. A possible design brief from these images would be:

Design brief
There is a problem with personal equipment used in gyms and fitness studios. In a gym, where a number of activities are taking place, bags are left

Figure 1.2 Mood board for sports lifestyle

unattended while people are taking part. There is a need for extra security for sports bags as these often contain personal valuables and equipment.

When writing a design brief, it is important to include the problem or situation first, illustrating the design need. You can then go on to talk about the target users and the area where you want to try to produce a solution.

KEY TERM

DESIGN BRIEF – short clear statement of what you intend to design and make

ACTIVITY

1. On a theme of sport, complete a mind map with branches finishing with possible projects. Share the results with other people to see if they could suggest more branches or alternative problem areas or projects.

2. Put together a mood board creating an image set for:

   • outdoor activities for young adults

   • leisure time for mature adults

   • playgroup activities for nursery children.

3. Share the mood boards with your class, describing the images and style you were trying to show. Use the feedback to improve your display.

4. Write a detailed design brief based upon each of the mood boards. Create a class display to see the range of design briefs.

1.2 ANALYSING A DESIGN BRIEF

LEARNING OUTCOME

By the end of this section you should have developed a knowledge and understanding of:

• analysing a design brief.

A design brief is a short, clear statement of what you intend to design and make. It may contain information about the target users and the context for the design problem.

You will have to analyse the design brief in order to identify areas of further research that will be necessary to ensure the final design is successful.

The 6Ws

Analysing your design brief involves asking questions to find out exactly what you should design and make. A good way of doing this is by asking Who, What, Where, When, Why, and How questions about your proposed product.

Who	Who are your range of users?
What	What has the product got to do? What other similar products exist?
Where	Where will it be used?

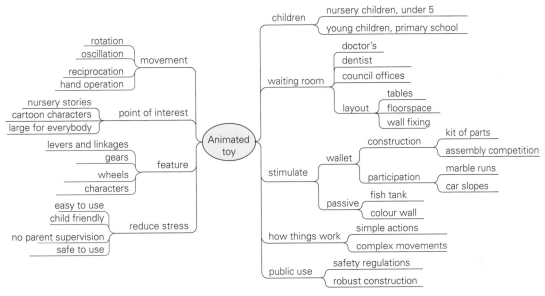

Figure 1.3 Mind map for animated toy

When   When will it be used?
Why   Why is it needed?
How   How will it be made? How much will it cost? How many are needed?

Using the 6Ws will help you to plan your future research activity.

 Mind mapping

An alternative approach to design brief analysis would be to use mind mapping. Mind mapping can be used to identify areas that will need to be researched prior to writing a design specification.

From this diagram, it is possible for you to analyse the design brief and see areas where you need to collect information.

Areas where further information/research is needed:

- children – age range of users, sizes of reach, grip, manipulation skills

- waiting rooms – size, available space, noise, other patients
- types of stimulus for children including points of interest and features
- client need – what do people who use waiting rooms want?
- customer needs – what do children/parents want?
- types of mechanisms – what mechanisms would be suitable/safe?

Each of these areas could be researched to gather information which would then be used in a detailed specification. It is important at this stage to collect information from a variety of sources.

EXAMINER'S TIP

Always analyse your design brief fully as it will help you to identify the most useful information you need in order to develop your design ideas.

KEY TERM

ANALYSE – examine critically so as to identify the most important aspects of the design brief

ACTIVITY

1. Design brief – Design and make a toy to help young children develop hand–eye coordination. The toy should involve lights and switches. Analyse the brief. In what areas will you need to carry out further research?

2. Animated toys are often aimed at adults for use on a work desk. Create a mind map specific to this age group. How would the areas that you need to research be different if the toy was aimed at children?

1.3 EXISTING PRODUCT ANALYSIS

LEARNING OUTCOMES

By the end of this section you should have developed a knowledge and understanding of:

- how to analyse an existing product
- the difference between primary and secondary product analysis
- how to identify trends in existing products
- how to use the information you find in your design work.

Analysing existing products is an important way of gaining an understanding of the features and functions of products that are already available. It allows you to identify possible improvements to existing designs and will help you to identify your target user requirements.

Analysing existing products

You will probably need to carry out a detailed product analysis of two products in order to gain sufficient information to fully aid your future design activity. It is essential that, when you undertake existing product analysis, you aim to gain as much information as possible. It is recommended that you do the following when carrying out product analysis:

- Photograph the product before and during the analysis exercise. Draw the product if you do not have access to photography.
- Consider the good and bad features of the product.
- Disassemble the products – to see how they are formed, made, joined.
- Identify all the materials and production methods used.
- Identify the assembly methods used.
- Ask users for their opinions of the product.
- Identify how the product satisfies the users' needs.
- Identify any special features that would appeal to the user group, e.g. ergonomic handle.
- Identify any laws or regulations that apply to the product.

Primary product analysis

This method involves the physical handling and disassembly of the product. It allows you to gain detailed information about materials, construction methods, function, operation, ergonomic features, etc. It is the method which will allow you to gain most information about the product.

Secondary product analysis

This method of product analysis relies on working from image. Images are often downloaded from the Internet or taken from magazines. This method can be limited, as you have to interpret the information from the picture. This very often results in a low level of attainment as you can do little more than describe what you see.

You will need to present the information you have gained, using a clear and concise method. It is recommended that you provide a summary of your key findings. These can then be used to aid the writing of your design specification.

Methods for existing product analysis

Whether you are undertaking primary or secondary product analysis you will need to gain detailed information about the products you are examining.

Using the 6Ws approach will help you to gain valuable information about the product. Some example questions are given below:

- What is the product's function?
- What is the product made from?
- Why is it made from these materials?
- What construction methods have been used?
- What are the likely quantities of production?
- Where was it made?
- Who is the target user?
- How much does it cost?
- What is the environmental impact of the product?
- How has the designer considered aesthetics and ergonomics?

You will need to create your own list of questions based upon the 6Ws to ensure that you fully analyse your selected existing products.

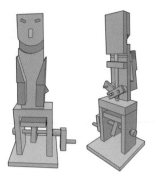

Figure 1.4 Happy clapper animation toy

ACTIVITY

1. Use the **6Ws** to examine the happy clapper animation toy shown in Figure 1.4.

▶ Identification of complex associations linking principles of good design and technological knowledge

It is important that designers have a good understanding of the interrelationship of the use of materials and components, the manufacturing process, new and emerging technologies, the user and the environmental implications of products. The relationships between these different aspects are complex and will depend upon many factors. The success of a product will be dependant upon the designer achieving the correct balance between all of these factors. It is important that as a designer you consider each of these factors in your own work and also when you are examining the work of others. If you are designing a product for use in a developing economy such as a water pump, would the aesthetics or ease of maintenance be the most important factor? Would using the latest materials and production methods be important?

When carrying out existing product analysis you can consider the 'principles of good design and technological knowledge'.

ACTIVITY

1. Look around your home at products. Make a list of those you consider well designed; also list those products which do not really fulfil their required purpose.

2. On the list, suggest tests which should have been carried out before the less successful products were sold.

KEY POINT

- Secondary product analysis can be of limited value. Always try to undertake primary existing product research.

KEY TERMS

ANALYSE – to examine critically in order to identify the most important aspects of the existing product
DISASSEMBLE – to take the existing product apart in a controlled way
PRODUCTION METHODS – the way in which the product is made
ASSEMBLY METHODS – the way in which the product is put together
PRIMARY RESEARCH – research carried out using the actual product which can be handled/disassembled
SECONDARY RESEARCH – research carried out using images of products

1.4 RESEARCH, DATA AND ANALYSIS

By the end of this section you should have developed a knowledge and understanding of:

- how to carry out different types of research
- how to present the data you have gathered
- how to analyse the data.

When beginning to design a product, you need information in order to make decisions and propose different design options. The information gained through existing product research will be invaluable to you as you start designing. However, further information must be found if your design is to be successful.

Research

You will need to find additional information to ensure that your product meets your users' needs and functions as intended. This may involve you in conducting user interviews or questionnaires, researching size data for the position or mounting of your design or researching size data relating to your user (ergonomics). As with existing product analysis, it is possible to carry out research activities using both primary and secondary research methods. From your research you will obtain two types of information:

- objective information – information based on fact
- subjective information – information based on opinion rather than fact.

Visits and interviews

You may be able to arrange to visit an 'expert' linked to the area you are designing. This would allow you to interview them and gain valuable information to aid your designing. You will need to accurately record any useful information they give you.

Surveys and questionnaires

These are an effective way of gathering information from a lot of users or potential users. You must, however, ensure that you plan the questions you will ask carefully. Many students ask questions which are of limited value to their design work. It is a good idea to test your questionnaire carefully to ensure that your target users can understand the questions.

EXAMINER'S TIP

Using primary sources of information such as interviews and visits may be more time-efficient than carrying out questionnaires or surveys. You must choose the method which will give you the best information to aid designing but balance this with the time constraints of the project that you are undertaking.

Environment

It is important to consider the environment where the product will be used. A product design for domestic use may have totally different aesthetic qualities when compared to a product that is to be used in an industrial plant. The environment may present particular issues that will affect the design of your product. Exposure to high humidity, dust, mud, water, low temperature and so on will affect the design of your product. If your product is designed for use in the 'domestic market', you will need to consider the aesthetic qualities of the area where it will be used and also the aesthetic qualities of similar products.

ACTIVITY

1. **A product is to be used in a greenhouse. What conditions would you need to consider during the design of the product?**

Figure 1.5 Greenhouse environment

Secondary research

This type of research involves you in looking at the work of other people. You can collect information for secondary research from such sources as:

- books and magazines
- the Internet
- CD-ROMs.

You will need to be selective about the research information you include and use in your folio. You should only include information that has a clear relevance to your design project.

All secondary information gathered from the work of other people must have clear references to credit the source. It is important to show your analysis or modification of the information gained.

If your research has identified a particular set of components or sub-assemblies you must credit the original data and include details of the components or sub-assemblies in your research on facts and sizes.

Ergonomics and anthropometrics

People are important in all designs. Designers need to make sure that the product 'fits' the target user group. **Ergonomics** is concerned with designing according to human need, in order to optimise the relationship between the product and the person using the product. The best designs are 'inclusive', allowing use by all people.

Anthropometrics refers to the measurement of humans, for the purpose of understanding physical variation between different people. Anthropometric data is widely used by designers to optimise product designs to ensure they 'fit' with their intended users.

It is important that you gather data that relates to your target group of users. You will need to look at the information available for sizes of people, especially hands, fingers and reach. These will be key pieces of information for interaction between people and your product.

You will need to search data tables to find the information you need. Fig. 1.7 shows the sizes of a hand. The percentiles data shows the range of sizes for the population. The usual figures used are 5th as the smallest and 95th as the largest and this range covers most of the population.

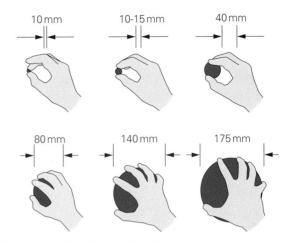

Figure 1.6 Hand and grip sizes

45	**Hand breadth**. The breadth of the hand, measured across the ends of the metacarpal bones (metacarpal-phalangeal joints).						
					Percentiles		
	Sample		1st	5th	50th	95th	99th
A	Men	cm	8.1	8.4	9.0	9.8	10.0
		(in)	(3.2)	(3.3)	(3.5)	(3.9)	(3.9)
B	Women	cm	7.1	7.3	7.9	8.6	8.9
		(in)	(2.8)	(2.9)	(3.1)	(3.4)	(3.5)

46	**Hand length**. The distance from the base of the hand at the wrist crease to the tip of the middle finger.						
					Percentiles		
	Sample		1st	5th	50th	95th	99th
A	Men	cm	17.3	17.9	19.3	21.1	21.9
		(in)	(6.8)	(7.1)	(7.6)	(8.3)	(8.6)
B	Women	cm	15.9	16.5	18.0	19.7	20.5
		(in)	(6.3)	(6.5)	(7.1)	(7.8)	(8.1)

47	**Hand circumference**. The circumference of the hand, measured around the knuckles (metacarpal-phalangeal joints).						
					Percentiles		
	Sample		1st	5th	50th	95th	99th
A	Men	cm	19.2	19.9	21.3	23.0	23.7
		(in)	(7.6)	(7.8)	(8.4)	(9.1)	(9.3)
B	Women	cm	16.7	17.3	18.6	20.0	20.7
		(in)	(6.6)	(6.8)	(7.3)	(7.9)	(8.2)

Figure 1.7 Static human physical characteristics – hands

KEY TERMS

AESTHETICS – the look of the product, its shape, form

ERGONOMICS – how the product relates/interacts with the human form – holding, carrying, etc.

ANTHROPOMETRICS – the measurement of humans to understand the physical variation between different people

Presenting data

The research activities that you will undertake will result in the collection of large amounts of data. The data will need to be presented in a way that makes it easy to understand and use whilst you are designing. Written data can be summarised into a series of bullet points. Numerical data such as the results of questionnaires can be presented visually. You can do this using:

- tables
- line graphs
- bar charts
- pie charts.

Tables

If you are using questionnaires as a method of gathering information, you will need to quickly bring together all the information you have found. Tables are a very good way of summarising the result of each question.

Line graphs

Line graphs usually have a horizontal and vertical axis. They are good at displaying trends in data. They are often used to present statistical information such as sales figures, stock market performance or crime data.

Bar charts

Bar charts usually have a horizontal and vertical axis. Information is shown as a series of bars of the same width with a gap in between each bar. The bars can be drawn either horizontally or vertically.

Pie charts

A pie chart is a diagram where the whole is represented as a circle. The circle is then divided into sectors to show the data as a proportion or percentage of the whole.

Analysing data

This is probably the most important aspect of the research you will undertake. Without quality analysis, your research activity may be of limited value. Analysing the results of your research carefully will allow you to identify the key information that will need to be considered during your design work in order for your design to be successful. This can be done using 'bullet point' statements that explain what have you found out, how the information is useful to you and how it will influence your design.

EXAMINER'S TIP

Present the results of your research clearly. Add a page at the end of your research section where you bring together all the results of your research activity. This should be called 'summary of research results'. Use bullet points to identify the key information from the research you have carried out. These bullet points can be used to guide the writing of your design specification.

1.5 DEVELOPING A DESIGN SPECIFICATION

By the end of this section you should have developed a knowledge and understanding of:

- what a design specification is
- how to develop a design specification
- how to present your design specification.

The specification is one of the key aspects of your design folio. It will provide guidance for your design activity and will be used to measure the success of your final prototype or product.

The design specification

A design specification is a list of specific points or conditions that your design should meet. It should be based around the information you have gained from carrying out research with your user group and from other areas such as existing product analysis and ergonomic data.

Presenting the specification

The specification is easier to use and follow if it is presented as a series of bullet points rather than in a paragraph format. You should use ICT to present your specification as this will save time later when you need to evaluate your designs and product against it. You will be able to simply reprint it rather than rewrite each point again.

The specification must be ordered, grouping together common areas such as function, customer, styling, manufacturing, environmental issues, life expectancy, etc.

The questions in the table below will help you formulate the specification.

SPECIFICATION TABLE		
Item	Area	Detail
1	Function	What the product is intended to do
2	Performance	Will it be used regularly or occasionally? Does the use exert a loading on the system?
3	Target Group	Who are the primary group it is aimed at?
4	Environment	Where will it be used? Does this mean the project will have to be built to fit the environment?
5	Limitations	Are there size and weight limits? Functional limits?
6	Appearance	What form could the outside case or structure be? What will be most suitable for the target group? What colour, shape, textures?
7	Ergonomics	Is there a specific size and shape it must be to fit the target group? Are there operational requirements dictated by the hand-eye coordination requirements?

SPECIFICATION TABLE		
Item	Area	Detail
8	Materials	Does the function decide on the range to use? Which is the most suitable and why? What materials properties are you looking for?
9	Manufacture	What are the range of tools and processes available to use? How will the product be made? Can you use machine tools, CNC machinery?
10	Durability and Reliability	Will the product be used in a way that could cause early failure? Do the materials chosen need to resist any specific environmental condition? How can you ensure the product will work each time it is used?
11	Health and Safety	Could there be risks during the manufacture of the product? Are there risks for the user of the product? Does the product pose a hygiene risk and can it be kept clean in use? Are there regulations the product must meet for safe use?
12	Sustainability Issues	Does the design consider the 6Rs? Is there an energy cost in normal use?
13	Instructions	Will the customer require information on how to use the product?
14	Maintenance	How will the product be kept in working order? Are there parts that will need renewing to maintain the best performance of the product? How easy will it be to replace parts?
15	Costs	Is there a budget for the construction process? What is the target price for the buyer? Is there an ongoing cost to use the product?
16	Life Cycle	How long do you expect the product to last? What are the critical functions?

Table 1.1 Specification table

KEY POINT

- Your specification is a checklist that will be referred to throughout the design project. Your specification needs to be clear and concise. You should include all of the criteria that are relevant to your proposed product.

ACTIVITY

1. **Use the specification table in Table 1.1 to write a specification for your mobile phone or MP3 music player.**

KEY TERM

SPECIFICATION – list of features that your intended product should have – each is a performance target that your product should meet and will be evaluated against

EXAMINER'S TIPS

- Remember that the **specific**ation needs to be **specific** to your product.
- Write your specification as a series of bullet points.
- Aim to produce a clear concise specification, one that accurately states what it is that you are designing.
- Ask someone to read your specification. Do they understand what you are designing based upon the information they have read?
- Avoid vague statements that could apply to almost any product.
- Use ICT to produce your specification. It can then be easily reproduced as required throughout the design process.

1.6 GENERATING IDEAS AND COMMUNICATING DESIGN

LEARNING OUTCOMES

By the end of this section you should have developed a knowledge and understanding of:

- how to present your design ideas
- the use of annotation to communicate your design
- modelling techniques to develop your design
- the use of ICT/CAD/CAM in design development
- testing and evaluating ideas
- presentation of the final design proposal.

You should be very creative in your thinking about possible product designs. Use your research and the design specification to inform your design ideas. Original ideas will develop from your creative thinking about existing products and how they can be developed further.

Recording and drawing techniques

You need to develop freehand drawing techniques to quickly record your thoughts. This means that you should not use drawing instruments. Your initial thoughts should be quick and free flowing. Using drawing instruments will slow down this process. Use of colour helps to improve the understanding of quick sketches. Add notes to the design sketches rather than labels. Remember you will not meet the examiner. You need to tell them the reasons for decisions by communicating with them through your annotation of ideas.

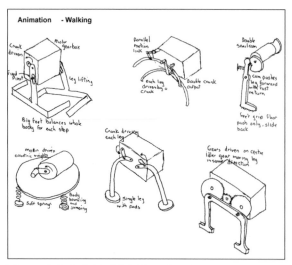

Figure 1.8 Quick initial idea sketches

Initial design techniques

You will need to use the systems approach to list the possibilities for your design. You will need to split your system into three parts: **input, process** and **output**.

You are not expected to design original circuits, mechanisms or pneumatics circuits. The systems analysis could be presented as a table, circuit diagrams or pictures of sub-systems.

An alternative approach would be to expand your 'starting thoughts' sheet.

You should add detail to your initial thoughts to give more information about how the idea would fit the design need and specification.

The sketches you make can be a record of your thinking. Each sketch could be a separate idea, detailing both the system and the casing or structure. Equally, you may want to develop an idea from your 'starting thoughts', making improvements until you are happy with the design. Both of these approaches may involve some trial modelling and use of CAD.

Project : Timing of events		
INPUT	**PROCESS**	**OUTPUT**
Push switch	555 timer chip as monostable	buzzer
Touch sensitive switch	Logic gates	lights
Movement switch	VR1 35K, R3 1K, IC1 NE555 (7 4 8 / 6 3 / 2 1 5), R2 47K, C1 220µF, R4 220, D1	Sounds – single, warbling, siren
Light gate		LED display
Movement sensor		LCD count

Table 1.2 Systems diagram

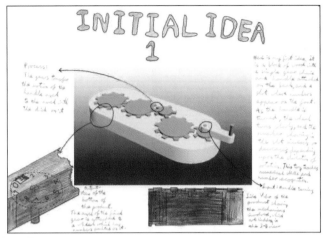

Figure 1.9 Initial thoughts sheet

As you develop and finalise your ideas, you will need to check these against the requirements of the specification. You will need to consider the materials and production processes available to you, as these will impact upon the final shape and form of your product.

The whole function of your design will need to be examined. Sub-systems will need to be assembled together to ensure signal matching and correct operation.

Working drawings

On a working drawing, you could show the whole design assembly or an isometric exploded diagram to show how it is put together. You will need to show dimensions of each part for manufacture.

Presentation drawings

Once you have developed your design, it is necessary to display the prototype for other people to see. This style of drawing is often used to show a client before production can start. It allows you to finally put together all the elements to see if the project will work as you first imagined. Presentation drawings are usually three-dimensional (3D) coloured representations of exactly what the final product will look like.

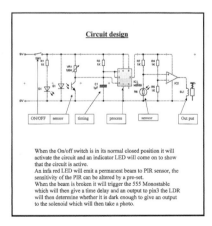

Figure 1.10 Design idea with functional detail

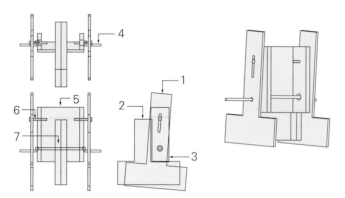

Figure 1.11 Detailed drawing of parts

Walker Assembly		
Part No.	Name	Number required
1	Outer leg	2
2	Middle Leg (glue together)	2
3	Side	2
4	Crank arm	2
5	Back	1
6	25mm M3 engineering screws	2
7	Gearbox (not shown)	1

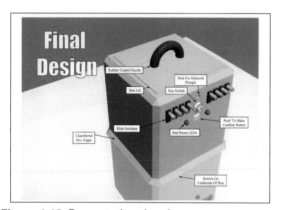

Figure 1.12 Presentation drawing

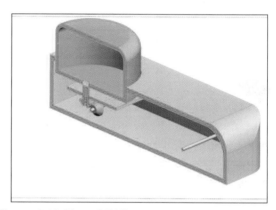

Figure 1.13 Use of CAD

Use of ICT/CAD/CAM to support design development

In your control systems course, ICT can be used freely to help develop good quality design work and practical products.

Planning the printed circuit board (PCB) is a most important development process. Most programs allow you to move components to better fit the size of copper-clad board you can use. The components will have connections which will move at the same time. The number of jump leads (zero ohm links) will be kept to a minimum. When you have arranged the components, you can look at the real view of the PCB with all the parts shown on the top of the board. You need to examine how close the components are, to ensure that you can construct the board and that no section will get too hot in use. The top view will give you the layout and can be printed to show where parts are fitted. The copper side shows you the copper tracking to be etched or cut in the copper clad board.

ACTIVITY

1. Use a CAD modelling method to show a final idea for a casing for a games timer.

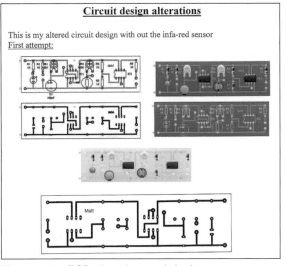

Figure 1.14 PCB planning and design

EXAMINER'S TIPS

- Present a wide range of ideas using a variety of presentation techniques from freehand sketches and CAD.
- Use quick simple sketches to show your initial ideas.
- Explain your ideas clearly using annotation.
- Use colour and rendering to enhance design communication.
- Explain to the examiner how you are developing your product – use sketches and notes to show any changes and modifications.
- Produce a 3D presentation drawing of your product – use colour and rendering to enhance your drawing.
- Produce a dimensioned working drawing of all the parts of your product.

1.7 MAKING REASONED DECISIONS ABOUT MATERIALS AND COMPONENTS

LEARNING OUTCOME

By the end of this section you should have developed a knowledge and understanding of:

- How to select appropriate materials and components for your product.

During the design development and modelling process, you will need to decide on the types of materials that you will use to make your product. You must look realistically at what your product needs and what users would expect. The choice of materials and components should be based upon the qualities and characteristics of the materials available with the best available material or component being selected.

Material selection

When selecting the materials and components for each part of your design, you need to be clear about function of the component/product and service conditions.

The manufacturing equipment in your workshop will allow differing materials and processes to be used. There would be no point in selecting a material or manufacturing process that you cannot use because of a lack of equipment.

You need to show you have considered different material options, made choices and explained the reasons for the selection of your chosen materials. The selection of materials may involve you in testing materials, trial constructions and looking at catalogues to check sizes of components.

Components and sub-assemblies can be selected using information from the internet and catalogues. For electronic parts, voltage and power ratings need to be considered. Quite often, size can be the deciding factor. Can you fit the part in the space or would the larger size make the whole casing too big?

Material	My use – alarm	construction	durability	finish
aluminium	casing	folding, pop rivet, self tapping screws	able to take knocks, surface scratches	self finish, paint
ABS	casing	vacuum forming	shock resistant	self finish
plywood	casing	lap joints, PVA glue, panel pins, screws	able to take knocks, surface damage	needs waterproofing, paint, varnish

Table 1.3 Materials selection

ACTIVITY

1. A hanging toy to stimulate young children lying in a cot, pram or buggy is required. Produce an 'initial thoughts' sheet for the product. The product should move continuously with a battery driven motor.

2. Children enjoy playing games and having competitions. A timer is needed to tell children when it is the end of their turn. Produce a systems diagram for a timing product.

1.8 MODELLING AND TRIALLING TECHNIQUES

By the end of this section you should have developed a knowledge and understanding of:

- the purpose of modelling of designs
- modelling techniques.

Before a final prototype is built, designers often make a model to check working parts, construction processes or the visual impact of the product. Model makers create these trial products to test function or the reaction of consumers. Modelling allows designs to be tested prior to production.

Even at this stage CAD/CAM can be used to practice construction methods and check whether it is appropriate.

Systems kits and simulation software

There are a large number of systems kits and simulation software programs available to help you model and develop your ideas. Specialist kits are available for the areas of mechanisms, electronics and pneumatics.

Use of modelling materials

Basic materials such as card, foam, foam board, corriflute or polystyrene sheet can be used to create models. Quite often you will need to make changes and improvements to a model, so a temporary method of fixing materials such as a paper fastener is ideal.

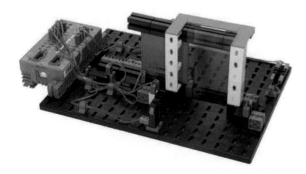

Figure 1.15 Fischertechnik construction kit system – sliding door control

Figure 1.16 Foam board model

To make stronger models that will resist some use in testing, it is possible to use quick assembly methods. Aluminium can be pop riveted, thin plywood (aero ply) and thin MDF can be joined with a hot glue gun. Nuts and bolts can also be used for fixing components.

Breadboard, CAD simulation, systems approach

When looking at the function of the design using components, it is necessary to carry out real modelling. The trial methods you use need to have correct functioning components so you can check the system is operating correctly.

Breadboards will allow you to work with real components and construct the circuit with wire links. A number of breadboards can be clipped together for larger circuits. Complex circuits can be difficult to fault find when there are a large number of wire links. To fault find successfully when using breadboard you have to work in a methodical manner. Breadboards are useful for developing sub-systems and matching together.

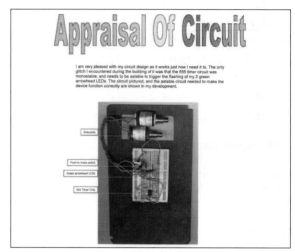

Figure 1.17 Annotated breadboard modelling

Some students like to solder components into copper strip boards which are especially good at ensuring all the joints are sound. Parts of the system can be made and tested before joining into a full system.

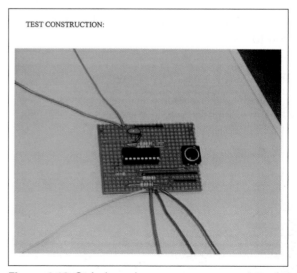

Figure 1.18 Strip board

The use of simulation programs allows you to use sets of components that you may not have immediately available. If the selected component combination does not work, others can be selected. This is true for digital electronics where you can follow a number of different approaches to get the same product result. PIC chips can now be simulated and simple instructions written for the PICs to operate. Using simulations helps prevent damage to actual components.

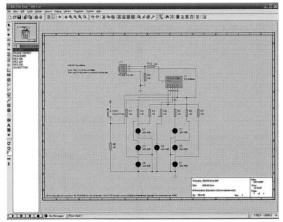

Figure 1.19 Virtual simulation of circuit function (PICAXE VSM screenshot – www.picaxevsm.com)

Other digital electronic simulations will allow you to see the operation of components such as a decade counter. It is part of an integrated program that allows you to go directly to the PCB layout for the circuit.

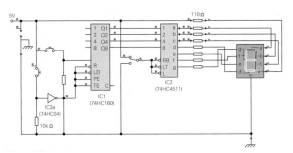

Figure 1.20 Yenka circuit simulation

In this egg timer, modelling shows the voltage levels on each link during the simulated operation with sound and light outputs showing the time period has been completed.

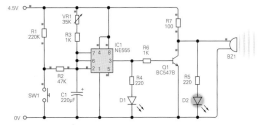

Egg timer - provides an automatic egg timer.

Click on the **Run** button to to simulate the circuit. Once simulating you can click on variable resistor **VR1** to adjust the cooking time. Switch **SW1** will start the timer - a buzzer will sound when the time expired.

You can see the PCB layout for this circuit by clicking on the **PCB Layout** tab at the bottom of the window.

Figure 1.21 Egg timer circuit

The simulation operation can also be run in 'real world' to create images of the PCB.

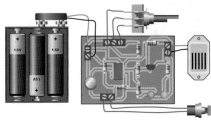

Egg timer - provides an automatic egg timer.

Click on the **Run** button to simulate the circuit. Once simulating you can click on variable resistor **VR1** to adjust the cooking time. Switch **SW1** will start the timer - a buzzer will sound when the time expired.

Figure 1.22 'Real world' simulation from circuit wizard

ACTIVITY

A charity wishes to thank supporters who put money into their boxes with a sound and light display every time money is dropped in the box.

1. Use block diagrams to design the system with at least two alternatives at each stage.
2. Use electronic simulation to model the system.

1.9 DIGITAL MEDIA AND NEW TECHNOLOGIES

LEARNING OUTCOME

By the end of this section you should have developed a knowledge and understanding of:

• how digital media and new technology may be used in your coursework.

The opportunities created by the growth of digital technology are numerous. In your portfolio work you may use digital images, drawing software or simulation software. If you use an electronic folio you may incorporate video, sound and animation into your work.

Uses of digital media and new technologies

The growth in digital technology has opened many opportunities for designers to both develop and show their products to potential users. The integration with CAD allows the designer to mix pictures of products with the places the product will be used. Photo software programs allow you to change and merge images to improve presentation.

Using these methods allows the user to 'see' the product in its final format before manufacture.

Many design companies are now allowing

Figure 1.23 CAD virtual life simulation

their clients to see products in the operating environment. Virtual worlds are being created allowing you to walk through buildings and see the layout of rooms with interior detail.

The ability to model designs from your CAD drawings is now available. You can directly manufacture models using **rapid prototyping** in resin and powder.

Stereolithography (SLA) builds accurate three-dimensional plastic components a layer at a time. A computer-controlled laser beam draws cross sections of a component on the surface of a vat of liquid plastic. The plastic will harden where it has been touched by the laser. Once one layer is completed it is lowered into the vat of liquid plastic a small distance, and the next layer is drawn on top of the first.

Selective laser sintering (SLS) uses thermoplastics such as polycarbonate, nylon, or glass-filled nylon. The laser fixes a solid traced out on top of a powder surface. The work platform moves down and another layer of powder is pulled across the surface. The platform moves down until the object is completed.

Fused deposition modelling (FDM) has a filament of thermoplastic squeezed hot from a tube onto a cooled platform which moves down. The extrusion head moves across the platform building up the shape. It can work in fast modelling mode or slow high precision mode making solid structural walls.

Three-dimensional printing (3DP) has an unbound powder layer in which an inkjet prints an adhesive. Layers of glued particles are slowly built up as the platform drops. It is a very quick modelling method, which does not require specialist knowledge to operate.

Laminated object manufacturing (LOM) uses layers of adhesive-coated paper, plastic or metal laminates which are successively glued together with heated rollers. It is cut with a laser cutter tracing the outline on each layer. The waste parts are cross hatched to make them easy to remove. All the layers are laid before the waste is separated. It is a low cost method using readily available materials.

Figure 1.24 Product of rapid prototyping

1.10 PRODUCTION PLANNING

LEARNING OUTCOMES

By the end of this section you should have developed a knowledge and understanding of:

- the importance of production planning
- the information required in a production plan.

> *When you have completed your design work you are ready to start making. You should at this point know exactly what dimensions and quantities of materials and components are needed to complete your product.*

Parts list/cutting list

You will need to examine your working drawings to create a parts/cutting list for your product. This needs to be done early in the planning process as materials or components may need to be ordered. A cutting/parts list will help organise the making process.

EGG TIMER

part no	description	material	no. off	size / item	length	width	unit cost	total cost
1	vacuum formed	ABS	1	2.0 mm (sheet)	300 mm	200 mm	£9.70 per sq m	58p
2	back	ABS	1	2.0 mm (sheet)	150 mm	150 mm	£9.70 per sq m	22p
3	back fixing screws	Screw, self tapping	1	12 mm × 6 guage			1p each	1p
4		Battery Holder	1	2 × AA			20p each	20p
5		Circuit Board, Printed	1	100 mm × 160 mm			£2.10 each	£2.10
6		Diode, light emitting (LED)	2	Standard (5 mm)			11p each	22p
7		Integrated Circuit Socket	1	8 pin			7p each	7p
8		Integrated Circuits (IC's)	1	556 Timer			50p each	50p
9		Resistor, fixed	1	100R			3p each	3p
10		Resistor, fixed	2	220R			3p each	6p
11		Resistor, fixed	2	1K			3p each	6p
12		Resistor, fixed	1	47K			3p each	3p
13		Resistor, fixed	1	220K			3p each	3p
14		Capacitor, electrolytic	1	220µ			8p each	8p
15		Resistor, variable	1	47K			42p each	42p
16		Switch, push	1	Push to Make			18p each	18p
17		Buzzer	1	12v			65p each	65p
18		Wire	1	Stranded	2 mm		6p per m	0p
19		Cable Tie	4	80 mm			50p each	£2.00
20		Machine Screw, pan head	4	M5 × 30 mm			7p each	28p
							Total	£7.72

Figure 1.25 Cutting list of materials and components

Plan, organise and record production

You need to plan the sequence of the making of your prototype so you do not waste time.

The more detail you put into your planning grid, the clearer you will be about the stages of production. Your production plan should consider the following elements:

- **Time** – You will need to plan your use of time carefully. A Gantt chart is a very good way to plan the efficient use of time.
- **Materials** – Make a detailed list of all the materials and pre-manufactured components you are going to need. Do this early in the making process to ensure that materials are available
- **Tools/Equipment/Processes** – List the tools, equipment and processes you intend to use. Suggest alternative methods of production that you may use should a piece of manufacturing equipment such as a laser cutter fail.

PLANNING FOR MANUFACTURE

Process	Materials	Tools	Time	Quality Control	Alternative Making	Safety/Risk Assessment
Rounding edges of panels	2 × 150 × 70 × 6 mm MDF, 2 × 150 × 300 × 6 mm MDF, and 2 × 300 × 70 × 6 mm MDF	Router	25 min	Test router on scrap piece of wood before using it on the panels; rub the rounded edge with a finger to determine smoothness.	Fine or coarse sandpaper	Goggles, tie away apron from machinery, keep fingers away from cutter when the machine is on.
Cutting axle holes	2 × 300 × 70 × 6 mm MDF and 1 × 150 × 84 × 4 mm MDF	Pillar drill	10 min	Place the axles inside and ensure that there is little friction.	Hand drill	Goggles, tie away apron from machinery.
Cutting clock hole	1 × 150 × 300 × 6 mm MDF	Pillar drill with tank cutter	15 min	Lubricate the cutter during usage and sand the sharp inner edges afterwards.	Cad/Cam laser cutter or milling machine	Goggles, tie away apron from machinery, keep fingers away from cutter when the machine is on.
Creating lap joints	2 × 150 × 70 × 6 mm MDF and 2 × 150 × 300 × 6 mm MDF	Router	20 min	Test router on scrap pieces of wood before using it on the panels and check that the pieces of wood align properly.	N/A	Goggles, tie away apron from machinery, keep fingers away from cutter when the machine is on.
Turning and drilling the brass axle	28 by 10 mm Ø brass cylinder	Centre lathe	30 min	Check the measurements on the lathe with a ruler; reset the lathe measurer to 0 before working.	N/A	Goggles, tie away apron from machinery.

Figure 1.26 Planning for production

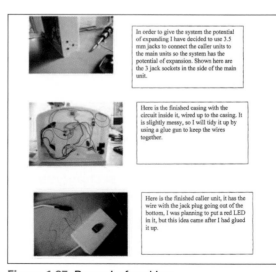

In order to give the system the potential of expanding I have decided to use 3.5 mm jacks to connect the caller units to the main units so the system has the potential of expansion. Shown here are the 3 jack sockets in the side of the main unit.

Here is the finished casing with the circuit inside it, wired up to the casing. It is slightly messy, so I will tidy it up by using a glue gun to keep the wires together.

Here is the finished caller unit, it has the wire with the jack plug going out of the bottom, I was planning to put a red LED in it, but this idea came after I had glued it up.

Figure 1.27 Record of making

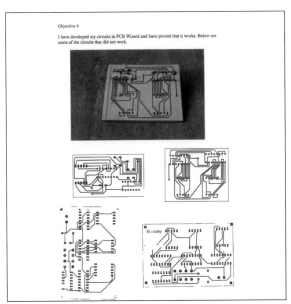

Objective 4

I have developed my circuits in PCB Wizard and have proved that it works. Below are some of the circuits that did not work.

Figure 1.28 Economic planning for PCB to reduce the size

- **Risk assessment** – It is important that you identify in your planning any health and safety risks in the making process and how you will minimise these risks.

As you make your product, you should make a photographic record which clearly shows the key stages of making, economic use of materials and health and safety. It can be like a visual notebook which you can reflect on when evaluating your use of resources.

Economic use of materials

To work in a sustainable way you should not waste resources. You need to plan how you would cut up your materials to minimise waste. In the planning of your PCB design, you have to make the smallest or the best shape for the enclosure or case.

STEP	TASK	MATERIALS	TOOLS/PROCESSES	QUALITY CHECK
1	Create a PCB design of my circuit.	N/A	PCB Wizard	Make sure the PCB board is the smallest possible design to make sure that it will be able to fit onto the boards the school will provide.
2	Print out the PCB design on acetate. Make sure I have my name flipped on the axis and the PCB board perimeter set.	Acetate	PCB Wizard, printer	Make sure all lines are apparent on the acetate and my name is shown the right way around.
3	Place the size PCB board I need in a UV tank and place my circuit design from the acetate onto the board. Leave for three minutes.	Acetate, PCB board	UV tank	When removing the board make sure all the lines and pads from the acetate are shown on the PCB board.
4	Place the board into photo developer until the image of the circuit becomes completely clear. Then take the board out of the developer and wash it with water.	PCB board	Photo developer	Make sure all the lines and components are clearly defined on the board. If not, then put the board in the developer unit until it does, though this should not take too long.
5	Place the PCB board in the acid tank for anything from 15–60 minutes. Check every 10 minutes or so to see if the layers of copper are showing.	PCB board	Acid tank	Make sure that all of the copper for the tracks is showing. Remove any excess copper.
6	Polish the PCB board with a polishing block until the copper shines. Remove any excess copper. Wash the PCB.	PCB board	Polishing block	Wash away the excess copper. Make sure the copper shines fairly bright so that it is clean and free of impurities.
7	Place the PCB into tin crystals and wait until the copper track becomes coated in the tin. Wash the PCB again.	PCB board	Tin crystals	Make sure the track is fully coated in the tin crystals and shines silver. Wash off any excess.
8	Drill holes in the component places.	PCB board	Drill	Make sure that the holes are drilled accurately and carefully. Failure to drill the holes accurately could mean the PCB will not work as the measurements have to be exact. Wash off excess debris.
9	Solder in components using my circuit diagram to help me.	PCB board, Circuit diagram, PCB layout.	Soldering iron, solder, all components. (see components list in section 4)	Be careful when soldering in components. Make sure tracks aren't linked by solder. Remove any excess solder or cross tracking solder by using the soldering iron or solder remover.
10	Wire the seven segment displays and micro switches in from the wires.	Wires, seven segment displays PCB board, circuit diagram, PCB layout, Seven segment information.	Soldering iron, solder	Make sure all the wires attach to the appropriate outputs and inputs of the PIC chip.
11	Attach a PP3 battery to the battery clip and test the circuit.	N/A	Battery	Make sure the PCB board works by running three tests. One hitting targets that give 5 points to over 100, one hitting only targets that give 10 points to over 100, and one that alternates between the 2 targets.

Figure 1.29 Sequence for PCB manufacture

▶ Process planning – flow charts, block diagrams and tables

In addition to the overall plan of making, you will need to produce some more detailed planning. What is the actual work order for making the PCB? What detailed sequence of making is required for the enclosure? These detailed plans should include reference to health and safety.

Fig. 1.29 shows the detailed sequence for PCB manufacture.

KEY POINT

- The success of your product will be related to the quality of your planning. Keep a diary of the making process of your product as this will help you with your evaluation.

EXAMINER'S TIP

Produce your plan before you start making. Keep a diary of the making process – use of time, problems encountered and modifications.

▶ 1.11 CRITICAL EVALUATION SKILLS

By the end of this section you should have developed a knowledge and understanding of:

- critical evaluation skills.

When looking at a product, even one you have made, you need a critical method of assessing quality and whether the product meets the user need. Before a new product is launched the producer would test a prototype with a group of people to see if it is fit for purpose. As part of your controlled assessment tasks you will need to undertake evaluation activities.

▶ Testing against the specification

Look at your specification. Take each point in turn. Has your design met the specification point? Explain how it has or has not done so. Avoid giving one word or tick/cross responses.

The table below shows a student's testing of a toy against the specification with some results.

EVALUATION OF FINAL PRODUCT AGAINST THE FINAL SPECIFICATION AND DESIGN BRIEF

FINAL SPECIFICATION	HOW CAN I TEST THIS?	RESULTS
THE TOY MUST BE SAFE AS YOUNG CHILDREN ARE USING IT.	FIND OUT WHETHER IT COMPLIES WITH BRITISH SAFETY STANDARDS. LOOK FOR ANY SHARP CORNERS, PROTRUDING RODS OR SMALL PIECES THAT COULD BE SWALLOWED.	THE TOY HAS ONLY TWO PROTRUDING CORNERS WHICH ARE NOT SHARP. IT HAS NO OTHER DANGEROUS PROTRUSIONS OR SMALL PIECES.
THE TOY MUST HAVE EDUCATIONAL VALUE AND MOTION.	DOES THE TOY TEACH THE USER ANYTHING? IS THERE A MECHANISM?	THE TOY TEACHES A CHILD HOW TO TELL THE TIME. THE MECHANISM IS A COMPOUND GEAR TRAIN.
THE TOY SHOULD BE MADE OUT OF A ROBUST AND SMOOTH MATERIAL	TEST A SCRAP PIECE OF MATERIAL, INVESTIGATING WHETHER IT WILL STAND UP TO THE FORCES OF USE AND HAS A SMOOTH SURFACE.	THE MDF STOOD UP TO THE FORCES THAT WOULD BE EXERTED ON IT BY A CHILD USER. IT ALSO HAS A SMOOTH SURFACE.
THE TOY MUST BE NO BIGGER THAN SHOE-BOX SIZE AND SHOULD NOT WEIGH MORE THAN 2KG.	MEASURE THE DIMENSIONS AND MEASURE THE MASS.	THE TOY WAS LESS THAN 2KG AND UNDER SHOE-BOX SIZE.
THE TOY SHOULD BE EASY TO USE.	GIVE IT TO A POTENTIAL USER	THE CHILD QUICKLY GRASPED HOW TO USE THE TOY.
THE TOY SHOULD BE ATTRACTIVE AND EYE CATCHING.	COMPARE IT TO OTHER MARKET COMPETITORS IN TERMS OF COLOUR.	THE TOY WAS NOT THE MOST EYE CATCHING, BUT MANAGED TO BE ATTRACTIVE.
THE TOY MUST COST NO MORE THAN £15.00.	CHECK THE COST OF MATERIALS.	THE TOY CAME IN UNDER BUDGET.
THE TOY MUST BE COMPLETED IN LESS THAN 60 HOURS.	LOOK AT THE TIME TAKEN DISPLAYED ON THE GANTT CHART.	THE TOY WAS COMPLETED WITHIN THE SIXTY HOUR TIME LIMIT.

Figure 1.30 Specification check

User testing

You should test your product with your target user group. If your design is to be used by elderly people, you should test it with elderly people. Do not be tempted to test your design with people in your teaching group if these don't represent your target market!

When carrying out user testing you should:

- Observe the users – Record their reaction and comments about the product as they handle it.
- Test function – Can the users use it easily? Do they need instructions?

- Check health and safety – Are there any obvious problems on edges, gaps, sizes, materials?
- Conclusions – Record what the user thinks about the product and any changes or improvements they suggest.
- Record – Take photographs of people handling the product. Take measurements related to function and modifications.

Problems and solutions sheet

During manufacture you will make many changes. When you meet problems, you will modify the design to overcome them. All these developments must be recorded. This will provide evidence of your creative responses to difficulties which is assessed in both controlled assessment units. The record can be in the form of a diary with sketches or photographs.

Modification of ideas

The purpose of evaluation is to learn how to improve and develop a better product. You need to evaluate your product and make proposals for improvement. You should be realistic about your work and think carefully about the next stage of the development of your prototype.

The following pages show a student's evaluation of a fish feeder.

Fig. 1.31 shows a survey of a number of possible customers with conclusions for improvement. The two areas for improvement are function where the system is reviewed, and the styling of the case or structure.

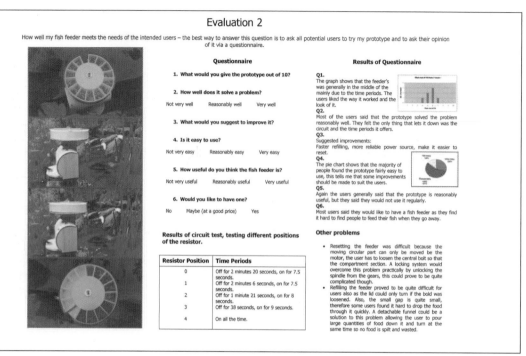

Figure 1.31 Survey of customers to test product

Evaluation 2A

Evaluating whether or not my prototype fish feeder meets each of my detailed specifications from OB2.

Specifications	Test	Result	Mark out of 10
My product will have to be large enough to contain pellets and flakes.	Put fish flakes and fish pellets in the compartments.	The prototype meets this specification as the compartments can easily hold fish pellets and flakes. However pellets are more practical as the flakes are small enough to get caught in between moving parts	9
My product will be battery powered so it is more practical.	See if the prototype can be powered by batteries.	The prototype meets this specification as the feeder is all powered by 2 9V batteries.	10
My product must be quick and easy to use.	Ask someone else to use it and see what they think.	The prototype meets this specification in some ways as the person found it easy to set a time period, easy to switch on, easy to change the batteries. However, refilling was time consuming.	8
My product will have to be capable of being mounted on a variety of surfaces.	See if it can be mounted on a fish tank and by a pond.	The prototype meets this specification in some ways as it can be mounted on a fish tank and clamped onto a flat surface. However, some users may find that it is difficult to mount the feeder.	7
My product will be able to feed fish from one to two times a day.	Change the variable resistor and time the time periods at different positions.	The prototype does not meet this specification as the circuit that was available to me could not deliver such long time periods as shown in evaluation 1.	0
My product will have to be waterproof so it can be used outside.	Check the materials used and if there are any gaps in them.	The prototype meets this specification in some ways as a great deal of it is made of plastic. It also has a lid covering the food and plastic covering the circuit and motor. However, there are a few gaps in which water could get inside of the feeder onto the circuit.	7
My product will have an indicator for the limits of fish food per compartment.	See if the compartments can hold too much food for a fish.	The prototype meets this specification in a way because I have worked out that the largest amount of food that will fit in each compartment is not enough to over feed more than 2 fish. Users can simply put less food in also.	9
My product will be made mostly of plastic as it is self coloured and water proof.	Look at the materials used.	The prototype meets this specification as a large amount of it is made from plastic.	9
My product will be made from some metal. Preferably metal that does not rust.	Look at the materials used and work out if they will rust.	The prototype meets this specification in some ways as it has metal parts however the metal that was available to me will rust.	8
My product will not be made from wood as it is not suitable.	Look at the materials used.	The prototype does not meet this specification because I used wood to box my circuit because it was easier to use other than plastic as it is hard to shape and glue together.	0
My product will be designed so it is possible for it to be made with the processes available at school.	Look at design and see whether changes were made because of school processes	The prototype meets this specification in some ways as I did not have to change the mechanism of the feeder. However, a suitable circuit was not available to me and I had to change the way the circuit was boxed from the design.	7
My product will require processes involving plastic and circuits. (E.g. Press forming, soldering)	Look at what processes were used to make the prototype.	The prototype meets this specification in some ways as I did use a lot of processes involving plastic and circuits. However, I did use processes involving metal and wood. (E.g. welding)	8
My product must be consistent so users can trust it.	Test the prototype over a long period of time to see if it does not work.	The product meets this specification in some ways because the circuit is very reliable giving consistent time intervals and the gear box never jams. However I have found that the circuit runs the batteries down quickly so it may be better for the feeder to be powered by the mains.	8
My products controls must be easy to use and ergonomic.	Ask someone to use the prototype and see if they find it difficult to use.	The prototype meets this specification as the person found it easy to use the on and off switch and the variable resistor. These controls are accessible and easy to change. The feeder is quickly and easily mounted on a fish tank and easily clamped on a flat surface to be moved by a pond.	9
			99 140

Overall I think my system is reasonable in meeting my specifications, however some specifications are not met at all. The score of 99 out of 140 is over half way, however this score is not entirely useful as some specifications are obviously more important than others.

Figure 1.32 Specification comments for evaluation

Evaluation 1

Recap on the aim of my project and the extent to which my prototype fish feeder meets them.

My intention in this project was to design and make a prototype system that was able to feed the users fish for up to two weeks reliably.
At the start of this project I produced many specifications about how it should perform. These are included in objectives one and two.
Now I need to evaluate whether my system meets these specifications:

Specifications
- The device must be simple and easy to use.

I tried to make my prototype as simple as possible. The only things that the user has to worry about is the on and off switch, which is very simple, the variable resistor controlling the time periods and refilling the feeder. I think the prototype meets this specification.
- The device must be able to feed fish at least once a day.

The prototype meets this specification as it can feed fish once a day, however it feeds too many compartments too often as a suitable circuit with the right time intervals was not available to me.
- The compartments must be large enough to hold enough food for one feeding.

The prototype meets this specification well as the compartments hold roughly two pinches of food.
- The device must be able to be positioned over a tank and a pond.

The prototype can be mounted on a fish tank and on a flat surface. However, positioning it over a pond may prove to be quite difficult for some users.
- When attached to a tank or over a pond the device must be secure.

The prototype is reasonably secure when mounted, however wind could cause the weight of it to fail.
- The device must be able to feed fish for approximately two weeks.

The prototype does not meet this specification as it empties in one day as the circuit does not give long time intervals.
- The device must be consistent and reliable.

I think that the prototype meets this specification because the circuit gives constant time intervals and the gear box never jams.
- The device must warn the user when it is empty.

The prototype does no meet this specification, however it has a see through lid so the user can see if the feeder needs refilling.
- The device must have no sharp edges so it is safe in a house hold.

The prototype has no sharp edges and would be safe in a house hold.
- The controls must be easy to use.

The controls on the prototype are easy to get to and easy to use.

I originally produced two attempts at specifications for my system. Firstly, a general list in objective one as a starting point for my objective two research. Secondly, at the end of objective two, a detailed list of specifications against which I will compare my finished system.

To find out if my fish feeder meets all of my specifications I will need to test it in a variety of ways. Some of these tests may be quite involved, some may be simple and quick but it is important to evaluate it against all of the specifications to come with an objective picture as to see how good it is.

Prototype mounted on a fish tank.   Prototype mounted over a pond with a clamp.

Prototype ready to feed.   Prototype feeding.

Prototype feeding.   Prototype after feeding.

Figure 1.32 continued

Fig. 1.33 shows how a specification check is made and useful comments are made about how the final design meets the needs. The function is reviewed in detail.

Fig. 1.34 shows how a comparison is made to the specification with differences, similarities and a summary of the important changes. It is really a snag sheet saying how the student changed and improved the design.

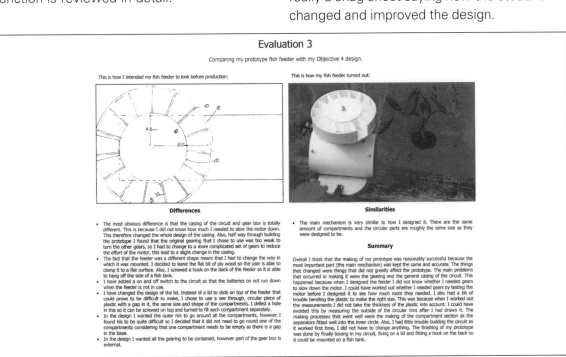

Evaluation 3

Comparing my prototype fish feeder with my Objective 4 design.

This is how I intended my fish feeder to look before production:

This is how my fish feeder turned out:

Differences
- The most obvious difference is that the casing of the circuit and gear box is totally different. This is because I did not know how much I needed to slow the motor down. This therefore changed the whole design of the casing. Also, half way through building the prototype I found that the original gearing that I chose to use was too weak to turn the other gears, so I had to change to a more complicated set of gears to reduce the effort of the motor, this lead to a slight change in the casing.
- The fact that the feeder was a different shape meant that I had to change the way in which it was mounted. I decided to leave the flat bit of ply wood so the user is able to clamp it to a flat surface. Also, I screwed a hook on the back of the feeder so it is able to hang off the side of a fish tank.
- I have added a on and off switch to the circuit so that the batteries on not run down when the feeder is not in use.
- I have changed the design of the lid. Instead of a lid to slide on top of the feeder that could prove to be difficult to make, I chose to use a see through, circular piece of plastic with a gap in it, the same size and shape of the compartments. I drilled a hole in this so it can be screwed on top and turned to fill each compartment separately.
- In the design I wanted the outer rim to go around all the compartments, however I found his to be quite difficult so I decided that it did not need to go round one of the compartments considering that one compartment needs to be empty as there is a gap in the base.
- In the design I wanted all the gearing to be contained, however part of the gear box is external.

Similarities
- The main mechanism is very similar to how I designed it. There are the same amount of compartments and the circular parts are roughly the same size as they were designed to be.

Summary

Overall I think that the making of my prototype was reasonably successful because the most important part (the main mechanism) was kept the same and accurate. The things that changed were things that did not greatly affect the prototype. The main problems that occurred in making it were the gearing and the general casing of the circuit. This happened because when I designed the feeder I did not know whether I needed gears to slow down the motor. I could have worked out whether I needed gears by testing the motor before I designed it to see how much room they needed. I also had a bit of trouble bending the plastic to make the right size. This was because I did not take the thickness of the plastic into account. I could have avoided this by measuring the outside of the circular rims after I had drawn it. The making processes that went well were the making of the compartment section as the separators fitted well into the inner circle. Also, I had little trouble building the circuit as it worked first time, I did not have to change anything. The finishing of my prototype was done by finally boxing in my circuit, fixing on a lid and fitting a hook on the back so it could be mounted on a fish tank.

Figure 1.33 Changes during manufacture

CHAPTER 2

MATERIALS FOR CONTROL SYSTEMS

This chapter introduces a range of resistant materials: wood, metal and plastics. It will help you prepare for the written examinations and also help you to identify suitable materials when undertaking design and make controlled assessment tasks. In order to make reasoned decisions about materials, you need to consider different aspects of materials, including information about their uses, properties, availability and environmental issues.

LEARNING OUTCOMES

By the end of this chapter you should have developed a knowledge and understanding of:

- the general classification of materials
- market forms of materials
- properties and performance characteristics of materials
- finishing processes applied to materials to improve performance and appearance
- smart and modern materials
- environmental issues and sustainability issues
- the use of pre-manufactured components and sub-assemblies.

2.1 THE GENERAL CLASSIFICATION OF MATERIALS

Metals

Ferrous metals contain, along with iron, differing amounts of carbon. The amount of carbon added to the iron depends on the type of steel and the properties required. For example, high carbon steel, used to make drills, files and chisels, contains much more carbon than mild steel used to make nuts and bolts.

KEY POINT

- There are two 'families' of metals: ferrous and non-ferrous metals. **Ferrous metals** such as steel contain iron. **Non-ferrous metals** such as aluminium and copper do not contain iron.

Both ferrous and non-ferrous metals can be sub-divided into two further categories: pure metals and alloys.

Pure metals are made from one single element. Examples include aluminium, copper, iron, lead, tin, zinc, silver and gold.

Alloys are metals that are a mixture of two or more pure metals with other elements to produce a 'tailor-made' metal with special properties not otherwise available in a single metal.

Metals	Alloy materials	Qualities	Uses	School use
Cast iron	>2.1%carbon, can add silicon, manganese, phosphorus	Can be brittle. Toughened when alloyed	Cast with moulds into a variety of shapes. Car brake drums, vices and machine parts	Can be cast from patterns in a foundry for solid base structures
Mild steel	0.1–0.33% carbon	Tough, able to take shocks, good machining when lead added, good welding	Structural steel in various shapes, bright drawn bar used in all engineering. Nuts and bolts, screws, nails	Main construction material, good value for money, easy to form, machine, join
Medium carbon steel	0.34–0.6% carbon	Tough for stressed use, e.g. hammering	Springs, hammers, high tensile wire, rails	Forged into stressed components
Tool steel	0.9–1.3% carbon	Strong cutting edge	Cold chisel, hand files, cutting tools	Forged into cutting tools, chisels
High speed steel M42 grade	1.10% carbon, 3.8% chromium, 9.5% molybdenum, 1.5% tungsten, 1.2% vanadium, 5% cobalt	Known as HSS. Able to cut at high speeds and feeds, even when hot	Cutting tools: drills, taps, milling cutters, tool bits, gear cutters, saw blades	Hacksaw blades, drills, taps and dies, milling cutters
Stainless steel	0.15% carbon, 18% chromium and 10% nickel	Corrosion resistant, keeps sharp edge	Cutlery, catering equipment, surgical instruments,	Rod and bar for corrosion resistance. Difficult to cut food containers

Table 2.1 Common ferrous metals

Metals	Alloy materials	Qualities	Uses	School use
Copper	Pure metal, Cu	Melting point 1084° C. Good electrical and thermal conductor, ductile, malleable. Joins easily with solder and braze	Electrical wiring and tracks, water piping, joints and water tanks	Printed circuit board, wires, sheet, tube and rod for construction
Brass	Copper and zinc, mainly 60/40, but can be 30–50% zinc	Melting point 900 to 940° C. Malleable and ductile. Very easy to beat into shapes. Good corrosion resistance, especially sea water	Good corrosion resistance, electrical conductor. Boat fittings. Casting into valves and joints for water and gas	Sheet, rod, strip for construction. Water resistant. Forms easily, can be joined with degrees of silver solder for adjacent joints
Aluminium	Pure metal. Difficult to solder and weld	Melting point 660° C. Soft and malleable, easily machined, cast, and extruded. Ductile, easy to shape. Good conductor	Resists corrosion, low density. Cooking utensils, foil for cooking, cans for drinks, window frames.	Sheet, tube and rod for construction. Self coloured but can be colour anodised
Aluminium alloy	Often with copper, zinc, manganese, silicon, or magnesium. Types: Duralumin (copper, aluminium); Magnox (magnesium, aluminium); Silumin (aluminium, silicon)	Wrought and cast into complex shapes. High strength to weight ratio, age hardens. Silicon content makes liquid metal flow into detailed shapes	Special projects where weight and strength are important. Aircraft parts, engine blocks. Special heat treatment process develops strength after forming	Casting alloys LM series. High strength sheet
ALU composite	Laminate of low density polythene core sandwiched between 0.3 mm aluminium sheet	Strong, stiff sheet which cuts very easily. Available in 2 and 3 mm sheets	Aerospace light structures	Available pre-coloured for high quality modelling and construction. Structural shapes

Table 2.2 Common non-ferrous metals

Metals are produced from ores found in the earth. They are not a renewable resource and their extraction can cause environmental problems.

The choice of metal for your design projects will be dependent upon your design situation and the manufacturing processes available to you.

Solder is a commonly used alloy for low temperature joining of metals. It is a special alloy made to melt at specific temperatures. Soft solder is made for joining components on circuit boards. The process can be carried out either by hand soldering or machine processing with a solder bath. Solder paste is screen printed onto circuit boards. The paste contains small beads of solder and flux; it must be sticky to hold components before melting in ovens or hot vapour.

▶ Plastics

There are two 'families' of plastic, these are **thermoplastics** and **thermosetting** plastics.

Thermoplastics

Thermoplastics such as acrylic and polythene can be heated to make them soft so that they can be shaped or formed. When the plastics cool they become rigid. You can reheat and reform a thermoplastic at any point during its life. When used for injection moulding this allows all the waste off-cuts to be remilled and reused immediately.

Thermoplastics have **'plastic memory'**. This is the ability of thermoplastics to return to their original state after reheating.

Thermoplastics such as acrylic are commonly used in school for the manufacture of boxes or cases for projects.

KEY TERMS

FERROUS METALS – metals such as steel which contain iron

NON-FERROUS METALS – metals such as aluminium and copper which do not contain iron

PURE METALS – metals which are made from one single element. Examples include aluminium, copper, iron, lead, tin, zinc, silver and gold

ALLOYS – metals that are a mixture of two or more pure metals with other elements to produce a 'tailor-made' metal with special properties not otherwise available in a single metal

Plastic	Properties	Working qualities	Uses	School use
ABS (acrylonitrile butadiene styrene)	Good impact strength, resistant to chemical attack	Light, able to take knocks, not crack sensitive	Kitchen products, strong cases for products	Sheet for box making, good crack resistance
High impact polystyrene (HIPS)	Toughened grade, shock proof	Cheap material, softens easily	Toys, packaging, containers	Easy vacuum forming, cut into pieces, joined with solvent or cement
Polystyrene expanded foam – styrofoam	Light, insulation. Closed cell is waterproof	White foam – open cell, coarse structure, cut with hot wire. Blue foam – closed cell, rigid, cut easily	Packaging products, beads for upholstery, insulation boards	Modelling materials. Styrofoam cut on CNC milling machine
Polypropylene corrugated board – corriflute	Rigid, tough board, lightweight	Rigid board cut easily with craft knife, 4 mm sheets	Originally for boxes in fishing industry. Simple joining pegs use the hollow tube structure	4 mm sheet joined by plastic connectors, click rivets, gluing and stitching
Polycarbonate	Supreme impact resistance and toughness. Good optically	Can be sawn and drilled. Softens when heated	Glazing, interior fittings, safety guarding. Optical and medical instruments	Display cases and areas of impact problems. Can be thermoformed easily
PVC	Good electrical insulator, tough, rubbery. Good chemical resistance	Rigid when unplasticised, very flexible grade when plasticised	Drain pipes, cable insulation, hosepipes, inflatable boat	Rigid pipes with push fit joints. Flexible sheet
Rigid foam PVC	Inner foam with smooth outer surface	Rigid board for mounting posters, easily cut	Exhibition and displays	Flexible foam easily thermoformed with press tools to make cases

Plastic	Properties	Working qualities	Uses	School use
Acrylic–polymethyl methacrylate (PMMA)	Good impact resistance, good light transmission. Wide range of colours. Notch sensitive	Machines easily, softens and bends in sheet, scratches but can be polished	Illuminated signs, clear covers for equipment	Flat sheet forming, rod. Light transmitter. Shaped on laser cutter with polished edges
Nylon–polyamide	Tough, hard wearing, self-lubricating for moving parts	Machines well, able to take threads. Excellent chemical resistance	Containers for aggressive chemicals. Engineering plastic – bearings, gear wheels. Casings for electrical hand machines	Gears and bearings. Chemical and water resistance. Hinges and cupboard fittings

Table 2.3 Comparing thermoplastics

Thermosetting plastics

Thermosetting plastics are made solid by heat and pressure or by a catalyst. The final processing cannot be changed by reheating. Thermosetting plastics are particularly useful for making products that need to keep their shape and are resistant to heat such as electrical switches and sockets.

Different plastics products require different working properties. Plasticisers can be added to the plastic to make it soft and pliable. Dyes and pigments are added to the plastic to make particular colours.

Thermosetting plastics are not often moulded in school workshops as they require rigid moulds and may need heat and pressure.

Glass reinforced plastic

Glass reinforced plastic (GRP, commonly known as fibreglass) is produced by laminating layers of stranded glass-fibre matting in polyester resin which is a thermosetting plastic. To make a GRP moulding, a mould has to be produced using resistant materials. The mould is polished and cleaned before a coat of release agent is applied to make it easy to remove the finished moulding. When the release agent is fully dried, gel-coat resin is mixed with the correct amount of liquid catalyst and brushed onto the mould to a thickness of about 5 mm. The gel coat is left to harden (gel) until it is slightly 'tacky'. Lay-up resin is then mixed with catalyst and brushed over the gel coat to give an even layer of about 2 mm thickness. The glass-fibre matting is cut into strips and pressed into the lay-up resin all over the mould. It is very important that all of the glass-fibre mat is soaked in resin to give a strong moulding. The mat is 'stippled' into the resin with a brush to remove any air bubbles. The process is repeated to build up the required thickness of moulding before being left to 'cure'.

Plastic	Properties	Working qualities	Uses	School use
Urea formaldehyde	Stiff, hard, strong, brittle	Heat and electrical insulator. Use up to 80° C	Electrical fittings, appliance parts, coated paper	Adhesive for wood, potting components
Melamine formaldehyde	Stiff, hard, strong, scratch resistant, low water absorption	Brittle, resists chemicals. Wide range of colours and finishes. Use up to 130° C	Tableware, laminates for work surfaces	Hard wearing surfaces for chipboard
Polyester resin	Stiff, hard, brittle (except when used with glass fibre). Good chemical and heat resistance	Liquid for mixing with glass fibre. Mixes with colours well. Good outdoors. Contracts when cured. Use up to 95° C	Casting, encapsulating and embedding. Structural panels in boats, car bodies, chairs, containers	Resins with catalyst used with types of glass fibre for GRP structures
Epoxy resin	Soft and rubbery but when reinforced has high strength. Resists heat up to 250° C	Two part paste, good adhesion for bonding dissimilar materials	Potting electrical components, laminating paper, surface coating, PCB, tanks	Fixing components, adhesive for unlike materials

Table 2.4 **Comparing thermosetting plastics**

Smart plastics

These have viscosities determined by physical conditions of temperature and stress. Polymorph operates at a lower temperature with softening taking place at 62° C but then hardens to an engineering material which can be drilled and sawn.

Another family of plastics are visco-elastic, being soft and mouldable but which become hard with fast loading and shock. The higher the stress, the harder the material becomes. They can be used as shock absorbers.

KEY TERMS

THERMOPLASTICS – plastics such as acrylic and polythene which can be heated to make them soft so that they can be shaped or formed. When they cool they return to a rigid state. This process can be repeated many times

PLASTIC MEMORY – the ability of thermoplastics to return to their original state after reheating

THERMOSETTING PLASTICS – plastics which are formed to shape then hardened by heat and pressure or by a catalyst, but this can only be done once. Thermosetting plastics are particularly useful for making products that need to keep their shape and are resistant to heat

▶ Wood

Woods can be divided into three broad classifications. These are:

- softwoods
- hardwoods
- timber composites and manufactured boards.

Hardwoods such as oak, ash and beech come from broad-leaved, deciduous trees, that is, trees that shed their leaves in autumn. **Softwoods** such as pine come from coniferous (cone-bearing) trees that remain evergreen all year round.

Timber composites and **manufactured boards** are wood-based materials that are made by compressing and bonding thin sheets of wood, pulp or particles with adhesive.

Softwoods are generally cheaper than hardwoods because of their rate of growth. The terms softwood and hardwood describe the cellular structure of the tree and do not mean that hardwoods are hard or that softwoods are soft. Wood is a natural material, which can be **sustainable** if it is taken from managed woodlands.

Solid woods contain moisture and as they dry out they shrink. This can cause the wood to twist, warp and split if not dried and stored correctly.

Softwoods

Softwood trees are fast growing with a cycle time of about 30 years. Softwoods are not very durable, if not protected from the environment. Softwoods are commonly used in the building industry as a structural material for floor beams, roof frames and windows.

The most common name you will find for this material is **pine** or **red deal**. Our main source of softwood is northern Europe and Russia.

Name	Source	Properties/working characteristics	Uses
Redwood (Scots Pine)	Northern Europe, Russia	Straight grain, knotty, easy to work, finishes well, durable. Widely available and relatively cheap	Most commonly used, construction work. Suitable for all inside work but needs protection when used outdoors
Western Red Cedar	USA, Canada	Lightweight, knot-free, straight grain, contains natural oils that protect from weather, insects, dry rot. Fine, silky surface	Outdoor joinery, e.g. cladding of buildings, wall panelling
Parana Pine	South America	Hard, straight grain, almost knot-free, available in wide boards	Good quality inside joinery such as staircases and built-in furniture
Whitewood (Spruce)	Northern Europe, Canada, USA	Fairly strong, resistant to splitting, easy to work	General indoor furniture

Table 2.5 Common softwoods

Hardwoods

Hardwoods are slow growing when compared with softwoods. They are commonly used for high quality furniture. The cost is much greater than softwoods and availability is limited to specialist wood yards.

Timber composites and manufactured boards

Manufactured boards are made from thin sheets or particles of wood which are fixed together with different glues, dependent on the grade of performance required. The

Name	Source	Properties/working characteristics	Uses
Beech	UK and Europe	Very tough, hard, straight and close-grained. It withstands wear and shocks. Polishes well. Liable to warp	Chairs, flooring, tools, turnery, toys, steam bent furniture
Ash	UK and Europe	Wide-grained, tough, very flexible, finishes well	Tool handles, sports equipment including cricket stumps and hockey sticks, ladders
Elm	UK and Europe	Tough, flexible, durable, water resistant, liable to warp.It can be difficult to work due to its cross grain	Garden furniture (treated), turnery, interior furniture
Oak	Europe	Heavy, hard, tough, open-grain, finishes well. Good outdoors. Due to it containing tannic acid, it will corode steel screws, leaving a blue stain	Boat building, floors, gate posts, high class furniture and fittings
Mahogany	Africa, South America	Easy to work, wide boards available, polishes quite well, but has interlocking grain which makes it difficult to work	Indoor furniture, shop fittings, veneers used to face manufactured boards
Teak	Burma, India	Hard, durable, natural oils resist moisture, fire, acids and alkalis. Straight grain, works well. Very expensive	Laboratory benches, high class furniture, veneers, garden furniture, traditional boat decks

Table 2.6 Common hardwoods

density of the board can be varied depending upon the amount of pressure used when forming the chips, fibre or pulp into the board. Manufactured boards offer a number of advantages over natural woods. These include:

- Manufactured boards are constructed to make them more stable than solid woods.

Material	Composition	Qualities	Uses	School uses
Plywood	Thin layers of wood veneer laid alternately at right angles with adhesive, odd number of layers	Stable wood in wide sheets. Can be waterproof depending on grade of glue	Structural board for flat roofs, shuttering board for concrete. Small boat building	Projects requiring wide boards. Construction of flat shapes
Aeroply	Very thin layers of birch veneer glued alternately	Very flexible sheet. Light cream colour	Built up curved laminates, furniture, decorative items, lights	Modelling material to be curved, could be used for moulds
Chipboard	Small chips (2–3 mm) of waste timber mixed with glue, compressed into flat board	Flat board of constant composition. Not good with moisture	Faced with vinyl or melamine for kitchen cupboards and worktops	When sheets glued bulks up for a mould. As backboard when faced
Medium density fibreboard (MDF)	Wood fibre mixed with formaldehyde glue then compressed	Flat boards with fine composition of varying density dependant on compression	High density faced with fine veneer for 'quality' furniture. Better surface finish than chipboard	Sheets glue up into mould blocks. Finer finish when shaped. Associated dust hazard
Hardboard	Pulped wood fibre compressed to thin sheets	Very smooth front surface easily fixed to framing. Can have surface pattern moulded in	Thin sheets used for the back of cupboards. Covers large area cheaply	Thin sheets for models. Fixing to frames for quick casing
Maplex board	Unbleached wood fibre. Formed with water pressure and heat	1 mm board, strong, bendable. Cuts cleanly with machine and hand tools	Material for interiors, furniture and consumer products. Can be finished with paints, varnishes, veneers	General purpose modelling, lightweight constructions. Easily used with laser cutter

Table 2.7 Manufactured boards and composites

- Manufactured boards are available in larger sheet sizes than wood cut directly from trees. Sheets as large as 2440 mm × 1220 mm can be purchased.
- Manufactured boards tend to be less expensive than hardwoods and softwoods.

KEY TERMS

HARDWOODS – trees such as oak, ash and beech which come from broad-leaved, deciduous trees, that is, trees that shed their leaves in autumn

SOFTWOODS – trees such as pine which come from coniferous (cone-bearing) trees that remain evergreen all year round

MANUFACTURED BOARDS – wood-based materials made by compressing and bonding thin sheets of wood, pulp or particles with adhesive

2.2 MARKET FORMS AND SELECTION OF MATERIALS

Materials are supplied by manufacturers in standard forms and sizes. Designers need to know about the standard forms and sizes of materials to ensure that both production time and materials are not wasted by having to change the material into a different shape or size.

Metals

The most commonly used metals can be bought from metal stockholders and suppliers in a range of **standard** shapes and sizes. It is important that you consider your designs carefully to ensure that standard sizes are used.

For example, 9 mm diameter round bar is not available. You should consider using either 8 or 10 mm instead. Reducing the size of the 10 mm bar to 9 mm by machining would be time consuming and would add to production costs and create waste.

We also need to consider the cost, because non-ferrous metals are much more expensive than ferrous metals and so we only use them when we need their particular properties.

Metal	Wire	Bar	Flat	Tube	Shaped sections
Mild steel		Round	Strip	Round	Angle
		Square	Sheet	Square	Channel
		Hexagon	Plate	Rectangular	Tee
					H section
Aluminium alloy	0.5–3 mm thick	Round	Strip	Round	Angle
		Square	Sheet	Square	Channel
		Hexagon	Plate	Rectangular	Tee
Copper	0.5–3 mm thick	Round	Strip	Round	
		Square	Sheet		
Brass	0.5–3 mm thick	Round	Strip	Round	Angle
		Square	Sheet		
		Hexagon			

Table 2.8 Metal forms commonly available

A wide range of sizes is available, but not all metals are made in the full range of sizes.

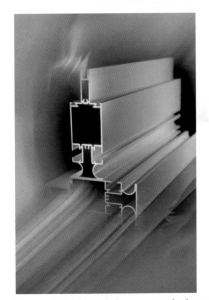

Figure 2.2 Aluminium extruded sections

Round bar: measured across the diameter.

Square bar: measured across the flats (AF).

Hexagonal bar: measured across the flats (AF).

Flat bar: measured width x thickness.

Equal bar: measured length x width of external faces x material thickness.

Channels: measured flange x web x thickness.

Hollow bar: measured outside diameter (OD) x inside diameter (ID).

Figure 2.1 Shapes and sections of materials

3	4	5	6	7	8	9	10	11	12	13	14	15	16
17	18	19	20	22	24	25	26	28	30	32	35	36	38
40	42	45	48	50	52	55	56	60	65	70	75	80	85
90	100	105	110	115	120	125	130	140	150	160	180	200	

Table 2.9 Diameters of rounds bright drawn/turned stock size range

width	3	5	6	8	10	12	15	20	25
10	x	x	x						
13	X	x	x						
16	X	x	x						
20	X	x	x	x	x	x			
25	X	x	x	x	x	x	x	x	
30	X	x	x	x	x	x	x	x	
40	X	x	x	x	x	x	x	x	x
45		x			x				
50	x	x	x	x	x	x	x	x	x
60		x	x	x	x	x	x	x	
65		x	x	x	x	x	x	x	
70		x	x	x	x			x	
75		x			x	x			x
80		x	x	x	x	x	x	x	x
90		x	x	x	x				
100			x	x	x	x	x	x	

Table 2.10 Size availability of flat bar sections

Aluminium can be extruded in a variety of sections. Aluminium profile is ideal for many applications, such as tables, frames, protective guards, protective enclosures, work tables, machine stands, test rigs, racking, machine guards and support columns.

Tubes

KEY TERMS

WELDED STEEL TUBE – rolled from flat strip then edged welded, used for conduit for electrical cables, low cost

BAR – a length of round, square, hexagonal or octagonal metal

STRIP – rectangular sectioned metal

SHEET – metal up to 3 mm thick

TUBE – hollow metal sections which may be round, square or rectangular

EXTRUSION – a forming process where a ram pushes the material through a die. The process can make simple squares but also complex shapes

CASTING – a forming process for liquid materials into a mould

ACTIVITY

1. Prepare a stock list of the metal materials available in your school.

2. Present the information as a table and give details of :
   - name of metal
   - type (ferrous or non-ferrous)
   - form (round, square, strip, etc.)
   - size
   - cost
   - typical application.

▶ Plastics

Plastic is produced as powder, granules, pellets and liquid which can then be moulded directly into the shapes required for particular products. Some standard forms of plastics are produced for general use. Plastic products can be made **self-coloured** by adding colour pigments to the raw material.

Because plastic is easy to form, it is often cheaper to use than other materials. It is possible to give plastics the appearance of other materials by the use of colour and texture.

Standard forms of plastic include:

Film – The applications for plastic film are wide ranging, from potato chip bags and other food packaging, to transparency film, protective overlay material, high-tech semi-conductor materials and a large variety of medical uses.

Sheet – For vacuum forming plastic sheet is made by calendaring, with the rolls shaping the soft sheet to the required thickness. High quality acrylic sheet is made by either 'vertical casting' or extrusion. Extruded acrylic sheet is more economical than cast sheet and is suitable for general purpose applications. Extruded sheet can however have limitations in machining and fabrication. Extruded sheet will have lower physical properties than cast acrylic sheet and is typically limited to a maximum thickness of 6 mm.

Round rod – Acetyl round rod is easily machined and a good surface finish can be achieved. It has a low rate of water absorption and is suitable for contact with food. It is available in natural (off-white) or black (dark grey).

Granules and pellets – This form of plastic is used in injection, extrusion and rotational moulding machines for a wide range of products. The base material is always white. Colour is added with pigment pellets that are added in the hopper before going into the melting zone on the machine. The feed screws mix the pigment with the plastic for the final colour. Where a number of colours are needed, such as in car rear lights, the injection processes are with separate injectors and moulds on the same machine.

Figure 2.3 Plastic granules for processing

Powder form – Many plastics are supplied in powder form, such as vinyl, nylon and polythene, to be used for dip coating. Heated metals are coated with plastic by spraying or dipping. The heat of the core metal fuses the plastic to give a smooth surface.

Wood

Softwoods and hardwoods

Rough sawn wood is often planed to give a smooth surface to the wood. Planed wood can either be planed on both sides (**PBS**) or planed all round (**PAR**). Planed wood is more expensive than rough sawn wood and is only used where a smooth finish and accurate size are needed.

When you buy wood you should buy the standard sizes as these are cheaper. Be careful when you see a knot as it can mean there is a bend or twist in the wood. End splits or 'shakes' are another common fault and can sometimes extend right up the board. These are usually caused by too-rapid drying. Other defects to look out for are 'cupped' boards, where there is a warped curve across the width, and sapwood on the edge of boards (which is a lighter colour than the rest of the board), which is attractive to woodworm.

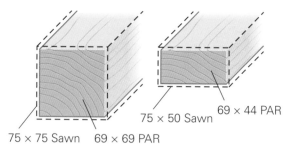

75 × 75 Sawn   69 × 69 PAR

75 × 50 Sawn

69 × 44 PAR

Figure 2.4 Typical planed timber sizes

Hardwoods are sawn into slabs of 50, 75, 100, 150 mm across the width of the tree. In the next conversion stage the wood is cut to more accurate dimensions when dried.

Widths of 50 mm, rising in 10 mm increments are available dependant upon the species of tree.

Thickness: 19 mm, 25 mm, 32 mm, 38 mm, 50 mm, 63 mm, 75 mm, and 100 mm, rising thereafter in 25 mm increments, are available.

Manufactured boards

These are produced in large sheets. Much of the material used to make the boards comes from the waste products of timber conversion and machining.

Type of board	Board sizes	Standard thicknesses
MDF	2440 × 1220 mm; 2440 × 607 mm; 1220 × 607 mm	3; 6; 9; 12; 16; 18 mm
Plywood	2440 × 1220 mm	4; 6; 9; 12 mm
Blockboard	2440 × 1220 mm	18 mm
Chipboard	2440 × 1220 mm; 1220 × 607 mm	12 mm; 18 mm
Hardboard	2240 × 1220	3 mm; 6 mm

Table 2.11 Standard sizes of manufactured boards

KEY POINT

- All natural wood has a grain which restricts how you can use it. Shaping the end grain will cause it to split where it is not supported. Solid wood will change shape and decay if used outside without protection.

KEY TERMS

PBS – wood that has been 'planed both sides'
PAR – wood that has been 'planed all round'.
MANUFACTURED BOARD – a sheet of wood-based material mostly made from waste timber products
WOOD CONVERSION – an initial cutting process for bulk timber with a band saw at a saw mill

2.3 PERFORMANCE CHARACTERISTICS OF MATERIALS

It is important to consider the performance characteristics of a material in order to ensure that you select the appropriate material to meet the demands that will be made of it when in use. Inappropriate selection could result in product failure or excessive cost if the material chosen has characteristics beyond those required.

Definitions of properties

Strength is the ability to support loads without breaking. Resisting stress from tension, compression or shear.

Elasticity is the ability of a material to stretch and return to its original shape. The property can be seen as the 'springiness' of materials. The limit of elasticity is often taken as the strength of the material before any permanent deformation takes place.

Conductivity is related to the atomic structure of materials. It is the ability to let electrons move with an electric charge. Thermal conductivity is the passing of heat with random movement of electrons. Most metals are good conductors. Most plastics are poor conductors or insulators.

Ductility is a measure of the ability of a material to be deformed in a plastic manner without hardening and fracture. At the limit of ductility materials will harden and become brittle and eventually fracture. Large strains happen when forces act on ductile metal. Typically the best materials are mild steel, aluminium, brass, copper, lead, nylon and Teflon.

Plasticity is the property of a material to smoothly deform without becoming brittle. The material will remain deformed when the load is removed. Additives are put into thermoplastics to improve this property for injection moulding to maintain flow into the mould.

Hardness is the resistance of a material to being scratched, indented or deformed. Usually hard materials are also brittle.

Tension is a force that pulls the internal structure apart. The pulling force will first make the material stretch elastically, which is reversible. Then a ductile movement occurs which deforms the material, stretching it out of shape. A characteristic of tensile failure is a narrowing of the section and increased length of the material. The break ends of the material may look like fibres pulled apart.

Compression is the squashing force which pushes the atoms closer together. All materials can take a higher compression force than tension. The usual mode of failure is when part of the structure shears off, caused by the squeezing action. Premature failure can occur in thin sections by buckling, well below the expected compression values.

Torsion is the twisting force on a structure.

Shear is used to shape materials. Cutting tools such as sheet metal cutters are very hard and shear off the parts of the material being cut. The action of the cutter gives a very high compression force at a small point which is beyond the compressive strength of the material, ductile failure occurs with a permanent change of shape in the material removed.

Bending: Long beams or even book shelves will undergo bending when loaded in the middle. When there is a centre loading of a beam that has supports at both sides, the top surface will be in compression and the bottom surface will be in tension.

ACTIVITY

1. Get a selection of ferrous and non-ferrous metals together. Cut the pieces to 100 mm. Using a vice and a hammer, insert each metal with 50 mm protruding from the top of the vice. Bend the metal to 90° with a hammer, then reverse back 180°. Count how many cycles the metal can make before failure.

2.4 PROPERTIES AND APPLICATIONS OF MATERIALS

Metals

The chemical and atomic structure of metals gives them a unique range of properties. Ferrous metals have the ability to form by deformation, both cold and hot. Using heat to join metals produces a local alloy at the joint which is of equal strength.

Figure 2.5 **Machined and joined steel structure**

Wasting and reshaping by machining methods allows complex shapes to be manufactured with great accuracy.

Some non-ferrous metals can be shaped in the molten state by casting into moulds. 'Low temperature casting' with pewter allows simple moulds to be made in MDF, which can be shaped with CNC machine tools.

Aluminium alloys are cast with sand moulds to complex shapes. An alloy with a small amount of copper can be heat treated and age hardened to equal mild steel.

Damp atmospheres can be a problem for some metals and a barrier to keep out oxygen and water is required to stop rusting which will reduce the section of the metal and reduce its overall strength.

Plastics

Plastics have a good strength to weight ratio but their strength is generally lower than other structural materials. They have good corrosion resistance making them suitable for use in 'harsh' environments.

Thermoplastics are widely used in many different applications. They are easily moulded and any waste material created during production can be re-used, making their use economically viable. However, in applications where the plastic may come into contact with heat (in the region of 100°C), thermoplastics will soften and lose rigidity, making them unsuitable for use.

Thermosetting plastics can withstand higher temperatures without any loss of rigidity which makes them ideal for use in products such as electrical switches and sockets.

All thermoplastics can be vacuum formed. The most useful thickness is 1.0 mm to 2.5 mm.

Shrinkage will occur as the material cools on to the former. You need to allow for this when designing the vacuum forming mould.

Alternative manufacturing methods for thermoplastics are injection moulding and extrusion. The preparation and molten state of the plastic is the same for both processes. The plastic is heated until molten. When the plastic is molten, additives are used to modify the material properties in the finished product. Mineral powder stiffens the plastic and reduces any flexing; it can also improve the temperature operating range of the product. Chopped glass fibre is added to improve the toughness. Feedscrews deliver the molten plastic to the tooling.

Polyester resin and glass fibre have two very different properties but when combined, produce a very useful material which has strength and resilience. GRP (glass-reinforced plastic) is an important construction material.

PCB boards are made with an epoxy resin and laminated with paper, cotton or woven glass for insulation with a copper film. The gradings are:

* CEM/1: cotton paper and epoxy
* FR4: woven glass and epoxy.

Adhesives

Adhesives are commonly used to join thermoplastics. These use the chemical structure of polymers to make strong joints. Solvent cements soften the surface of the plastic by breaking the chemical bonds, they then remake the bonds as the solvent evaporates. The 'new' bonds then include the parts to be joined.

Tensol cement is a solvent cement. The work must be held together while the solvent evaporates. Surrounding surfaces need protection from the solvent.

Epoxy resin is a two-part adhesive, with resin and hardener mixed together just before use.

PVA (Poly Vinyl Acetate) is a water-based polymer adhesive for use on absorbent surfaces such as wood, paper, card and leather. When the water evaporates the polymers cross links and become solid.

Super glues are special plastic liquids which cure on exposure to air. **Cyanoacrylate adhesive** is an acrylic resin which

polymerises in the presence of water, forming long chain molecules bonding surfaces together. This adhesive sets very quickly – in less than a minute – with full bonding strength in two hours.

Thermoplastics can also be welded with a heat gun using a filler rod. The heat is sufficient to produce melting of the plastic for 'welding' the parts. If the edges are shaped to accept the rod, the melting will produce a good solid joint.

KEY POINT

* Processing of plastic with solvents or heat produces fumes which could be harmful. Always ensure there is adequate ventilation to remove fumes.

KEY TERM

SOLVENT CEMENT – chemical liquid mixed with powder or pellets of the materials you are to join, which puts the monomer in solution

▶ Properties and applications of timber and composites

A special property of all woods is elasticity. The natural springiness of the wood fibre within the bulk of timber gives the materials a high elastic limit. Wood has good flexural properties and repeated bending does not degrade or work harden the material. There is little warning at the end of the elastic range before failure takes place.

The cell structure of wood makes glues and adhesive very effective. Liquid and paste glues can get into the structure, making a secure bond.

Wood is not a homogenous material; it has different strength qualities along the grain and across the grain. The end grain is difficult to shape without splitting.

Hardwoods are more durable and resist the effects of water or rotting more than softwoods. Rates of growth are slower than softwoods. This makes hardwoods more dense and solid. Teak and mahogany have some chemical resistance. Oak and elm when used in wet situations have natural resistance to rot, but they must remain wet.

Hardwoods require sharp tools to shape and finish them. The finishing coat applied to hardwoods may be waxing, oiling or varnishing to show the coloured grain.

Softwood is a cheap, fast grown material commonly used in the building industry. Increased moisture content will lead to fungus rot which is commonly seen in window frames. Pressure treating softwood with tanalin gives a much longer life to wood products such as roofing timbers.

Softwood is easily cut and machined, giving little wear to the tools. If knots are avoided, it is a soft, smooth material ideal for construction projects. It will accept staining, varnishing and painting to produce a good quality finish.

Timber composites combine some of the best qualities of wood and produce wide, stable, thin boards. They have differing properties and their selection is dependent on the use of the product. MDF and chipboard are used as bulk boards for flooring, cupboard sides and can be faced with melamine film for an aesthetic finish with wood grain or solid colours. Kitchen worktops have a hard wearing Formica surface. Wood veneers are added to timber composites for use in furniture making.

Plywood is made by 'laminating' or gluing together a number of layers known as veneers or plies. Each layer is glued to the previous one with the grain running at 90°. This gives stability and multi-directional strength to the board and means it is unlikely to bend, twist or warp. There is always an odd number of veneers – 3, 5, 7, etc. When waterproof glues and hardwood veneers are used in the construction, it makes marine plywood for boat building and exterior projects. Birch plywood is a less expensive material to use for indoor projects.

Aeroply consists of three thin birch veneers. It is flexible and easily formed and laminated. Layers of aeroply can be glued and curved in one direction using either a two-part mould or a vacuum bag. When the glue is hardened, the curved structure is strong and resilient.

KEY TERMS

HOMOGENOUS – the same all through the material, no differing properties in any direction

WOOD FIBRE – the grain along the length of the timber, collections of cells

WOOD CELL – the natural base unit built into grain, fixed side by side in elongated form like drinking straws

2.5 FINISHING PROCESSES

Metal finishes

Primers and paints

Three coats of paint are applied to protect the metal; these are primer, undercoat and top coat. The primer coat is applied to the bare metal and helps the undercoat and top coat paints adhere to the metal.

An undercoat is applied as the preparation for the final coat. An oil-based gloss finish would be applied last.

Traditional oil-based primers and undercoats are available but acrylic paints are now more commonly used. Acrylic paint dries quicker and allows quicker application of coats.

'Hammerite' is a 'one-coat' paint, available in a smooth or hammered finish that gives a quick-drying protective finish for ferrous metals without the need for a primer or undercoat.

Electroplating

This process enables metals to be protected and their appearance improved by coating the surface of the metal with a thin film of metal. The thin film is fused electrically onto the surface.

Anodising

Anodising is a process carried out on aluminium. The process is similar to electroplating except no additional metal is used. Aluminium develops a thin film of oxide that forms a protective layer. This layer can be thickened by anodising. Coloured dyes are often added to provide an attractive metallic surface finish.

Dip coating

Dip coating can be carried out in school using polythene in powder form. Metal is heated to 180°C and is then plunged into a tank of 'fluidised' polythene powder for a few seconds. Products that are dip coated include refrigerator shelves and tool handles for electrical screwdrivers and pliers.

Wood finishes

Varnishes

Polyurethane varnishes give a clear, tough and hardwearing finish. They provide a plastic coating without actually penetrating the surface of the wood. They are available in matt, satin and gloss finishes. To achieve a high quality finish, up to six coats of polyurethane varnish may be applied. A very fine grade of glasspaper should be used to rub down between each coat of varnish. If the product is to be in contact with water, marine or 'yacht' varnish should be used.

Primers and paints

There are three stages to painting wood. A coat of primer is applied to seal the wood, followed by an undercoat, then a final gloss coat.

Paint can be applied by spraying, brushing or rolling. Emulsion paints are water-based and not very durable. Oil-based paints, including non-drip types, are tough, hardwearing and weatherproof. Acrylic paints are quick drying and can be applied straight onto wood.

Oils

Oils give a natural finish to wood. They are usually applied by cloth or brush. The type of oil used will be dependant upon the final function of the product. Danish oil is made mainly from linseed oil and is used for furniture. Olive oil can be applied to kitchenware that will come into contact with food as it is colourless and odourless.

Wax

Wax polish can be applied on top of bare wood or wood sealed with French polish. Beeswax is a traditional wax polish. Silicone wax is used where greater protection is needed from sources of heat.

EXAMINER'S TIP

When examination questions ask you to name a suitable finish, your answer needs to be precise and explain which finish is most suitable. Single word answers such as 'paint' or 'varnish' are unlikely to gain credit.

Plastics: self-finishing and polishing

Acrylic sheet is the most commonly used plastic in school. Acrylic is supplied with a backing paper or plastic film on the surface. When working the material, it is important that this film is left in place to prevent scratches to the pre-finished surface.

The edges of the plastic will become rough and scratched when sawn. These edges will need a finishing process applied to remove the scratches. The process is as follows:

1. Drawfile to remove deep scratches.

2. Rub the edges with silicon carbide (wet and dry) paper.

3. Apply polishing compound to a soft calico buffing mop. Use the mop to polish the edge of the acrylic.

Labelling

Functional prototypes often need to be modified and improved. It is important to use labels to identify inputs for the processing system and then to identify the outputs. The designer/developer will need information about the prototype to make any necessary modifications.

In electronic circuits, colour-coded wires can be used but it is more effective if number tags are added to wires when they are bundled or tied together. An alternative is to use ribbon cable that can easily be colour coded.

The visible exterior controls on the system need information for the user to ensure correct operation. Controls such as on/off switches, volume adjustment and time adjustment should be clearly labelled.

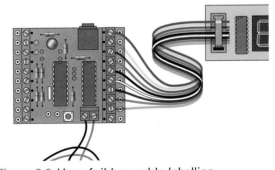

Figure 2.6 Use of ribbon cable labelling

Protection from working environment

High power handling transistors, like those in a conventional audio amplifier, and high speed integrated circuits, such as the central processing unit (CPU) of a personal computer, generate heat which could lead to component damage. These components require the use of thermal grease in addition to the heatsinks.

Thermally conductive paste improves the efficiency of a heatsink by filling air gaps that occur when the irregular surface of a heat-generating component is pressed against the irregular surface of an aluminium heatsink.

When soldering components into a PCB, the soldering process requires a flux to react with the copper and tinned leads. Some of the fluxes are very reactive and need washing from the copper board. Spray varnishes can be used to finish and seal the soldered joint to prevent corrosion.

When circuits are used in extreme environments, the whole circuit can be encapsulated with a resin compound. While this process keeps moisture out, it traps heat in, since most resins are poor conductors of heat.

Ferrous metals need a protective barrier to stop corrosion. The barrier could be a coating of plastic or paint, but equally galvanic protection can be used. Non ferrous metals used in construction projects are self-protecting, where the oxides are stable. For aluminium, the oxide layer can be increased with anodising and coloured before sealing.

Plastic requires little protection from items such as liquid. Abrasion can be a problem as most plastic surfaces are soft, although nylon is hard and is able to absorb knocks and shocks. ABS has a rubber content to increase its resilience.

Wood products need protection from liquids since the cell structure will soak up liquids and then distort the product. If moisture levels go above 20 per cent, fungus rot will start.

Wood fibre products are very poor when damp as they swell and distort. The cut edges in items like kitchen worktops must be sealed.

Protection from wear in use

Metals do not wear if lubricated for rotation and sliding. It is even better if you can use brass or bronze as a bearing material. Bearings help spread the load. The best type has ball bearings that run in a case fixed to the body with the shaft in the middle.

Nylon is an excellent bearing material for light loads; it has a waxy nature which reduces friction.

KEY TERMS

HEATSINK – aluminium extrusion with fins that will dissipate heat from components
RESILIENCE – ability to take shocks without breaking
ROT – a fungus attack in wet wood
BEARINGS – a fixed hole or slot that has another part rotating or sliding through, often made of a special material with added lubrication to reduce friction

2.6 SMART AND MODERN MATERIALS

Most materials that we use in products have properties which remain more or less constant in use. 'Smart' materials are different; they respond to external factors such as differences in light or pressure, magnetism, electric field, temperature levels and change in some way. They are described as 'smart' because they seem to be intelligent or have a mind of their own. Smart materials are now being used in everyday products. Examples include sunglass lenses (and spectacle frames) which darken as light intensity increases and stick-on thermometers whose colour changes to indicate temperature. Smart materials are now even used in clothing!

▶ Quantum tunnelling composite (QTC)

Quantum tunnelling composite (QTC) is a patented technology developed in the UK by Peratech Limited, based on original discoveries by David and Chris Lussey, the company's founders.

QTC has the unique ability to smoothly change from an electrical insulator to a metal-like conductor when placed under pressure. While in an unstressed state, the QTC material is a near-perfect insulator; with any form of deformation the material starts to conduct and with sufficient pressure, metallic conductivity levels can be achieved and a tiny piece of QTC measuring 4 mm square and 1.5 mm thick can pass a current of up to 10 amps when squeezed.

Uses of QTC – pressure-sensing and switching

The potential of the QTC material for transition from an insulator to a conductor is influenced by how much deformation the material is experiencing as a result of applied mechanical pressure.

QTC can be used to produce low profile, low cost, pressure activated switches or sensors that display variable resistance with applied

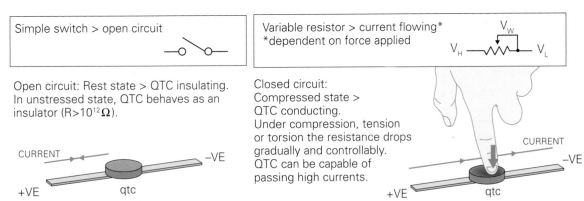

Simple switch > open circuit

Open circuit: Rest state > QTC insulating. In unstressed state, QTC behaves as an insulator ($R > 10^{12}\,\Omega$).

Variable resistor > current flowing*
*dependent on force applied

Closed circuit:
Compressed state >
QTC conducting.
Under compression, tension or torsion the resistance drops gradually and controllably. QTC can be capable of passing high currents.

Figure 2.7 A QTC pill application (Peratech Ltd)

force and return to the insulated state when the force is removed. The difference between a QTC switch and a QTC sensor is only the speed and amount of physical input required to achieve the required switching point or resistance range.

QTC can be tailored to suit different force, pressure or touch sensing applications – from sensing feather-light or finger operation to heavy pressure applications.

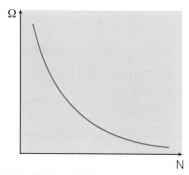

Figure 2.8 A QTC switching graph

The graph shows the effect of varying the current at constant voltage, with increasing pressure on a QTC pill. The transition from insulator to conductor follows a smooth and repeatable curve, with the resistance dropping exponentially.

In theory, the resistance of QTC decreases exponentially with compression – subsequently allowing increasing current flow through the material. In practice, uniform compression is rarely achieved and therefore the resistance change with compression will deviate from a true exponential.

QTC is currently available in a number of forms. Each formulation of QTC offers different potential for practical use and they all show a striking resistance change when deformed by squeezing, pulling or twisting.

KEY POINT

- QTC pills can have connections on both sides, by having wires pressed onto the surface. The resistance changes between each face as the pill is stressed. The pills can also be placed across a gap in conductors by connecting to the same side of the pill.

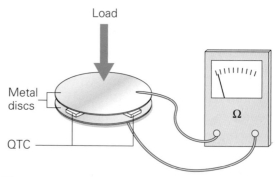

Figure 2.9 Practical use of QTC pills

Properties and applications of shape-memory materials

Materials are said to show a shape-memory effect if they can be deformed and fixed into a temporary shape, and recover their original, permanent shape only on exposure to an external stimulus.

Shape memory alloys (SMA)

Nitol is the most well known shape memory alloy, being an alloy of nickel and titanium. By heat treating the wire, it can be made to remember a shape.

Example

A wire is made straight then bent to a shape, such as a paper clip. When the wire is heated above 70°C, the wire will revert to the original straight shape and will remain in this shape when cooled.

The wire can also be heat treated to remember different shapes. It simply has to be held in the required shape and then heated to 500°C in a small oven for a few minutes. This means you can create smart springs and other components that a few years ago would have been difficult for engineers to produce.

The basic use of SMA is a pull force and for this the wire is formed when cold by drawing through a die to make thinner and longer wire. During the heat cycle, the wire then shortens to its original length, but during cooling it will return to the longer length. The cycle of heating and cooling can be repeated millions of times. The physical change point is called the transition temperature.

Nitol has a high electrical resistance, which can be used to heat the wire by connecting to a battery, the current heating the wire to the transition temperature.

Nitol SMA wire is sold in diameters from 5 mm to 50 microns. The widely available size is 100 microns, which is 100/1000 mm (0.1 mm diameter). It has been formed to give about 5 per cent shortening at the transition temperature of 70°C to 80°C.

If you are using a working length of 150 mm the shortening is $150 \times 5/100 = 7.5$ mm. This small movement can be amplified by using levers.

- When using this SMA wire, it needs a small force to hold it straight of 0.3 N.
- Pulling force when heated is 1.5 N.
- Resistance is 150 ohms per metre.
- Maximum current in the wire 180 mA.

- Maximum power is 5 watts per metre.
- Times for shortening is 0.1 second, relaxation 1.0 second – ideal, could be longer.
- Transition temperature – pulling starts at 68°C and ends at 78°C; relaxation starts at 52°C and ends at 42°C.

You can use the electrical resistance to heat the wire with a small battery. If you connect a 9 volt PP3 battery you will have to use a series resistor with the SMA wire. If the SMA wire is 150 mm long the voltage drop would be:

resistance 150 ohms/metre $\times$ 0.150 metre = 22.5 ohms

voltage across SMA wire V = I $\times$ R 180 mA is 0.18 A

V = 0.18×22.5 = 4.05 volts

The voltage across series resistor is 9 volts minus 4.05 volts = 4.95 volts. The value of series resistor is:

R = V/I

4.95/0.18 A = 27.5 ohms, nearest value 27 or 33 ohms, but remember it needs to be a high power resistor of 3W.

Figure 2.10 Memory spring

If SMA is used as the output of a system, a power transistor can be used on the interface to control the current.

You cannot solder the wire, therefore crimp connections or screw blocks must be used to make connections.

SMA two-way memory spring

Depending upon the final forming process, two types of spring can be made. The contraction type smart spring 'remembers' that it should be closed and is supplied in a contracted condition. The spring can be extended up to a recommended maximum of 150 mm when it is cool. When it is heated, by passing an electrical current not exceeding 3A, the spring returns to its closed condition with a pulling force. The force will lift a 1 kg weight vertically. When it is cool the spring 'feels' soft and pliable; above 70°C – the transition temperature – it is like a stiff metal spring and cannot be extended again until it has cooled down.

Such springs can have many industrial applications, e.g. in fire applications where they replace single-use only fusible links in sprinkler systems, the spring will reset as the heat of a fire decreases. Memory springs open and close with considerable force and can be used in applications where movement is needed at the opening and closing threshold temperatures.

Magnetic shape memory (MSM)

These alloys are ferromagnetic materials that change size and shape when a magnetic field is applied to them. The field can be focused onto a small area with a ferrite core. The movement occurs from a change with internal structure of the solid material. Blocks of molecules flick between two states.

Shape memory polymers (SMP)

These are easy to see and demonstrate with acrylics. The acrylic is heated to a softening point then a shape is forced into the surface of the acrylic. This will deform the material. If the acrylic is then filed to remove the indentation and then reheated, the 'squeezed-in shape' will rise out of the surface.

Suitable materials have been refined to give more movement with dynamic shape 'memory'.

In the softened state, SMP can be stretched up to 200 per cent, then cooled to lock in this stress. When re-softened to an elastic state, it will recover if left unloaded, returning to the initial shape.

There are applications where SMP can be tightly compressed, cooled, then left indefinitely in a rigid state. When needed the SMP is heated and flips to its original shape. The transition point of softening can be managed with a type of polymer with a range from 30°C to 260°C.

Some possible applications include **custom reusable mandrels**, reusable moulds, replica optics and deployment mechanisms for outer space.

Shape memory composites

The development of **Shape memory composites** progressed in a space contract with NASA for a 'self deploying gossamer support structure'. Shape memory technology benefits NASA by allowing large items, such as satellite dishes and solar panels, to be packed into smaller launch vehicles. This technology will make it possible for very large satellite dishes to be compacted for launch and then deployed in space.

Figure 2.11 Gossamer space structure

These plastics are thermally activated by increasing temperature by exposure to electric current or light illumination. New polymers with shapes of films, tubes, arches or spirals are activated by ultra violet light and have medical applications.

▶ Properties and applications of nano materials

Nanotechnology utilises materials and properties which are only available in very small sizes. These atom- and molecule-sized materials have opened up a new technology, with tools and processes to manufacture novel products.

It is difficult to imagine the size of a nano product. The scale is similar to the size of the earth in relation to a 1p coin – that is the relationship of one metre to one nanometre. It is a millionth part of a millimetre.

When atoms are joined to make new materials, new properties are discovered which are not available in normal bulk size products. For example, large carbon blocks

are soft and have limited use as refractory insulation when melting special metals and some electrical resistance uses. Carbon nano tubes are very strong and are better conductors than copper.

Nano technology can promise new research in areas such as microelectronics, sustainable energies and biomedicine. Using nanomaterials and composites will yield results when attempting to create materials that are stronger and lighter or have improved conductivity, heat and UV resistance. There are also new technologies in plastics, inks, pigments and coatings.

There is a whole new technology used when constructing nano products. How, for example, do you see and manipulate these particles? Nanohand technology helps develop tools to pick and place nano-sized materials.

In the nano state, atoms join to make sheets in a material called Fullerene. These sheets are rolled into tubes many sheets thick. The new material is very strong and stiff. Carbon nano tubes are a building block for composites which have increased stiffness. For example, when mixed with polymers it

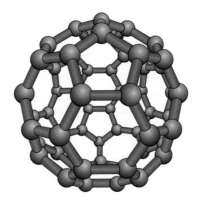

Figure 2.12 A buckyball of carbon 1 nm diameter

can make tennis rackets of superior lightness and strength.

Another carbon structure is a hollow spherical form called 'buckyballs' which can be filled with medicine. When filled with nano metals it can be delivered to areas of malignant growth so they can be seen on MRI scans. There are more developments for medicine than any other field in the future.

Nano particles of semiconductor materials are made as **quantum dots** which have light-changing properties. The smaller the nano particles, the more blue it shows; as the particles get larger, the more red it is. If the quantum dots are used on photovoltaic (solar) cells, there is an increased voltage output as the incoming light makes the dots' energy fluoresce before being captured in the cell.

By narrowly controlling the particles distribution (PSD) of the quantum dot crystals to within 10 nanometers, discrete colours can be emitted with wave lengths representing the entire visible spectrum. By controlling the light output of LEDs, it is possible to produce light nearer to the warm white light needed for home use. Quantum dots are also being explored for use in future quantum computing.

Hydrogen fuel cells will see big improvements if the active membrane and catalysts are made of nano particles. Sustainable solar powered water purification happens with a photoelectrocatalytic fuel cell which is powered by visible light, making electric current as a by-product.

Nano coating of metals can help improve working qualities. Sputtering techniques in a vacuum chamber already coat drills and cutting tools with tungsten and chromium to dramatically improve abrasion resistance.

Figure 2.13 **Printed solar cell**

Research and development has led to recent progress in dye-sensitised solar cells (DSCs), which use light-harvesting dye to improve the optical absorption of stained nanostructure electrodes. Costing only 10–20 per cent of equivalent silicon products, the new devices might make it possible for more people to use solar energy, bringing the costs closer to the cost of electricity from conventional sources.

Figure 2.14 **Applications of nano composites**

Carbon nano tubes have exceptional qualities:

- high strength – up to 1000 times greater than steel
- electrical conductivity – superior to metals
- thermal conductivity – superior to metals.

Nanotubes are multi-walled with the following characteristics:

- number of walls: 3 to 15,
- outer mean diameter: 13 to 16 nanometres
- inner mean diameter: 4 nanometres
- length: 1 to over 10 nanometres

The material appears as lumpy black powder ready for adding to resins to create composites. It can replace carbon fibre reinforcement. The polymer composites are good electrical conductors, so offer many development possibilities, even new types of transistors and capacitors. If mixed with inks it is possible to print circuits directly onto a substrate, since the ink and carbon nano tube will be conductive.

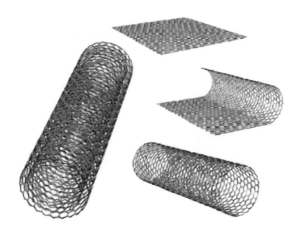

Figure 2.15 Nano carbon tubes

Safety – there are serious safety considerations when the product is so small. Research is being carried out about how the body reacts to such materials. Are there skin reactions to materials entering the pores? If breathed in, is it as serious as previous problematic material such as asbestos? The material should not be handled and only used with good fume extraction. The Health and Safety Executive are still considering the safety rules for its use.

Phase change materials (PCMs)

Latent heat storage is achieved when there is a phase change between states, such as solid–liquid, solid–solid, but gas changes are not used. When heated, PCMs absorb energy until the phase change point (melting point) when they absorb energy while remaining at the same temperature. They continue to absorb heat energy until all the product is liquid. When the ambient temperature falls, the PCM releases heat until all of the product is solid. The working point can be in a range from −5°C to 190°C. PCMs can be used to keep products warm or cool. They can modify the environment to remove extreme temperatures.

For example, a phase-change lining in a food transport vehicle can eliminate the need for on-board mechanical refrigeration. As the vehicle warms up, the material starts to change and 'sucks' heat from the contents, keeping it all cool.

Piezo electric crystal

Piezo crystal is made from minerals, ceramics or polymers. Transducers react to energy, changing it from one version to another.

When a piezo electric material is deformed, e.g. by tapping with a pencil or dropping money onto it, a voltage appears across it. This voltage can be used as an input signal to a system.

If a voltage is applied to the piezo material, it deforms, producing a movement. The deformation is sufficient to produce a sound wave, with a frequency to match the output signal.

The product can be a disc for fixing to your own base, then used as input or output. The crystal is also supplied in a complete package for use as a sounder or siren.

Figure 2.16 Piezo crystal disc

Piezo cable is coaxial with copper conductor surrounded by the piezo polymer. The sensor cable uses polyvinylidene fluoride (PVDF) as the piezo element. The cable is used in security and signalling systems. It can be fixed to a wall or buried in the ground and generates a signal from sound or vibrations. It is a good input for alarm circuits.

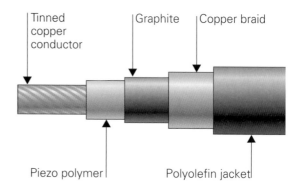

Figure 2.17 Piezo electric sensor cable

2.7 ENVIRONMENTAL AND SUSTAINABILITY ISSUES

Environmental and sustainability issues are a thread that runs through all your work on this examination course. We all need to be responsible producers and consumers. We cannot continue to abuse the world with the removal of resources and creation of pollution. It is one world and we have to protect the future. You need to look at all manufacturing activity and make choices as to whether it is sustainable and a good use of resources.

Life cycle assessment

When looking at the work of other designers and producers, the whole environment must be considered in your analysis. The life cycle assessment of a product needs to be reviewed in terms of energy used in the whole process, from raw materials through production, usage and final disposal. The use of resources is an issue when finite materials are being consumed. The mining and preparation of materials and use of chemicals can cause social problems for remote areas. Cost issues are complex when considering the 'real cost' of production. Are the raw materials costs covering the extraction and conversion a proper reward for the area? Exploitation of resources and people is now

INPUTS		OUTPUTS
	Raw materials	
Energy	All products are created from raw materials. There is an energy cost to extract oil, ores and timber and in growing livestock	Concentrated ores and materials
	Transporting raw materials	
Energy Raw materials	Consider the transportation of raw materials both nationally and internationally. There is an environmental impact from transporting goods	Atmospheric pollutants
	Processing raw materials	
Energy Raw materials	Transforming raw materials by chemical and physical processing – such as ores in stock metals, oils into plastics	Solid waste
	Manufacturing the product	
Energy Chemicals	Manufacturing industry requires energy to convert materials into products with machines, lighting and heating. Chemicals used in converting materials will have environmental impact Transporting components and distributing finished products to warehouse, to retail outlet and to customer	Pollution Fumes Chemicals
	Using the product	
Energy Raw materials	Some products require no energy in usage. Most hi-tech products require a considerable energy input to function and can have standby costs	Recycled packaging
	Disposal of the product	
Energy Raw materials	Collection of waste uses energy. There are raw material savings when materials are recycled	Pollution from land fill

Table 2.12 Energy needs in the life cycle of a product or system and environmental impact

being considered in the cost of products. Fairtrade and other similar organisations are trying to ensure the growers and producers of raw materials receive the correct value for their labour.

Impact of production

In the area of electronic and control systems, many special materials and production methods are used. Even the gold wire used inside integrated circuits has a local extraction and refinement problem as low technology chemicals are used to concentrate the ore.

Where materials are exclusive to an area, such as the demand for columbite-tantalite (CT) used in the production of small capacitors, the processing and money flow can upset the political balance of a country. Areas of West Africa are subject to conflict, with governments and militia trying to control production.

Lithium batteries are seen as great rechargeable batteries. The vast majority of the world's supply of lithium carbonate, the mineral used to make lithium-based batteries, is found in just four countries: China, Chile, Argentina and Bolivia. While production capacity will double in the next few years, the industry simply cannot produce enough lithium to build the hundreds of millions of large-format batteries needed to power the electric cars and plug-in hybrids of the future.

Figure 2.18 Large lithium battery for transport showing the separate cells

Environmental impacts of production are related to use of chemicals, heat processes and waste. Many regulations are in place to control substances which could damage health. Look at Chapter 9 for greater detail.

The main protection for the environment is the restriction on the use of chemicals in electrical and electronic equipment (the Restriction of the Use of Certain Hazardous Substances in Electrical and Electronic Equipment Regulations 2008 (the 'RoHS Regulations')). The aim is for manufacturers to look at processes and see if there could be a reduction in the exposure and use of damaging chemicals. For example, the

reduction in the amount of solvents used in the painting and finishing of a product. Many finishes are now water based.

In recent legislation the restrictions on use of chemicals have been widened. REACH is a new European Community Regulation on chemicals and their safe use. It deals with the **R**egistration, **E**valuation, **A**uthorisation and Restriction of **Ch**emical substances. The new law entered into force on 1 June 2007. The aim is to provide a high level of protection of human health and the environment from the use of chemicals.

Use and disposal of materials

In creating products, a wide range of materials are used in combination. Consumer products are very complex in their construction and use of materials, which makes full recycling very difficult. The **Waste Electrical and Electronic Equipment Directive** (WEEE) states products must be returned to the manufacturer for disposal. The manufacturer should then de-construct the product to fully recycle all the parts. If manufacturers know they are going to recycle the products at their cost, it will make them think about the whole construction process and the materials used.

Designers are trying to reduce the number of parts or materials used in a single product, making it simpler to sort and recycle. A 1984 Panasonic television, for instance, had 13 types of plastics, 39 plastic parts and took 140 seconds to take apart. The 2000 model contained just two types of plastic, eight plastic parts and took 78 seconds to disassemble.

The need to make electronics more

recyclable is one of the more subtle drivers pushing the increased use of aluminium for product cases – it's much more readily recycled than plastic.

A whole new thread of product design is now opening up. 'Take Back Design' is a very long-term relationship with a company which provides these devices. That is a powerful force for change.

Sustainability – use of materials

Sustainability is about the ability to keep producing the materials and not using finite resources. The impact on the environment should not cause problems with toxicity, use of water, biodiversity or social and moral problems for growers and producers.

Biomass is an example of a renewable, growing material which can be used for fuel and energy. Timber can be from a responsibly managed forest, where trees are replanted or allowed to regenerate naturally for future use, and the needs of the local people and wildlife are considered. This symbol is stamped onto wood and wood products to show the management.

Figure 2.19 Forest Stewardship Council symbol

You can make choices about the materials you use for constructing projects. It is difficult to make sustainable choices for circuit boards, mechanisms or pneumatic components. The best route is about conservation of materials and reuse of components. When modelling, ensure the parts can be used again, reducing the amount that is scrapped.

Some of the key issues when choosing materials are:

- Property of materials – will it function as you need it? Is it fit for purpose? Is it aesthetically pleasing to use?
- Is it needed? Is it from ethical sources?
- Are you using scarce resources or renewable materials?
- How far has it travelled?
- What are the embedded costs in energy and toxicity over the whole life cycle?
- How big is the carbon footprint?
- Is it recycled? Can it be recycled during construction and at the end of its life?

Rethink materials

Natural material does not always mean there is no environmental impact. Sometimes a synthetic material is the best, such as polymer-based damp proofing in buildings.

Reduce materials

When you use materials think about the energy trail. There is an energy cost at each stage of producing a material. The toxic impact in getting the raw materials can be high from the act of exploring and acquiring the oil or other materials. Pollution can also occur in the preparation and forming stages. At the end of the life of the product, can it be easily taken apart to reuse the material? All materials have an environmental impact so it is important to use less.

KEY TERMS

RETHINK – consider the impact on the environment of your design and make activity

REFUSE – do not use materials which are toxic or if people are exploited in their production

REDUCE – make the impact on the environment less. Consider how much energy is used in making the material. How far have the materials travelled? Can more be done with less materials?

RECYCLE – it generally uses less energy to take materials back to manufacturers than to create virgin materials

CO_2 EMISSIONS – when fossil fuels are burnt or converted, carbon dioxide is produced, contributing to global warming

2.8 PRE-MANUFACTURED COMPONENTS AND SUB-ASSEMBLIES

By using sub-assemblies, more complex products can be designed and made. This method of assembling systems is how products are commercially produced. Sub-systems can be tested and proven before they are joined to other systems. Testability is very important in complex systems.

▶ Radio-frequency identification (RFID)

This is an automatic identification system that stores details of products, sub-systems or components. The information is retrieved with an RFID reader at the warehouse or till when it is sold or dispatched.

The object has an RFID tag fixed to the packaging or on a person or animal and is tracked with radio waves. The reader, or transceiver, can be within a short distance of the tag or read from a great distance out of sight. Most tags have two parts. The largest is the aerial which can be used to gather energy for the circuit (passive), as well as being the receiver and transmitter. The second is the processor which reacts to the radio frequency signal; the integrated circuit stores the ID information. A future development is chipless RFID where the circuit can be directly printed onto the product.

Figure 2.20 Radio Frequency Identification (RFID) foil

High frequency RFID systems (850 MHz to 950 MHz and 2.4 GHz to 2.5 GHz) offer transmission ranges of more than 27 metres, although wavelengths in the 2.4 GHz range are absorbed by water (the human body) and therefore has limitations.

RFID is also called dedicated short range communication (DSRC).

Applications of passive RFID

Passive tags have a reading distance of about 100 mm when used in shops. Most tags signal by backscattering the carrier wave from the reader, that is just like having a mirror reflecting back this signal, but which also contains the ID data. The tags are 'unlocked' when placed on the pad by the till, otherwise the tag will trigger the shop door exit loops which sound an alarm.

They have uses in access cards on security doors, contactless payment and tracking products. In the Oyster travel card, used on London Transport, there is a writable EEPROM (Electrically Erasable Programmable Read-Only Memory) for storing data on the money value of the card. These toll cards are loaded with 'money' to be used on the

journey, and each charge point subtracts money.

One problem with passive RFID is the need for antenna to be very large compared to the operating chip. Future developments will reduce prices, when silicon on paper will produce smaller inlays inside paper. Very soon RFID will be as commonly used as bar codes.

Applications of active RFID

Active tags are sophisticated wireless devices with a power source, capable of communicating data at long range and operating in rugged environments for years at a time.

Active tags do differ in price, with a wide range available, unlike passive tags. Organisations must consider a wide range of properties and technological factors when selecting the correct system.

Typically active RFID tags – which contain a small battery – are used where the value of the product or information is high. Asset tracking is used in warehouses, offices and labs to follow valuable items on pallets, in containers or being carried by employees; readers are positioned on internal doors to

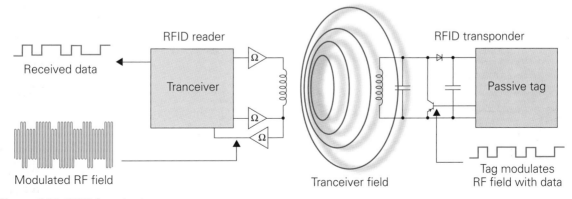

Figure 2.21 RFID functioning system

'see' a product's movement. When you visit a trade show the badge will contain information on you, which is 'given' to each stand you call at. Security in hospitals is improved when a wrist band is fitted to patients, especially babies, which will sound an alarm when they are moved out of the range of the antenna.

Electronic sub-assemblies

Electronic parts catalogue will show you a variety of pre-assembled parts or kits. The websites detailed below will allow you to look at the variety available.

www.rapideducation.co.uk

www.technobots.co.uk

www.ripmax.com

www.mutr.co.uk

www.tep.org.uk

www.maplin.co.uk

Over the next few pages you will be able to see a number of sub-systems that you can use in your own projects. When looking at security projects it is useful to have a keyboard input to give the secret code to operate your output.

For a mechanism-based project, a motor and gearbox are needed to drive the system at the required speed. In most kits you are able to modify the compound gearbox by varying the drive ratio.

Figure 2.23 Sub-assembly – motor kits, gearboxes

In another work area for projects, pneumatics models can be constructed via kits of valves and cylinders. Piping up can be easily completed with plastic push-on connections. If a system is available in your school you can complete modelling for Unit A511.

Figure 2.24 Sub-assembly – pneumatic motor

Putting in the sustainability strand may mean you need to think about solar power and how the energy can be used. Special motors and capacitors can be used to match capabilities.

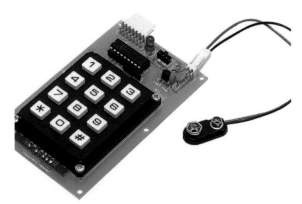

Figure 2.22 Sub-assembly – keyboard units

Figure 2.25 Sub-assembly – solar power

Figure 2.27 Sub-assembly – with PICAXE systems you can add your own parts

The input at the front of the system can be used to control later circuits. Ultrasonic sensors can help 'see' and control movement.

If you are working on projects for young children it is possible to find inputs to create interest for this age range.

More complex functions are possible with plug-in units to give wireless communication for remote connections for control or data transfer.

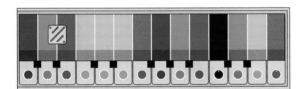

Figure 2.26 Sub-assembly – fun inputs can be used to trigger many different sounds

When looking at process units there are a number of DIL (dual in line) packages you can use containing specific functions. If you use PICAXE systems, you can vary the program to change process and outputs. You should aim to modify the circuit to make it fit your needs.

Figure 2.28 Sub-assembly – a radio unit remote control can be added with edge connectors

CHAPTER 3

TOOLS AND PROCESSES

LEARNING OUTCOMES

By the end of this chapter you should have developed a knowledge and understanding of:

- tools that are used in control systems projects
- machines that may be used in project manufacture
- measuring and testing tools
- health and safety when carrying out practical work.

3.1 TOOLS AND EQUIPMENT

Practical work for the Electronics and Control Systems course will involve a wide range of tools and equipment. The nature of the work means that if you are specialising in electronics, the tools used will differ from somebody specialising in mechanisms or pneumatics. There are however some tools that will be common to all three activities. In this chapter you will find descriptions and uses of most of the tools that you will use; the list is not exhaustive though.

Figure 3.1 Permanent fine liner, scriber and pencil

Marking out

A permanent fine line marker, a scriber and a pencil are shown in Fig. 3.1.

These will be sufficient for most marking out that is required on plastics, metals or wood. Each has advantages but they should be used

with care. It is easy to make a mark but not always easy to remove it. The **permanent** or **spirit marker** is particularly suited to use on plastics. It will not leave any scratches and marks can be removed later with a solvent, normally methylated spirit. Markers are available in a range of colours and should be chosen to give a good contrast against the colour of the material. These markers also have a use in electronic work when repairing PCB artwork or etch resist on a PCB, before carrying out the etching. On wood, ink from a permanent marker will soak in and the line becomes too wide to be accurate.

EXAMINER'S TIP

If a permanent marker with a larger line width is available it can be very useful in providing a good contrast background when marking on metals.

Figure 3.2 Woodworker's and engineer's squares

Marking out on metals is normally done with a **scriber**. This is a tool with a fine point, making it capable of extremely accurate lines with almost no thickness. It will scratch the surface, which means that a scriber should not be used on plastics or wood. Pencils are ideal for marking out on wood. The marks are clear and can be easily removed later; they cause no permanent damage and, if the pencil is sharp, are quite accurate.

Lines are often needed square to an edge; the only way of marking accurately is to use a

try square. A woodworker's try square is shown alongside an engineer's square in Fig. 3.2. The stock or thicker part of the square should be held against a true edge and the squared line is drawn against the blade of the square.

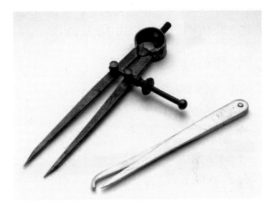

Figure 3.3 Oddleg callipers and dividers

Lines parallel to an edge can be drawn on metals using the **oddleg callipers** shown in Fig. 3.3. In a similar way a marking gauge can be used on wood. Either tool can be used to mark plastics but remember they will scratch the surface. The dividers shown in Fig. 3.3 are used when drawing circles or arcs, mainly on metal, but they can be used on wood or plastics. To prevent the point at the centre

Figure 3.4 Centre punch

from slipping, a centre punch, shown in Fig. 3.4 can be used lightly on the surface.

This multi-purpose tool is also used to mark the centre of a hole before drilling and for putting small marks around a profile when marking out metals.

Measuring and testing tools

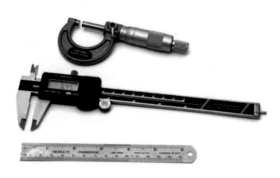

Figure 3.5 Micrometer, digital caliper and steel rule

Measuring and testing tools are often very expensive because of the accuracy that they work to. In industry, a **micrometer** or a **multimeter** will need calibrating regularly to ensure that they are still accurate; in school this is not normally done because of the expense. Fig. 3.5 shows a 0–25 mm micrometer, a digital caliper and a steel rule. The micrometer is normally used to take measurements when working on a lathe or milling machine. It can measure diameters to an accuracy of 0.01 mm but has the disadvantage that you have to learn how to read it. Digital versions are available but are quite expensive. To measure larger diameters, additional micrometers are needed, each one increasing the range by 25 mm. A more practical tool for accurate measurement is the digital caliper. This has a

number of advantages: it is easy to read, it can be used for depths and internal gaps and it can be instantly changed to read in inches.

EXAMINER'S TIP

For measuring the distance between two hole centres, first set the internal jaws to the diameter of one of the holes, then reset the reading to zero. When the jaws are then set from far edge to far edge on the holes, a centre to centre reading is given. This is very useful when measuring component pin spacing in electronics.

The **steel rule** is an accurate tool that is often marked in both inches and millimetres. Many rules will have 'standard at 20 °C' marked on them. This indicates that if they are used in very high or low temperatures the distances marked will not be quite accurate. For most purposes this can be ignored; it is only in industrial quality control that fine changes like this become important.

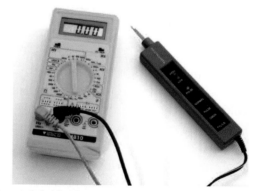

Figure 3.6 Multimeter and logic probe

The **multimeter** and **logic probe** shown in Fig. 3.6 are basic tools in electronics. The multimeter may be auto-ranging, which means that only the basic scale is chosen, or like the one shown where there are a number of scales for each type of reading.

EXAMINER'S TIP

When measuring resistor values do not hold both ends of the resistor in your fingers or your body resistance will be measured in parallel with the value you are trying to measure.

The **logic probe** makes checking a digital circuit very quick; two LEDs are normally used, green for low and red for high. There is normally a switch to change between CMOS and TTL logic levels. Many probes also have a pulse available which can be applied to a circuit by placing the probe at a suitable connection point.

▶ Cutting tools

A wide range of cutting tools are used in project work; some should only be used with a single material but many of them are suitable for more than one material. For example, woodworking tools can be used on plastics and tools intended for metals can also be used on plastics, but as a general rule woodworking tools should never be used on metals.

Figure 3.7 Tenon saw

All of the saws shown here have a *set* which allows the blade to cut a *kerf* slightly wider than the thickness of the blade itself. This avoids the blade binding in the cut.

A **tenon saw** is shown in Fig. 3.7. Intended for straight cutting on wood, it can also be used on plastic sheet materials; it should never be used on metals. It is good practice to keep one tenon saw purely for use on plastics as they can have a rapid blunting effect on the teeth. The brass back of the tenon saw keeps the blade true and adds weight to help reduce the effort needed in cutting; it does however limit the depth of cut.

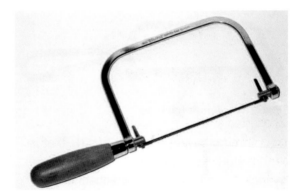

Figure 3.8 Coping saw

The **coping saw** shown in Fig. 3.8 is intended for cutting curves in wood; it can also be used successfully on plastics if a finer blade is used. The angle of the blade can be changed by rotating the handles at either end of the frame; this allows intricate shapes to be cut.

Metals are normally cut using a **hacksaw** (Fig. 3.9). There are various blade options available with more teeth per inch (tpi) being suitable for finer materials. Bimetal blades have very hard teeth combined with a flexible blade, leading to fewer breakages. To allow a

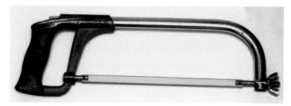

Figure 3.9 Hacksaw

greater depth to be cut, the blade can be turned through 90°. Teeth on a hacksaw blade should always face forward. A smaller version of the hacksaw is available as shown in Fig. 3.10; this is known as a **junior hacksaw**. It is very useful for cutting bolts to length and for cuts on sheet metals or plastics.

Figure 3.10 Junior hacksaw

The **piercing saw** is an unusual saw that is very useful when working on electronics casings or small parts in a mechanisms project; it is shown in Fig. 3.11. Some versions, such as the one shown, have an adjustable frame length allowing short pieces of blade to be used.

Strictly this is a jeweller's saw but the fine blades make it very suitable for cutting shapes in vacuum-formed casings. Blades in

Figure 3.11 Piercing saw

this saw should face toward the handle so that the saw cuts on the back stroke; this will keep the blade fully tensioned.

When used to cut switch inserts, a small hole must be drilled first to allow an end of the blade to be inserted before it is clamped in the saw frame.

 EXAMINER'S TIP

For all saws: when choosing a saw or blade make sure that at least two teeth are always in contact with the material being cut – this will avoid the blade jamming.

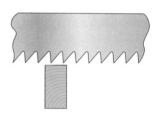

Choose a blade that keeps at least two teeth on the material as it cuts

Figure 3.12 Saw teeth

For cutting sheet materials **snips** can be used; in Fig. 3.13 compound action snips are shown, along with traditional tin snips and jeweller's snips. The compound action snips make cutting heavy material a lot easier because of the double lever action. Snips are also available with a curved blade for cutting around a circle.

Figure 3.13 Snips

Because snips shear rather than cut they will cause some distortion in the material being cut. This can be reduced by cutting the waste away in stages rather than all in one go.

Figure 3.14 Cutters and strippers

The range of **cutters** and **strippers** shown in Fig. 3.14 are intended for electronics work. When cutting through a wire the cutters or

long nose pliers can be used, but for stripping insulation the wire stripper is used. The yellow handled version is intended for larger cables and has no adjustment; instead a series of grooves are given, each for a particular thickness of cable. The red handled strippers can be adjusted for different wire thickness; this is the type usually used for electronics work.

Figure 3.15 Tap and die

Fig. 3.15 shows a **tap and die**; tools used for cutting a thread. Taps are made in sets, with at least two taps for each thread size. The first is tapered to give an easy start to the thread, the other tap, sometimes known as a plug or bottoming tap, has a full thread which can cut right to the bottom of a hole. The internal thread should be cut first using a **tap and tap wrench**; this is because there is no adjustment on the depth of the thread. The external thread is cut using a **die and diestock**. The one in Fig. 3.15 has no adjustment but split dies are normally used with the adjusting system shown in Fig. 3.16.

Figure 3.16 Split die

Tightening the centre screw will open the die, cutting a shallower thread. If the centre screw is loosened and the outer two tightened the split is closed and a full depth thread is cut. Most threads in Europe are now metric coarse, though on older equipment British Standard Fine (BSF) or British Standard Whitworth (BSW) threads are still found. The difference is in the pitch and inclusive angle of the thread.

In addition to the hand tools shown, there are a number of machines that can be used to speed up material preparation; some of these are only available to trained staff because of the dangers involved. The **scroll saw** is available in many schools. Fine cuts can be made but it is difficult to achieve an

Figure 3.17 Scroll saw

absolutely straight cut because of the narrow width of the blade. This saw is shown in Fig. 3.17. The air tube used to blow dust away from the cut can clearly be seen on the top arm.

The **circular saw** shown in Fig. 3.18 can be used on wood or plastics. Special blades are available for acrylic, in particular, to reduce chipping on the cut. The riving knife, which keeps the cut open as material is passed through, and the guard have been moved slightly to give a clearer picture of the blade. When marking work to be cut on this machine, remember that the blade is about 3 mm wide so always allow enough waste between cuts. The circular saw may only be used by trained staff.

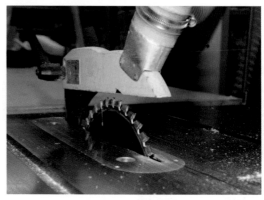

Figure 3.18 Circular saw

An alternative to the circular saw is the **bandsaw** shown in Fig. 3.19. This has many uses in project work but is only available to trained staff. When cutting out material for a vacuum-forming mould, it is ideal for cutting curves. The blade is a continuous band which rotates with the teeth facing down toward the saw table. As with the circular saw, as much of the blade as possible should be guarded.

Figure 3.19 Bandsaw

Shaping tools

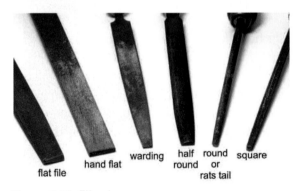

flat file / hand flat / warding / half round / round or rats tail / square

Figure 3.20 File shapes

Files, although designed for use on metals, can also be used on plastics. They are not really suited to wood as they will quickly clog. Fig. 3.20 shows the main file shapes available; they can all be obtained in different lengths and cut depth. The pointed tang at the handle end should always be firmly inserted into a handle. Before using a file check that the handle is secure. Files cut on

the forward stroke can be lifted or lightly dragged on the back stroke. The hand flat file has one safe edge which has no teeth. This allows an angle to be filed on one face without taking material from the other face.

 EXAMINER'S TIP

If a file is clogging or *pinning* on a material like aluminium, chalk can be rubbed into the teeth; this will help to keep the teeth clean. A clogged file can be cleaned with a file card which has many small wires that pull out the metal clogging the file.

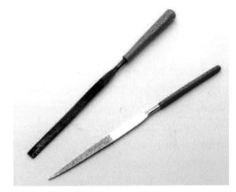

Figure 3.21 Needle files

Needle files and diamond needle files are available in more shapes or sections than the full size type of file. They are small and delicate and should be used with care. Uses will include finishing shaping of holes and slots in circuit packaging, as well as shaping small parts in mechanisms.

Smoothing planes and block planes will find a use when making tools or moulds for vacuum forming. If MDF or plywood is used, it will often need to be finished to size after having been rough cut on the circular saw or bandsaw. The smoothing plane is intended for use on natural timbers but it can be used successfully on plastics. The block plane shown in Fig. 3.22 has its blade set to a low angle which is ideal for plastics. If it is used on acrylic sheet, a good finish will be obtained.

Figure 3.22 Smoothing and block planes

For timber that has to be prepared to size in quantity, a **planer** will probably be used. This, like other potentially dangerous machines, is only available to trained staff. Fig. 3.23 shows the cutter block of a planer with one of the blades visible. There are three blades in total on this machine. The right-hand table is set lower than the left so work that is pushed

Figure 3.23 Planer blades

across the blades will be cut and then supported by the table as the wood goes through.

Drilling equipment

The ability to drill holes is required in all areas of Design and Technology when constructing and assembling a product. The following section will look at the equipment available and the cutting tools that actually make the holes.

Figure 3.24 Hand drill

The **hand drill** in Fig. 3.24 is a pattern that has been around for many years. It should not be dismissed though, as it is a sustainable product. It is environmentally sound, will last for many years and spare parts are available to allow repairs to take place. For small holes and for countersinking,

Figure 3.25 Cordless drill

it is ideal as there is good control over the depth reached.

A more usual tool to use for general purpose drilling is a **cordless drill** of the type shown in Fig. 3.25. For project work these tools are ideal, being fully portable and quick to recharge.

EXAMINER'S TIP

Always check that the drill is set to rotate clockwise for normal cutting. It is quite easy to accidentally knock the reversing lever; you will then find drilling very hard work!

When starting a hole it is important that the drill bit has a location point in the work. This can be provided with a **centre punch** shown in Fig. 3.4. The punched hole will allow a small drill to locate but for a large drill it is necessary to use a small 'pilot' hole that is opened out with the larger drill. When working on plastic sheet material, which is often highly polished, a drill may skid on the surface, causing damage. Masking tape used over the hole position gives the drill tip less chance of slipping.

Figure 3.26 Centre drill held in a tailstock chuck

If your work is circular or can be fitted into a lathe easily, the tailstock of the lathe should be used to hold a drill chuck and a centre drill used to start the hole. A centre drill has a thicker body that is more rigid than a small twist drill.

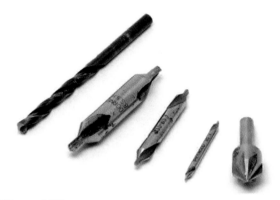

Figure 3.27

A **twist drill** is shown in Fig. 3.27 along with three sizes of centre drill and a countersink bit. Twist drills are available in diameters ranging from well below 1 mm to those above 30 mm. The larger sizes have a Morse taper shank, rather than parallel, and fit directly into either a lathe tailstock or a pillar drill.

Before use, drills should always be checked to ensure that the tip has not been blunted or broken off. If a shine is visible on the cutting edges, the drill is probably blunt.

The countersink bit is used for countersinking a hole to accept a screw or rivet head. The speed of rotation should be much slower than for a drill. When countersinking in a pillar drill, make sure that the depth stop has been set to prevent going too deep.

When drilling holes in a thin plastic casing for switches or other controls, there is a danger that a large drill will catch and distort the work.

One method of preventing this is to drill a small hole and open it out with a tapered reamer as shown in Fig. 3.28. Turned by hand this will give good control over the finished size of hole. The tapered nature of the hole means that it should not be used on thicker materials.

Figure 3.30 PCB drills

The PCB drills in Fig. 3.30 show clearly the thicker shank that prevents the drill bit 'wandering' from the hole location. The small size and brittle nature of these drills means that eye protection is absolutely essential when using them. When drilling holes in a PCB, they may start to become ragged around the edge; that is a sign of a blunt or broken drill, which should be changed immediately.

Figure 3.28 Tapered reamer

The **PCB drill** may be a small low voltage version held in a stand or it may be a small version of a pillar drill; whichever it is, the work must be held securely. Fig. 3.31 shows a simple method of doing this with a new piece of plywood or MDF used as a backing. The circuit board is held down with

Figure 3.29 Hand-held rotary tool

Fine finishing of holes can also be carried out using a hand-held rotary tool as shown in Fig. 3.29. These tools come with a variety of miniature attachments – grinding wheels and burrs being the most useful.

Figure 3.31 PCB drilling

masking tape which will prevent any movement.

Small collet sets are found in some PCB drilling machines. These will grip a drill more firmly than a three-jaw chuck but each collet will only hold a limited range of sizes. Hand held collet tools can be useful for holding drills when opening out a hole with a slightly larger drill.

Figure 3.32 Collet tools

Figure 3.33 Forstner and flat bit

For cutting wood there are a number of other patterns of drill that can be used. The Forstner bit allows a hole to be drilled with an almost flat base. These bits are normally used in a pillar drill with a slow speed to prevent burning. The flat bit can be used in either a

cordless drill or a pillar drill. Available in sizes of up to 30 mm diameter, they will quickly produce an accurate hole.

EXAMINER'S TIP

In any drilling operation you should remember to use eye protection. This is vital when using very small drills which break easily. As a rule, small diameter drills should be run at a faster speed than large ones. Make sure that the machine is set to a suitable speed. If smoke comes from the work or the material being cut discolours, stop and ask for advice.

Machine tools

Figure 3.34 Centre lathe

The **centre lathe** is one of the basic engineering machine tools. It allows work to be held and rotated while the cutting tool remains stationary. For control systems projects, it will be used when any circular material has to be finished to length or reduced in diameter.

For facing or cleaning the end face of a bar, the cutting tool should be moved across the work slowly, taking a small cut with the machine set on a high spindle speed. For reducing a diameter, the cut is set using the cross slide and the lathe carriage is then moved slowly along the bed with the large hand wheel. For circular work, a three-jaw self-centering chuck is used. If the material that is being cut is square or rectangular in section, a four-jaw independent chuck is used. This type of chuck is far more difficult to set the work up in and is less likely to be needed. It should be noted that the three-jaw chuck, though reasonably accurate, does not allow work to be removed and then replaced in the chuck; if it is replaced it will not run true. This does not matter if you are only facing the end, but if parallel turning is being done, it should be completed in one setting. The lathe tool should be checked to make sure that it is set at centre height. If it is under centre, a small piece will be left when the facing is carried out. If it is over centre, a rough area will appear.

EXAMINER'S TIPS

To quickly check the centre height:

- The lathe should be switched off and isolated.
- Find a straight piece of thin metal about 150 mm long – a steel rule can be used.
- Trap the metal between the lathe tool and the work in the chuck. If the tool is centre height, the metal will be vertical; if above or below centre, it will not be vertical.
- Adjustments will be carried out by a teacher or technician.

The lathe can be used for accurately drilling a hole in the end of a bar, as shown in Fig. 3.26. This method is far easier and more accurate than using a pillar drill.

The tool post shown in Fig. 3.35 shows a lathe tool held in a cam lock holder. The tool can quickly be adjusted up or down. Without this type of holder, packing pieces must be used to set the tool to centre height.

Health and safety reminders

- Eye protection must be worn.
- No loose clothing to be worn.
- Long hair must be tied back.
- Turn the chuck by hand before switching on to make sure there are no obstructions.
- Make sure that the chuck key is removed before switching on and after work is removed.
- Use both hands to operate the hand wheel, cross slide or compound slide.
- Make sure that spindle speed is correct for the material being cut and the diameter of work.

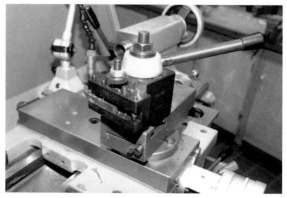

Figure 3.35 Lathe tool post

Figure 3.36 School-sized milling machine

Figure 3.37 Industrial milling machine

Milling machines can be used to cut slots and grooves or to achieve a flat surface. These machines will require a teacher or technician to carry out the setting and to ensure that all work is carried out safely. With a milling machine, the work is moved against a revolving cutter, which is the opposite of the lathe. The work is held either in a machine vice that is bolted to the milling table or it is clamped direct to the table. There are three axes of movement: the X axis which runs from left to right; the Y axis which is from front to back; and the Z axis for up and down movement. By using all three axes, the cutter can be positioned at any position relative to the work. The cutters used for project work will probably be restricted to end mills which can cut a horizontal or vertical surface, or slot drills which can cut a slot right through a piece of material. The slot drill has two cutting edges, one short and one long; these allow it to cut vertically down; an end mill can only cut down a small way before it has to be moved horizontally. It is possible to remove the cutter chuck and use a drill chuck; this allows the machine to become a drilling machine which can position holes very accurately.

The machine shown in Fig. 3.36 is a type often found in schools; the guarding of the cutter area can clearly be seen. The larger machine in Fig. 3.37 is more typical of an industrial milling machine.

Health and safety reminders

- Work must be secured in vice or clamped to milling table.
- Guards must be positioned before starting the machine.
- Eye protection must be worn.
- Hands must always remain on the safe side of the guard.
- You should be directly supervised on this machine.

Hand electrical tools

The **linisher** shown in Fig. 3.38 is useful for finishing wood or manufactured board to size. Used with care it can be quite accurate and give a good finish. There is a tendency though for the user to put too much pressure on the item being linished, resulting in large amounts being removed. The abrasive is an endless belt that rotates. Work is held firmly on the table and it can be supported by a

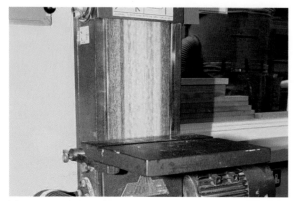

Figure 3.38 Linisher

fence to ensure that work is kept at 90° to the belt. These machines have a built-in dust extractor but this must be emptied regularly if it is to do its job. When producing vacuum-forming tools the table can be tilted slightly so that a taper or draft angle is produced on the side of the work. The work should be moved to right and left across the belt as you remove the waste to ensure that the belt wears evenly.

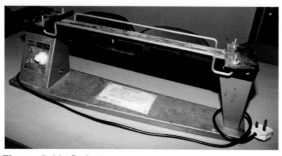

Figure 3.39 Strip heater

When bending plastics, a **strip heater**, sometimes known as a **line bender**, is used. This tool heats a narrow band on the plastics material before it is bent to shape. If the plastic is more than 2 mm thick it will be necessary to keep turning the plastic over to heat from opposite sides; this will make sure that the areas have been thoroughly heated

and the bend will be more even. Marking on the plastics can be done with a fine line permanent marker shown in Fig. 3.1.

The **plunge router** seen in Figs 3.40, 3.41 and 3.42 is a woodworking tool that can cut out a lot of hard work and will give accurate results if used carefully. Because of the dangers involved it should only be used under direct supervision. The router uses cutters, normally with edges made of tungsten carbide; the cutter then rotates at high speed against the work.

One of the problems of routing is the amount of dust produced; a typical extraction system can be seen in Fig. 3.40. Dust is removed as soon as it is cut and is passed through the hose to the extractor bag. Even with this system operating, a dust mask should be worn.

Extractor hose

Figure 3.40 Dust extractor

The depth stop seen in Fig. 3.41 is used to ensure that the cutter depth is fully controlled when it is 'plunged' into the work. The three fixed stops allow the moving stop to set a precise depth that can be duplicated for batch work.

Figure 3.41 Depth stop

To control the position of the router against the work, either a template or a fence, shown in Fig. 3.42, can be used which is pressed against the edge of the work. Setting up the router takes a long time, often much longer than doing the cut itself.

Figure 3.42 Fence

The basic tools for electronics construction are seen in Fig. 3.43. The **soldering iron and stand** will be required throughout the construction of a circuit. They should be properly maintained once the initial preparation for use has been carried out. A soldering tip when new will require careful tinning; this gives a coating of solder to the working tip of the iron. Each time it is used,

the tip should be wiped across the sponge, which is just damp; solder is then held against the tip until it is fully coated. Before the iron is switched on, the cable should be checked for any signs of burn marks. An iron with burns going through to the internal insulation must not be used. You should remember that the stand for the iron will get almost as hot as the tip of the iron, about 200°C; take care not to touch it.

Figure 3.43 Soldering iron

In addition to the danger of burns, the soldering process involves flux which can give off irritating fumes. In industry the fumes will be extracted above the work space; this does not always happen in a school, but small individual extractors may be available. The final danger to point out is that of the solder itself; if leaded solder is used, the lead is a toxic material and care should be taken to wash hands after handling it. Since 2006 soldering in industry has had to be carried out using lead-free solders. As it is not easy to tell the difference by looking at the solder, it should be assumed that solder you come into contact with is leaded.

Fig. 3.44 shows the tool that can be used if your soldering has gone wrong. The **de-soldering tool,** or **solder sucker,** as it is

Figure 3.44 De-soldering tool

often known will suck up excess solder which has been melted with the soldering iron. The device is a simple spring-action sucker which has to be 'set' by pressing in the plunger until it locks each time the tool is used. To remove a lot of solder it may have to be used two or three times.

Figure 3.45 Glass and wire brushes

One of the biggest problems when soldering is keeping the joints clean. Any grease or oxide on the joint will prevent the solder from attaching. This is a particular problem when re-soldering an old joint or when working on a PCB that has been made for some time and the pads are oxidised. The small wire brush has fine bristles made of brass that can quickly remove oxide. The same thing is done by a glass fibre pen but it can operate in a

smaller area. Both are useful tools if a joint is proving difficult to solder as shown in Fig. 3.45.

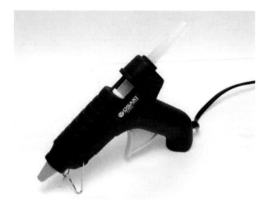

Figure 3.46 Hot melt glue gun

The **hot melt glue gun** shown in Fig. 3.46 is an invaluable tool for prototype work. It should be used with care otherwise large stringy blobs of glue will be left to spoil the appearance of your work. Use of hot melt adhesive should be considered as a permanent joining method.

Safety should be considered when using the glue gun as hot glue on the skin will continue to burn for some time; it does not cool down nearly as quickly as solder splashes. Checks on the cable should be carried out the same as for the soldering iron.

Holding tools

Tools used for holding work are essential for manufacturing. The most commonly used tool is probably the vice, two versions of which can be seen in Fig. 3.47.

The larger vice is intended for holding wood; if metals are held in it the jaws of the vice will be damaged. To overcome this many schools now use separate engineering vices such as the small one shown; these are held

Figure 3.47 Vices

in place in the wood vice. Most engineering vices will have hardened jaws that are patterned to give a better grip. Marks will be transferred if plastics are held unprotected in these jaws.

For quick movement of the jaws, a quick release catch may be found that will allow the moving jaw to be fully extended or pushed in a single movement.

Figure 3.48 G cramps

For the temporary holding of work to a bench or while adhesive is drying, **G cramps** are normally used. To protect the surface of your work, small pads of softer material can be used under the head of the G cramp.

Holding work for machining may involve the use of a **machine vice**. Though designed for holding metals, they can be used for other

materials. The advantage with a machine vice is that slots are available in the jaws to hold a round bar horizontal or vertical without slipping. The machine vice also has slots to allow it to be bolted to the table of a drilling or milling machine.

Figure 3.49 Machine vice

Holding a PCB while soldering components is not absolutely necessary but it does make the job a lot easier. The best method is shown in Fig. 3.50; this is a purpose-made clamp that allows a PCB to be moved to any angle.

Figure 3.50 PCB clamp

A simple method is a block of wood with a saw slot cut to hold a PCB that is pushed into it; this is shown in Fig. 3.51. If two of these blocks are available they will provide a secure and firm base.

Figure 3.51 Wooden PCB holder

Figure 3.53

▶ Assembly tools

When carrying out project work a variety of assembly tools will be needed. Some of these fit into the permanent joint category but many of them are tools for semi-permanent or temporary fixings – those that need to come undone again.

The **camlock** clamp shown in Fig. 3.52 on tripod legs is often used as a temporary fixing.

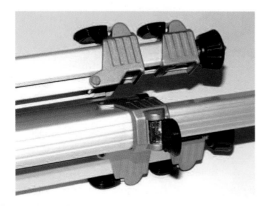

Figure 3.52 Cam lock

The first task to consider is that of tightening or loosening nuts, bolts or machine screws with a hexagon head. Fig. 3.53 shows a selection of tools that can be used for this job, some better suited than others.

The first shown is **locking pliers** or **mole grips**. They use a toggle clamp to lock onto a nut, bolt or shaft; the hardened, serrated jaws can leave marks on a shaft or bolt so care should be taken. Because the jaws close around a pivot point they are rarely parallel; grip is on two points rather than along a flat. The locking action allows them to be used for holding parts together while drilling or riveting.

The second tool shown is an **adjustable wrench** which should be tightened as much as possible to avoid slipping.

The **engineer's or combination pliers** have serrated jaws for grip and a cutting edge for wire; useful as a holding tool rather than as a tightening tool.

The first **spanner** shown is **open ended** at one end and has a **ring spanner** at the other. The ring spanner allows a greater range of fitting positions on a nut, useful when space is tight. This type of spanner is the same size at both ends.

Metric nuts and bolts are measured by the thread diameter but the spanner size will refer to the distance across the flats of the hexagon; a 12 mm spanner will fit a bolt head or nut measuring 12 mm across the flats. For awkward locations, the double ring spanner is used; this has different sizes at each end.

Screwdrivers will mainly be of the cross head or straight end variety. The condition of both types should be checked before use. Damage to a flat end screwdriver blade is easy to see but the cross head should be inspected closely for any rounding at the tip. Cross head screwdrivers are available with different angles ground at the tip; the most common is Pozidrive, but Philips screwdrivers, although mainly used in America, are still available. Each pattern should only be used on the screw it is intended for otherwise both screw and driver can be damaged.

Figure 3.54 Screwdrivers

A damaged screwdriver will damage the screw head and if a tight screw is being undone it will often become rounded to the point that it needs drilling out. Fig. 3.54 shows a close-up view of a tip with the three most useful sizes: 0 pt, 1 pt and 2 pt; the smallest being 0 pt, used mostly in electronics work.

For really delicate jobs, the **jeweller's**

screwdrivers shown in Fig. 3.55 will be necessary. The set will normally include a range of sizes with both flat and cross heads.

Figure 3.55 Jeweller's screwdrivers

Figure 3.56 Hammers

Hammers are available in different patterns for different jobs. The **ball pein hammer** at the top of Fig. 3.56 was originally used to form rivet heads; it is a type in general use by engineers. The lower hammer is a **Warrington or cross pein hammer**. This is a woodworking hammer intended for inserting nails or pins. The cross pein can be used to start a pin before turning the hammer over to use the face. Hammer heads are made from hardened steel and two hammers should never be struck together because of the danger of chips flying off. Before using a hammer check that the handle is tight on the head.

Figure 3.57 Hexagon keys

Many machines are assembled using **socket screws**. These have an internal hexagon head which requires a **hexagon key** to insert and remove them. Hexagon keys are available in imperial and metric sizes; care should be taken to use the correct size. Both of the sets shown in Fig. 3.58 have ball ends which allow the key to be at a slight angle to the screw. Hexagon keys, sometimes known as **allen keys** are also available with a 'tee' handle meaning that greater torque can be applied.

Figure 3.58

Figure 3.59 Socket wrench

When carrying out disassembly for product analysis, the tools in Fig. 3.58 may be required. The set shown allows a range of security heads to be unfastened. The torx fittings on the top row will work on either **standard torx screws** or those with a centre pin, and are only intended to be taken out by a qualified repairer. All of the tools in the set can be turned with a spanner or a socket wrench, shown in Fig. 3.59.

The final tool to be shown is a **torque wrench**; this is used when the nut or bolt must be tightened to a specified torque, normally for safety reasons. Car wheel nuts and cycle cranks are examples of this. The centre bar of the torque wrench remains still and as pressure is applied, the main bar will bend; a scale indicates the torque applied. An alternative pattern of torque wrench is set to the required torque and then turned until an internal clutch starts to slip; this is indicated by a clicking sound.

Figure 3.60 Torque wrench

Fine finishing and abrasives

The use of abrasives for finishing your work requires some knowledge of the nature of the abrasives available and of how to use them. Abrasives in most cases are natural materials; they abrade or wear away the material that they are being used on. The principle of using abrasives is that you replace deep scratches on a material with finer scratches as you work through the grades of abrasive, ending up with extremely fine scratches that can barely be seen.

The abrasives need to be hard enough to withstand the pressure of the material they are being used on.

Abrasives for the main groups of materials are described below.

For use on wood

Glass paper, which is no longer produced in the UK, had small abrasive particles of glass glued to the surface. It has been replaced by a number of alternatives: garnet paper, which uses crushed garnet as the abrasive, a semiprecious stone, has been available for many years and is very effective on both softwood and hardwood. **Aluminium oxide paper** is a more recent alternative which can last for far longer than any of the alternatives. All are available in a range of grades or grits, the higher the number the finer the grit.

As aluminium oxide and garnet papers are not waterproof they should never be used wet. They should be wrapped around a block of cork or softwood so that pressure is applied evenly; as far as possible they should be used with the grain of the wood. To achieve a good finish it will probably be necessary to use a minimum of three grades which are progressively smoother. Suitable grades for a fine finish are 180, 240 and 320.

For use on metal

For metals the traditional abrasive is **emery cloth**; this has the abrasive glued to a blue twill cloth and is available in rolls or sheets. Once again different grits are available to work toward a fine finish. Emery cloth can be torn to size; the roll is probably more convenient to use as the sides will not fray. Once torn, it can be folded around the tip of a file so that an even pressure can be maintained. For a fine finish on steel a few drops of oil can be added to the emery cloth. A suitable grade for general purpose is FF; that is the equivalent of 150 grit.

For use on plastics

Acrylic or polycarbonate is the material most likely to need an abrasive and it is usually the edges that have to be worked on. The abrasive to be used is usually **silicon carbide**, sometimes known as **wet and dry paper**. Aluminium oxide is also available as waterproof paper. When used wet the water will carry away the particles that have been cut and it will last much longer. Grades of wet and dry paper go down to a grit size of 1500 or more; 1200 grit will give a finish on acrylic that is perfectly smooth but slightly matt. If a polish is then applied, the edge will be as good as the face of the acrylic. Wet and dry paper can also be used on metals to achieve a fine finish.

In addition to the sheet and roll form of abrasives mentioned, it is possible to buy them made up as a flap wheel or a belt for use in a linisher.

▶ Surface protection and decoration

Surface protection of materials is one of the last processes carried out and the form it takes will depend on the final use of the item. For electronic project casings it may be that vacuum forming is used; in that case no further finish will be needed. Vacuum-forming plastics are available with a range of colours and textures which enhance the finish and add to the final appearance; an example of this is ABS with a thin laminate of acrylic.

When finishing steel, powder coating may be available; in this process the steel is heated and dipped into a container of powdered plastics, the powder is available in a range of colours. In the commercial process the steel is given a static charge that will attract the paint particles; it is then passed through an oven to melt the plastics onto the steel.

Alternative finishes include paint which can be brush applied or sprayed. If it is sprayed, the process should take place in a spray booth with an extractor to remove paint fumes.

If wood is used in a project it is often preferable to allow the grain to be seen. To achieve a long lasting finish, the wood can be sealed with shellac-based sanding sealer before wax is applied. The wax should be applied with fine wire wool and then buffed with a soft cloth.

With many project casings it is necessary to include information on the use of switches and controls. This can be done using vinyl cut lettering or it can be carried out quite effectively with a laser cutter onto an acrylic surface.

▶ 3.2 HEALTH AND SAFETY

Health and safety issues should be an important part of any practical activity. You should remember that while every precaution is taken to protect your safety when carrying out practical work, it is down to the individual to take responsibility for their own safety and that of others working in the same area.

There are two important distinctions to make when it comes to protection: **the machine or tool can be protected** or **the operator can be protected**. In some cases it is necessary to carry out both.

A noisy machine can be encased in soundproof material or the operator can be given ear protection to use. In the first case, once the machine is protected no worker will

have their hearing damaged; in the second case, each worker has to actively use the ear protection to avoid hearing damage.

The chart in Fig. 3.61 indicates some of the precautions that should be taken for particular activities. Knowledge of the risk involved should make you aware of what can happen; the appropriate steps should then be taken to minimise the risk. To help with this, schools and industry have to carry out **risk assessments**; these are checks on processes and machines to identify the risk involved. The risk assessor then identifies the measures that can be taken to minimise the risk. In a school you may only be aware that you are given instructions by your teacher on how to work safely; this information will have

	circular saw	planer thicknesser	pillar drill	lathe	milling machine	CNC machines	laser cutter	hand router	cordless drill	soldering	PCB manufacture	bench processes	pneumatics	chemicals
guarding or protection of the tool or machine														
chuck/cutter guard	✓	✓	✓	✓	✓	✓	✓	✓	✓					
emergency stop switch	✓	✓	✓	✓	✓	✓	✓							
danger from rotating parts	✓	✓	✓	✓	✓			✓	✓					
air pressure reduction													✓	
guarding or protection of the operator or user														
apron or overall			✓	✓	✓	✓			✓		✓	✓		✓
eye protection			✓	✓	✓				✓	✓			✓	
hand protection											✓			✓
ear protection	✓	✓												
long hair protection	✓	✓	✓	✓	✓				✓			✓		
COSHH documents										✓	✓			✓
dust/fume extraction	✓	✓					✓	✓	✓					✓
supervised use			✓	✓	✓	✓	✓	✓	✓	✓	✓	✓	✓	✓
no student use	✓	✓												

Figure 3.61 Health and safety

come from a written risk assessment which has to be reviewed regularly. As new machines become available, the risk assessment file is added to.

General points on safe practical work

- Put tools away when finished with.
- Report any breakages or damage.
- Never use equipment that you have not been shown how to use.
- Know where the emergency stops are.
- Never distract a person working on a machine.
- Alert other people who you consider to be in danger.

CHAPTER 4

COMPUTER APPLICATIONS

By the end of this chapter you should have developed a knowledge and understanding of:

- the benefits and uses of CAD for designing
- on-screen modelling methods
- text database and graphics software
- applications of CAD for project work
- CNC machines
- programmable control systems.

During the past 20 years the use of computers in industry, as well as in school, has increased dramatically. The capability of computers allows sophisticated work to be carried out, particularly in the areas of design and increasingly in manufacture. The software used in schools allows complex design problems to be resolved quickly; for example when auto routing a printed circuit layout or producing a 3D model of a mechanism. Additionally, software allows you to produce project documentation to a high standard. This chapter will look at the developments in both hardware and software and will show examples of methods of working which can be adapted to suit your own work.

4.1 TYPES OF GRAPHICS SOFTWARE

Vector graphics

Vector graphics software is based on 'line path'. The computer saves the start and end points as coordinates and then when it displays the line, the thinnest line possible is drawn between coordinates. This method is very economical on memory and is also excellent for scaling up or down.

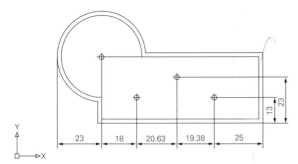

Figure 4.1 CAD drawing of a hinge showing the drawing origin

Raster graphics

Sometimes known as a bitmap a raster graphics image is used to put together a complete picture by mapping pixels. The pixels or picture elements are the smallest units in an image and are normally arranged in a two dimensional grid. When viewed closely the grid can be seen. The more pixels fitted into a set space, the better the image

will appear. The downside is that more memory is used to store the image. High resolution on a monitor screen can be 1280 × 1024 pixels; low resolution could be 640 × 480, with as few as 16 colours. The resolution of an image is most important when that image is captured; after that moment it cannot effectively be improved. Digital cameras and scanners have a maximum resolution; both can be set to give different quality images to conserve memory.

Figure 4.2 Examples of high and low resolution in a photo

4.2 USE OF CAD PACKAGES IN SCHOOL

Computer-aided design (CAD) does not fully replace the use of pencil and paper but it can save you a lot of time when you have become competent in the use of the software.

CAD software in schools is used in these main areas:

- 2D software such as 2D Design, AutoSketch and AutoCAD, all of which use vector graphics
- 2D software producing raster images such as Paint and all digital photo software
- 2D software for specific purposes such as circuit design and PCB design, Circuit Wizard and Crocodile Clips being the best known of these

- 3D software, sometimes called solid modelling; an example of this is ProDesktop or Autodesk Inventor.

Many of the programs used are complex and able to go far beyond what is needed in school; the secret is to learn the basic techniques thoroughly and add to them when the need arises.

Whenever a computer is used the same basic rules apply:

- Save the file before you have done any work on it.
- Resave, using the shortcut key Ctrl S, every five minutes or so.
- If you are trying to record development of

a design, resave using a version number every few minutes, e.g. casing design1, casing design2, etc. or use regular screenshots to record the development of the design.

- Never rely on storage in only one place – keep a backup.

- Never keep your only copy of a file on a memory stick.

- Keep work for a project together in a single folder with a name that relates to the project.

- Do not delete any files until the project is complete.

4.3 ON-SCREEN MODELLING

Using 2D vector graphics software

The most important thing to remember with line drawings is that accurate joins between two lines can only be produced using a grid or a snapping method. Most systems will give you a choice of tool. The most useful for straight lines are *snap to end* or *snap to middle*. For circles, the *centre point*, *quadrant* or *tangent* snap allow neat joins to be produced (Fig. 4.3). 2D Design calls the attachment methods *grid lock, step lock* and *attach*.

Restricting lines

As mentioned above, snap and grid can be used to good effect. There are additional features in many packages such as 'ortho', which is short for orthogonal. It is used in AutoCAD and AutoSketch to restrict lines to vertical or horizontal (See Fig. 4.4). 2D Design has 'radial lock', which restricts in 45° steps. This type of restriction can be very useful.

Figure 4.4 Restricted movement on lines

Coordinate systems

All CAD work will involve the use of a coordinate system; in some cases it is not actively used but you should know the meaning of the terms involved. The origin in a drawing is the 0,0 point on the grid from which all coordinate positions are measured. In most cases it can be reset, for example in 2D Design, *setup – drawing – user origin* allows the origin to be moved from its starting point at the bottom left of the sheet. Any grid reference taken from this point is known as absolute. A grid reference from the previous point used is relative. There is normally a bar on the screen which follows

snap positions

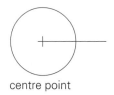 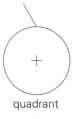

centre point   quadrant   tangent

Figure 4.3 Snap methods on a circle

Figure 4.5 2D Design coordinate display

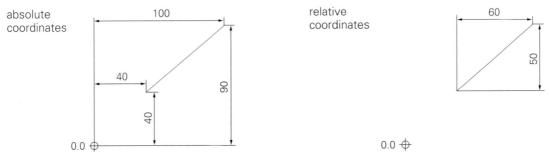

Figure 4.6 Absolute and relative coordinates for a line

cursor movement and gives relative and absolute coordinates. This system is also used in CAM and becomes very important when directing tool movement. It is usual to use either absolute *or* relative coordinates but not to mix the two (see Fig. 4.6).

Layers

Most graphics software offers this feature, as shown in Fig. 4.7. It is like having a pad of clear paper and choosing the sheet that you want to work on. The advantage is that unwanted layers can be switched off so that they are still there but are not visible; useful for construction lines, dimensions and notes.

Drawing attributes

An impressive title but it only means the properties of the lines in a drawing. These will include layer, colour, line weight and line type, as shown in Fig. 4.8. For example, on a drawing with hidden lines you can set the lines up on a layer called 'hidden detail', with a dashed line that is coloured red. As soon as you make the layer active, all lines will then appear as dashed red. For a simple drawing it is not worth going to this trouble but for more complex work it will help to organise the drawing. The colour attribute is used in laser cutting or milling to denote depth of cut.

Figure 4.7 Layers dialogue box in AutoCAD and 2D Design

Figure 4.8 Line attributes

Types of line

The solid line is the default but broken, chain, dotted and many other types of line are also available. Apart from the straight line and regular curve, one of the most useful is the polyline, literally a line made up of many parts. A series of mouse clicks will produce a segmented line which can automatically change to a smooth curve or can be changed manually.

Scale

The scale of the drawing is important – try to work in real measurements wherever possible, as this can be useful later if transferring to a computer-aided manufacturing or CAM system. Scale for the whole drawing can usually be set at the start. If the item you are drawing is too large or too small to fit on the page, set a scale that will allow it to fit. For example, if drawing an item 400 mm long and printing onto A4 paper, a scale of 1:2 or 1:3 would be appropriate. For an item that is 5 mm long, it may be better to draw to a scale of 10:1 to make it appear on the page as 50 mm.

Grouping

When moving objects about on the screen, it is sometimes useful to group them. This will allow a lot of objects to be selected with a single click, but the objects are only available in that file. Similar systems are available on different programs but the names may vary slightly. In AutoCAD, a *block* can be saved and used again, and when inserted, the objects are grouped together and can be moved on the screen as one item.

A group or block of objects that form a feature that you may want to use again can be saved as a separate file to form a library. This can save a lot of time when your drawing has the same feature used more than once or you want to transfer from one drawing to another.

Arrays

If a number of regularly spaced objects are needed, the array can be used: rectangular array for objects spaced in straight lines or a circular array for ones that move around a centre point. This is the quickest method for producing a template with a number of equally spaced holes on it.

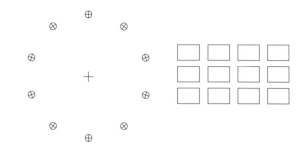

Figure 4.9 Circular and rectangular arrays

Dimensions

These can be added to the main drawing or placed on a separate layer. If a choice of standards is available, go for ISO, the international standard. In some packages the dimensions are associative; this means that if you change the length of a line, the dimension will also change. With others you will have to redraw the dimension. A dimension in a drawing is normally a group of objects. If you need to change a part of it, you can 'explode' or 'ungroup' to give access to the individual parts. Full circles should be dimensioned by diameter using the Ø symbol; for arcs use a radius dimension.

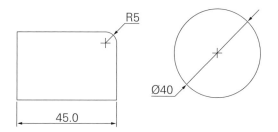

Figure 4.10 Dimension examples

Special shapes

Most software will include the basic geometrical shapes: rectangle, circle and polygon. The polygon can be set to the number of sides required, e.g. to 6 for a hexagon. Other useful shapes are the ellipse and arc. If an ellipse is not available separately, it is possible to 'squash' a circle to the required shape.

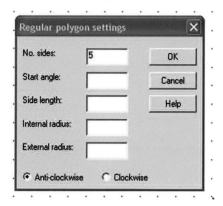

Figure 4.11 Polygon settings

Isometric drawing

Drawing to an isometric (30°) grid can be carried out quickly if it is available. 2D Design, AutoSketch and AutoCAD include this feature. 2D Design allows a transformation from a rectangle to isometric once the depth has been set. If a single isometric circle is required, the full circle is drawn and both the start and finish depths are set to 0 before transforming.

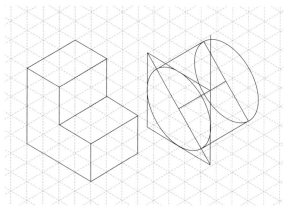

Figure 4.12 Isometric drawings using 2D Design

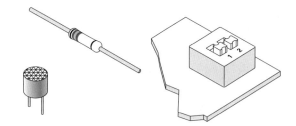

Figure 4.13 Isometric drawings using AutoCAD

Unwanted lines

Complete lines can be deleted, part lines can be trimmed and whole sections of the drawing can be removed. At this point you realise that you have just deleted a whole lesson's work. DO NOT PANIC! Use the 'Undo' command. With professional software such as AutoCAD, the number of 'Undo's can be set and is limitless within one drawing session. Software designed for schools will normally only allow a single or small number of Undo commands to be carried out. The opposite of this is 'Redo', not used so often but still helpful on occasions. The toolbar icon can be used but it is often quicker to use the keyboard shortcut: Ctrl + Z for 2D Design and Ctrl + U for AutoCAD and AutoSketch.

The working screen

When using CAD it is important to have your drawing as large as possible on the screen. The screen resolution should also be set to the highest possible rate. Try to get used to zooming as you work, it will give far greater accuracy and reduce eye strain. In some cases you will 'drag' out a zoom box, but in others a dynamic zoom is available. This means that you hold down the left mouse button while dragging diagonally from top right to bottom left, for zooming in, and the opposite direction to zoom out. 2D Design features Zoom Last which takes you back to the previous zoom level and x= which allows a zoom factor to be entered. For example, enter x=4 and the object will become four times larger on the screen; enter x=.5 and it is half the size.

Shortcut or 'hot' keys

These are very useful if you are doing a lot of CAD work. They do vary but the standard Windows shortcuts normally work.

Ctrl A – select all
Ctrl S – save
Ctrl X, Ctrl C, Ctrl V – cut, copy and paste
Ctrl G – group
Ctrl U – ungroup (undo on AutoCAD)
Hidden menus – right click over an existing menu and this will open the choices box.

What to do when the drawing is completed

Completed drawings can be 'outputted' using a number of different routes. **First make sure it is saved!**

- Send direct to a printer.
- Export to a CNC machine direct.
- Export to software that will convert the file for CNC machining; this is called post-processing.
- Export in a format that presentation software can use.
- Send electronically to a manufacturer.

4.4 ON-SCREEN MODELLING AND IMAGE MANIPULATION

Drawing in isometric or perspective is not true 3D drawing. In this section ProDesktop will be used to illustrate features though similar software could be used.

ProDesktop has three distinct modes of working: *design*, *engineering drawing* and *photo album* (Fig. 4.14).

The drawings produced can be interactive, meaning that a change in the design view will

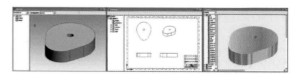

Figure 4.14 Three views showing the design, drawing and album modes

be reflected in the presentation or album view and the orthographic view.

ProDesktop will allow a complete model to be built which has virtual properties such as mass and centre of gravity that can be used. One of the most useful features is being able to build a working model of a mechanism, for example to test whether it will work. This type of design, known as an assembly, should have every part drawn as separate, saved files which are then assembled into a final version. It is important that all files needed are kept in the same folder. Electronic projects can be shown as exploded views to show how each part fits into the casing. The separate parts such as a switch can be sub-assemblies that are used in the main drawing.

Designs can be drawn completely in ProDesktop or they can be imported using a .dxf file. This type of file can be created in most 2D CAD software and allows work to be moved to another program; dxf stands for drawing exchange format.

In addition to proving that a concept will work, quite complex features such as threads can be modelled to give realism to a 3D drawing.

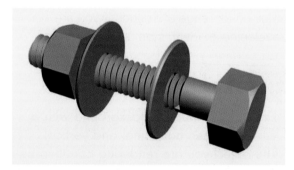

Figure 4.17 Threads drawn using the 'sweep profile – along helix' command

The drawing option allows an orthographic or working drawing to be produced very quickly; this can then be dimensioned and notes added before printing. Different drawing standards are available but ISO is a good

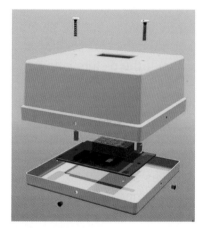

Figure 4.15 Exploded view of a project case

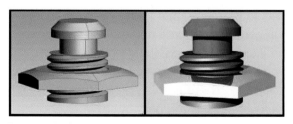

Figure 4.16 Design and album shot of a press switch sub-assembly

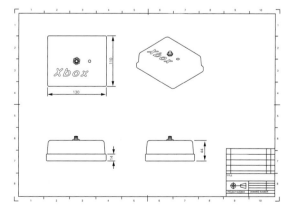

Figure 4.18 Orthographic drawing in 3rd angle projection with dimensions

choice. As mentioned previously, if a change is later made to the design it will also be shown in the engineering drawing.

The purpose of the photo album is to convert the vector drawing into a bitmap image which has realistic properties. A variety of standard materials can be applied or your own photos can be used to provide materials or backgrounds. It is easy at this stage to get carried away and spend far too long on the album shot. Once a clear image has been obtained (or range of images if you are developing an idea), stop, save and print.

EXAMINER'S TIP

Draw and extrude a background with a curve between horizontal and vertical. The object you are rendering can then be 'assembled' onto the background. By using a reflective material on the background you can produce realistic shadows.

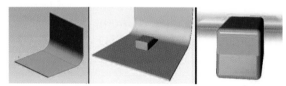

Figure 4.19 Using a solid background to produce shadows

Output

It is possible to print from any of the three types of drawing but for design folders the best results will come from the album and engineering drawing.

A number of CNC machines accept files direct from ProDesktop or in an industry standard format such as IGES or MEDUSA.

Other useful export options are the .bmp and .jpg and .tif files; files in these formats can be included in any word-processed document or edited with Paint or Photoshop.

When you export a file for use in another application, make sure that the render settings are at a high enough value for the final print size. A good starting point is the 1024 × 768 pixels option in image properties. Choosing presentation mode will apply anti-aliasing; this helps to remove the jagged edges that can occur.

Preparation of photographic images

Most digital cameras will provide JPEG files with the .jpg extension. This type of file can be compressed to take up less space on the memory card at the expense of some quality. For adding to a folder or if the photo is to be printed, set the camera resolution at the highest value. If the picture is to be used only on screen, a lower value will be sufficient. More advanced cameras will allow TIFF or RAW files to be saved. TIFF files saved with .tif extensions do not lose quality when they are saved; as a result the files can be quite large. RAW files save data exactly as the sensor in the camera sees it; this allows the user to process the file as they wish without any enforced loss of detail. When a file or set of files are downloaded to the computer they should be stored in a folder which indicates the content and date taken. Any work done on individual photos should then be saved under a different name so that the original is still there. There are a number of simple ways of getting the best out of your photos. If you have got a lot of unwanted detail around the edge it can be cropped to leave only the main subject. If no other tool is available the picture toolbar in Word® can be used. Colour, contrast, brightness and rotation can all be dealt with in the same way. If a program like Corel Photo-Paint is available, you have a lot more options; auto-equalize will adjust the balance between light and dark; contrast and brightness allow fine adjustments to be made. The resample control can be used to adjust image size if necessary to give a set size and resolution. For printing, a minimum of 300 dpi should be used for the resolution setting.

Figure 4.20 An image imported into Word® and cropped

4.5 TEXT, DATABASE AND GRAPHICS SOFTWARE

For project purposes the normal choice is Microsoft Office® which will provide you with either Word® or Publisher® for text input. Excel® is a good choice as a database. The graphics software already mentioned (Paint, Photoshop, Photoshop Elements or Corel Photo-Paint) are all suitable for working on bitmapped images.

A table of database information from Excel® can be placed on the clipboard by highlighting and copying. Once there it can be placed in

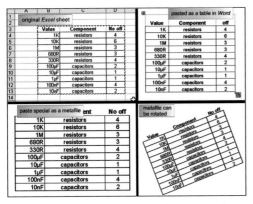

Figure 4.21 Pasting a table of information into Word®

the text document, either as an editable object using *paste* or by using *paste special* to paste it as a Windows® metafile. The first method converts your data to a Word® table, the second converts to a graphic image that can easily be scaled and behaves just as any other graphic file.

2D CAD software will also give the option of exporting an image as a metafile, a simple and effective way of adding graphics to text. In general, vector images can be saved as metafiles (with the .wmf file extension), for insertion into a project folder.

Pasting options

When pasting graphics into Word® you may have to use the picture toolbar to apply 'text wrap' to the object. This ensures that text will flow around and not through the graphic.

Cropping is another tool that will be needed. The crop tool acts in a different way to simply sizing an object. The crop tool will remove a section from each edge of the graphic without affecting the scale. As a general rule, remove as much of the background as possible while keeping an even border around the graphic image. When putting together a design folder go for a simple, readable font such as Arial and make sure that you use a readable point size, such as 11 or 12 point, for the main text.

Save work on a regular basis, do not rely on a single copy of the file, and do not rely on memory sticks as they can go missing.

To avoid having to add the same information to every sheet, make use of the header and footer facility; this will also add page numbers as you go along.

When checking work, a vital tool often missed is the spellchecker. It should be the last thing that you use before printing a design folder or committing it to a CD-ROM. Getting somebody else to read through the text is also useful as they can often spot quite basic mistakes.

A simple method of recording what you have done in any software is to use the PrtScn or print screen button on the keyboard. This does not literally print the screen but it does send a copy of the full screen to the clipboard from where it can be pasted into any application and later cropped to the area that you need.

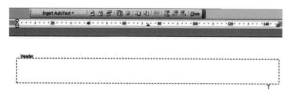

Figure 4.22 Header and footer menu in Word® with header area visible

4.6 STORING AND SHARING DATA

It is important that work is not just stored in one place. If you do that, sooner or later you may well lose work and these things have a habit of happening just before important deadlines! A system of regularly backing up your work onto either a CD or a memory stick will avoid the problem. Folder names and file names should be meaningful; if they are not, you may have to open a lot of files to find the one that you want.

Some files may be needed on a more regular basis, particularly the CAD drawings with parts that can be used in other drawings. Keep a folder as a library of parts; this can then be used for more than a single project.

When searching through a folder for drawings or photos, remember that the way the file is viewed can be changed. The normal view is probably the 'details' style; if you change this to thumbnails the contents of each photo or drawing can be seen immediately.

Figure 4.23 Folder contents with assembly and parts shown in thumbnail view

4.7 APPLICATIONS OF CAD/CAM

Designing

CAD can be used in many stages of designing but it is important to remember that it is not always appropriate or the most efficient route. Many designers will still produce early ideas using paper and pencil or modelling with real materials. A lot will depend on the area of designing being tackled. In electronics it is quite common to do all designing on screen, where it can be tested or simulated instantly. This approach is fine but you will need to carry out some basic research into integrated circuit (IC) function or in finding suitable circuits rather than hoping to do the whole thing yourself. Pneumatics projects will almost certainly include a lot of modelling with the equipment and unless you are really confident in your abilities, the CAD work for this type of project will come later. Software like Crocodile Clips is very useful for modelling mechanisms; you may also find that 2D drawing can be useful when planning the positions of components in a mechanism. Whatever it is that you are designing, the important thing is to use the most appropriate method to develop ideas. If you have access to systems boards for electronics it may be quicker to assemble and test a system on there first. Remember to take a photograph of any models produced in this way if it is for an assessed project.

Drawing loci

In mechanisms design, when links move it is important to know that they are not going to hit another part of the mechanism. The locus of a point is the path followed by that point as it moves and it can give important information. The locus will not always be needed but if you are designing a linkage that will fit into a tight space, it is an essential element of designing. It will also give important information about pivot points and the length of slots needed for the linkage to operate. The movements of a human limb can be viewed as loci; in ergonomic work a *manikin* is used for this. Commercial versions are quite expensive but you can put your own simple version together by drawing limb outlines and grouping them into position.

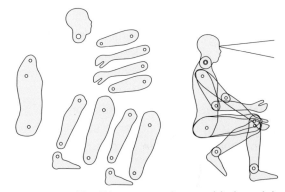

Figure 4.24 Manikin parts and assembled model

Calculations

Calculations for gearing or pulley systems can be carried out easily using a spreadsheet such as Excel®, as shown in Fig. 4.25. In many cases this is easier than using a calculator as a system can be modelled to give results from different gear or pulley ratios. Calculations for electronic systems can be carried out quickly and accurately in the same way, allowing substitution of either resistor or capacitor values.

driver teeth	driven teeth	reduction ratio (x1) X	input speed rpm	output speed
15	65	14.3333333	600	138.46154
8	50	6.25	600	96
20	56	2.8	600	214.28571

Figure 4.25 Excel® used for gear ratio calculation

Models and prototypes

With electronics it is easy to model using simulation software. The step that many people miss out is to use the test instruments that are available on screen. For example, when modelling a fast astable circuit it will not be possible to evaluate your circuit unless the on-screen oscilloscope is used or the signal is slowed down. The control of simulation speed is a valuable tool when trying to trace faults in high speed circuits. However good a simulation is, it must be tried for real at some stage, before committing your design to manufacture.

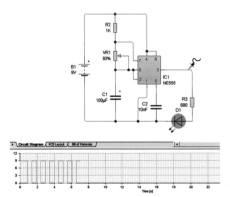

Figure 4.26 Astable circuit showing output on the oscilloscope

Use of PIC or programmable ICs has increased the level at which you can work. Once a basic circuit is produced, the rest is down to programming. When starting it is a good idea to use the flowchart that most systems provide. This will give a visual indication of what is happening when you simulate the program. Once again, the speed of simulation can be controlled so an action that will take a millisecond in real time can be slowed right down so that the result can be viewed.

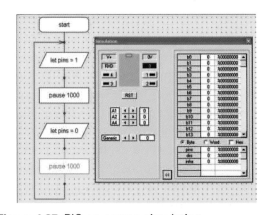

Figure 4.27 PIC on-screen simulation

Once the PIC program has been designed it must be made as a circuit. Simulation software is being developed to actually test the program when designing the circuit but it is not an essential feature as a blank dual in line (DIL) IC can be inserted into the design. Fig. 4.28 shows how a PCB can be developed from the circuit design in Fig. 4.29. The final artwork is shown in Fig. 4.30. This should be printed out onto good quality tracing paper or Mylar film ready for use in the photoetch process.

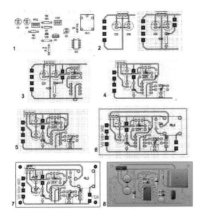

Figure 4.28 Sequence of development for the PCB layout

The sequence shown in Fig. 4.28 has been designed without using the circuit to PCB conversion facility that is available in the software. This conversion facility is known as 'autorouting'. It is possible to use the direct conversion but you may find that if you have carried out your own designing, your understanding of the circuit is better. There are advantages to both methods but generally a more compact board can be designed if you do the whole job yourself. Saving the sequence as a series of numbered files, as mentioned earlier in the chapter, will provide good evidence of development for the project folder.

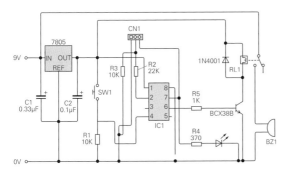

Figure 4.29 Schematic circuit

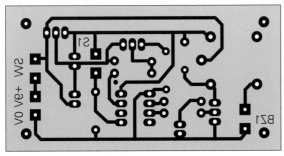

Figure 4.30 Artwork for the completed circuit

EXAMINER'S TIPS

When designing a PCB, remember the following points:

- Use the widest tracks that will fit on your circuit.
- Pad sizes should also be adjusted to the maximum that will fit. If you do this there is less risk of a break in the track or of drilling a pad totally away.
- Always have some text, e.g. your name, on the board so that you know which way up it goes.
- Put a mark near pin 1 on any ICs.
- Use terminal blocks for inputs and outputs.
- Keep tracks horizontal or vertical as far as possible.
- Measure component pin distances carefully.
- Use $0\,\Omega$ resistors instead of link wires.

PIC devices are not only useful in electronic projects but can also find a place in the control of valves in a pneumatic circuit.

A final point on PCB design using CAD is that in most cases it will save as a Gerber file, which can be sent directly to a commercial PCB manufacturer. The information enclosed in the file is broken down into pad sizes and positions, track position and width, followed by details of the screen layer with component information. The whole process can be carried out without the designer ever seeing the manufacturer.

▶ Laser cutter

Design of mechanisms, particularly when linkages are involved, will require testing at an early stage. Many schools now have access to a laser cutter and this will provide the means of making excellent quality acrylic models of linkages. Holes for pin joints can be laser cut with the rest of the profile rather than having to use a drill; complex outlines can also be produced. If a thicker piece of material is needed, it is possible to laminate and by adding holes to each part, a piece of acrylic rod can be used to dowel the laminate together.

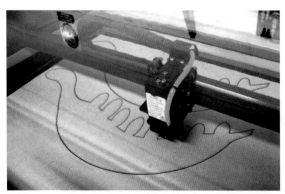

Figure 4.31 Laser cutter being used to produce a profile in MDF

In addition to working on acrylic, it is possible to use 3 mm MDF as the basis for a model and this can also be cut with the laser. For those who do not have access to a laser cutter, CAD can still provide a useful tool for modelling. If templates are accurately drawn, they can be printed and glued to sheet material, providing a clear outline to cut to. This method can be also be used later in a project, for example, when cutting holes in a vacuum-formed casing, the hole positions can be CAD drawn and printed out as a template with datum marks for lining up on the casing.

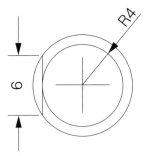

Figure 4.32 'D' hole template

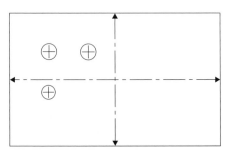

Figure 4.33 Template for top of electronics casing

 EXAMINER'S TIP

When drawing out a template, add a line of set length and dimension to it. When the template has been printed you can then measure the line with a ruler to ensure that it has printed out full size.

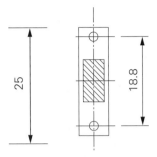

Figure 4.34 The 25 mm line can be measured to ensure accuracy

One-off and quantity production

One-off production is the making of an item or items using processes that do not always allow for easy duplication.

When vacuum forming, templates for producing the forming tool can be drawn using CAD. Holes in the vacuum forming for switches and controls can be marked onto the forming tool using a paper template to give accurate positioning and then centre punching or drilling a small diameter hole in the forming tool. When the forming takes

place, a small depression will appear that is enough to mark the hole.

Quantity production will probably be limited to a small batch but even so it is often worth setting up a machine for manufacture. In many projects, CAD/CAM will be used for one-off production even though the full benefit of the equipment will not be gained. One copy of the artwork for a PCB is required for a single circuit, but if more than one were required, a number of circuits can be blocked together and etched in one go.

Time is saved and, apart from the cost of the board, very little extra expense is involved. One of the main benefits of CAM is in the repeatability of the process. In industry, machines have to be kept working for as much of the day as is possible to gain most benefit from the investment.

Results gained from using CAM should be consistent and if tools on the machines are in good order, quality will be high. What should be remembered is that setting up the

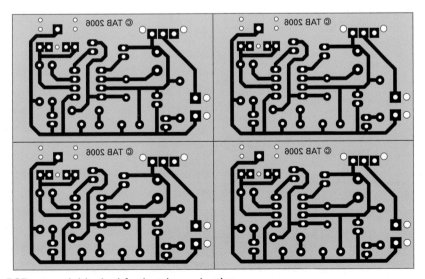

Figure 4.35 PCB artwork blocked for batch production

machine can take three or four times as long as the operation that will be carried out. Allow time in your planning for this. Once it is set, it may be worth producing a spare for the one part that you are making. It will often cost very little for materials but can save a lot of time if there is a mistake with the first one.

Figure 4.36 CNC vinyl cutter and close-up view of the cutting head

Figure 4.37 A project with vinyl cut labels

▶ Computer numerical control (CNC) machines

CNC machines come in a variety of forms but basically they are using the same principle. Tool position is controlled by sending electronic signals to operate motors that position either the tool or the work, and then the tool completes a cutting action. Machines that you may find in school using this system are a lathe, milling machine, router, laser cutter and vinyl cutter. Smaller machines have at most three axes of movement, usually known as the X, Y, and Z axis.

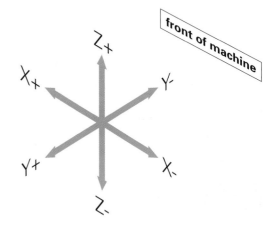

Figure 4.38–9 Layout of axes on a 3-axis milling machine

Movement can take place in a + or − direction for each axis of movement. Taking a vinyl or laser cutter as an example, if you want to cut a circle, the movement will be in the form of a series of steps, as shown in Fig. 4.40.

To provide fine movement like this, stepper motors are normally used, sometimes being geared down using spur gears or a stepped pulley to provide an even smaller movement. On the CNC router in Fig. 4.41, the X axis stepper motor can be seen on the right hand side of the machine.

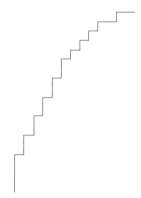

Figure 4.40 The cutter moves in small steps to form a curve

Figure 4.41 CNC router

The language of many CNC machines is *G&M codes,* these codes being used to pass instructions directly to the work holder, the tool holder or the drive motors. A program will have to take into account the order of work and also ensure that when the tool is moving to a new position, it does not hit the work. Most software currently being used will take a file that has been drawn in another package and convert it into G&M codes with

the code not being seen at all. It is useful to have an appreciation of what is happening because a certain amount of editing can be carried out direct on the code without having to write a totally new program. As with any other programming, it is good practice if you are writing code to include *REM* statements or annotation to each line of the program.

Industrial milling machines and routers will have extra axes of movement to ensure that the cutting tool can get to the ideal position rather than having to compromise. Machines with up to five axes are now common with even more being available on robotic based CNC machines.

All line drawings will need line thickness setting to 0.15 mm.
G codes

G00	Rapid positioning movement
G01	Linear movement
G02	Circular movement clockwise
G03	Circular movement counter clockwise
G12	Clockwise circular pocket milling
G13	Counter clockwise circular pocket milling

M codes

M00	Program stop
M03	Spindle on clockwise
M04	Spindle on counter clockwise
M05	Spindle stop
M06	Tool change
M08	Coolant on

Figure 4.42 Examples of G&M codes

4.8 PROGRAMMABLE CONTROL SYSTEMS

Programmable logic controllers (PLCs)

Programmable logic controllers or PLCs are now common in manufacturing industry. They are capable of handling multiple inputs and outputs and of sensing a variety of different conditions. The PLC will provide a sequence of operations once programmed and can be easily customised to match the needs of an individual user. Some PLCs will include the facility to measure analogue signals as part of their sensing function. An example of this is where an operation relies on a temperature range. The temperature is measured as an analogue value and then converted before being used in the process.

PLCs are often used to monitor and control pneumatic systems.

Microcontroller overview

These tiny programmable devices are now featuring increasingly in everyday life. Many of them are stand-alone individual devices that rarely need reprogramming. The other option is to have them controlled as part of a computer network where any updating can take place quickly and a number of the devices can be dealt with simultaneously. In either case, the microcontroller will contain the codes needed to operate independently; it is the means of changing the code that differs.

The latest systems will use embedded Internet in the microcontroller which allows a web server to send out fresh instructions when requested. In a factory, a network could quickly update a number of separate microcontrollers. In addition, if the microcontrollers are being used to monitor conditions of a machine or manufacturing operation, alterations can be carried out remotely; an engineer can manage a machine from thousands of miles away. You may have come across this with a computer being managed remotely by a service engineer on a helpline or even by your teacher in a computer suite. Machines can also be set to automatically send an email to an engineer if a breakdown occurs, allowing a repair to take place quickly and in many cases without even visiting the site.

Microcontrollers in cars are now common and most modern vehicles have controllers for engine management, braking, steering and stability control. Most will not require alteration in the life of the vehicle but engine management systems can be reprogrammed to cope with different conditions or to alter performance.

Microcontrollers have a CPU or central processing unit to carry out program instructions. They also have RAM or temporary memory for the program to use and ROM where the program and any set values are stored. A microcontroller can be embedded in another device such as a washing machine or TV where it will control the functions of the device. Microcontrollers are dedicated and will only carry out the one program that is held on them. This program can be overwritten, as necessary, if an update or improvement becomes available. Many of the microcontrollers used today use quite old technology as the CPU. The Z80, which gained popularity in the early Sinclair computers, is still being used, as is the 80386, which was at the heart of many school computers in the 1980s.

The PIC

The microcontroller developed by the firm Microchip is known as a PIC®. This is the family of microcontrollers used in most school projects. The board shown in Fig. 4.43 uses an 18-pin PIC and has a Darlington Driver output. Easy access to the inputs and outputs is available using terminal blocks.

Figure 4.43 18-pin PIC board

PICs are low cost devices and have now reached the point where they are almost a throwaway item. They come in a DIL package that is easily built into a circuit. Inputs can be either analogue or digital; the analogue inputs being converted into a numerical value once they have been read. The CPU is capable of carrying out logical operations and, in addition, it can make use of time delays that relate to real time. A small addition can be made to the circuit that will allow the device to operate in real time and keep track of the date as well. PICs are available as 8, 14, 18, 20, 28, or 40-pin versions. In general, the higher the number of pins, the more facilities

on the chip. A number of programming systems are available but the examples given here will use the PICAXE® system that can be downloaded free from the PICAXE website. The software uses a flowchart for programming or, for more advanced use, programs can be written in BASIC, a computer language that is not too hard to learn.

The first example given in Fig. 4.44 will develop a program to operate the PIC alarm circuit described earlier in the chapter.

The first two boxes in the chart switch pin 1 on and off with no delay; this sets up pin 1 as an output. It can also be done using the command 'let dirs = %00000010' . This can be used to set all pins up in one go as either input or output. The % sign tells the program to expect a binary number. Each 0 in the number is an input and each 1 is an output. Input 3 and output 0 on the 8-pin PIC cannot be changed; only in/out 1, 2 and 4 will be affected.

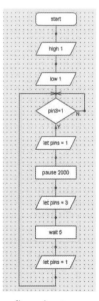

Figure 4.44 Alarm flowchart

The next box is where input 3 is checked for the sensor/switch being pressed. It will continually loop until that happens. When activated, the LED connected to output 0 will be switched on with the command 'let pins = 1'; this is followed by a 2000 ms or 2 second delay. The Darlington transistor at output 2 is then switched on as well as the first LED. The result of setting the output as 'let pins = 3' can be seen in Fig. 4.45. After a further 5 seconds, using the wait command this time, the output changes again to just output 0 being on. The flow of the program goes back to the checking pin 3 box and it is ready to detect another switching action.

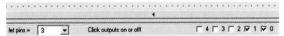

Figure 4.45 'Pins' dialogue box showing both outputs switched on

This type of program is known as linear, with each command following the next. In any longer program it is better to write a

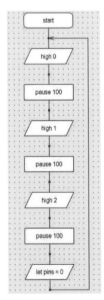

Figure 4.46 Linear flowchart

structured program using sub-routines. With this method the main program calls up a sub-routine which is then carried out. The return statement takes the flow back to the main program. No duplication of code using this method means shorter programs.

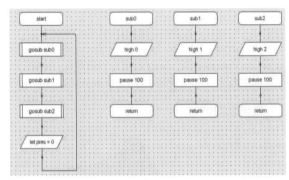

Figure 4.47 Structured flowchart

In addition to sensing a switch closing or opening, the PIC can also use a device like the Dallas DS18B20. This can be connected to an analogue input and will return the temperature in °C and store it in a variable. The big benefit of using a PIC approach to electronics is the speed that changes can be made. Altering a program and downloading it can be done in seconds with no changes to hardware needed.

Development of control programs should be treated in the same way as circuits for project folder purposes. Regular saving using a different file version will allow you to go back later to print out the development of the final program.

Robots in manufacturing

Use of robots within commercial manufacturing is now common, particularly among car manufacturers. They are strictly programmable devices with three or more axes of movement. Robot arms can be programmed or 'trained' to carry out complex tasks with a degree of precision that would not be possible using humans. In assembly work, where very small components are being picked and placed such as surface mount components in the electronics industry, it would be impossible for a human to achieve the accuracy and speed of a robot or machine. The components shown in Fig. 4.48 will be placed at the rate of

approximately one per second. The program used to control the placement robot sets the orientation of the component, polarity and position on the circuit board.

In the engineering industry, robot arms are commonly used to remove completed components from a CNC machine and load a new piece of work onto the machine. Advantages in this case are mainly in the reduction of workers needed to operate a production line.

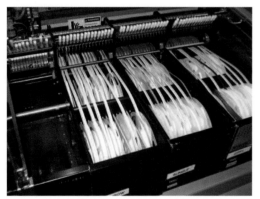

Figure 4.48 Surface mount components being fed into a 'placing' machine

Figure 4.49 Robot arm

KEY TERMS

PIC® – microcontroller produced by microchip

CPU – central processing unit – carries out arithmetical and logic operations

ROM – read only memory; once downloaded from the PC cannot be altered without another download

RAM – random access memory, sometimes known as volatile memory; it will clear when the circuit is switched off

VARIABLE – temporary storage can be 1 byte or 1 word (2 bytes); maximum value for 1 byte is 255; for 1 word is 63,335

ADC – analogue to digital converter

INTERRUPT – a means of taking instant control of the program

RESONATOR – provides the operating frequency for the device, either internal or external

RESET – means of getting back to the start of a program

BASIC – high level computer language

DEBUG – a command allowing values to be seen on a monitor screen
FLOWCHART – visual means of writing a program
BIT – smallest amount of data handled – literally a **binary digit**
BYTE – 8 bits
WORD – 16 bits
BINARY – the low level language of the computer – 1s and 0s

CHAPTER 5

MECHANISMS

5.1 GENERAL PRINCIPLES

By the end of this chapter you should have developed
a knowledge and understanding of:

- the language of mechanisms
- components used in mechanisms
- general principles involved in the design of mechanisms
- conversion and transmission of motion
- calculations.

A mechanism in the control sense can be defined in a number of ways:

- *a simple machine*
- *a device that will assist in the performance of human tasks*
- *a device to modify mechanical energy and transmit it in a more useful form*
- *a device consisting of fixed and moving parts that may be connected*
- *machines and mechanisms include the logical assembly of component parts to allow a system to achieve its purpose.*

A mechanism is all of these things and in this chapter you will find examples of well known mechanisms along with their practical applications.

KEY TERMS

LOAD – the weight or mass that is supported or moved by a mechanism

EFFORT – the input force applied to the mechanism. If the mechanism has a mechanical advantage, the distance moved by the effort will be greater than the distance moved by the load

FULCRUM – in a lever mechanism, the pivot about which the lever turns is known as the fulcrum. The position of the fulcrum relative to the load and effort will determine the class of lever

TORQUE – this is the turning force in a mechanism. High torque means that there is a lot of force going into the rotation; this is generally associated with a high gear ratio

FRICTION – this can be defined as a force resisting the relative motion of two surfaces

MECHANICAL ADVANTAGE – this is simply defined as load divided by effort or output force divided by input force. **IDEAL MECHANICAL ADVANTAGE** is what you would get if there was no friction in the mechanism. **ACTUAL MECHANICAL ADVANTAGE** is the real figure and is dependent on the amount of frictional loss in the mechanism

VELOCITY RATIO – The distance over which the force is applied divided by the distance over which the load is moved. The factor by which any applied force is multiplied; it is independent of friction

EFFICIENCY – this is a percentage, given by the formula: **M**echanical **A**dvantage/**V**elocity **R**atio or **MA/VR**

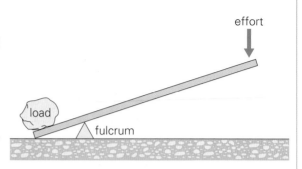

Figure 5.1

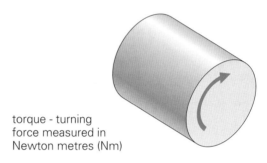

torque - turning force measured in Newton metres (Nm)

Figure 5.2

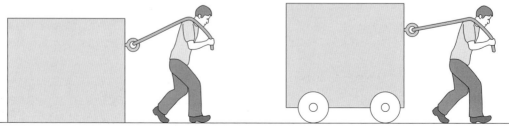

Figure 5.3 Using wheels will reduce the friction

5.2 COMPONENTS

Wheel

This can be viewed as a lever rotating about a centre point or axis. In a cartwheel the effort is applied at the rim, the load is at the outer radius of the axle.

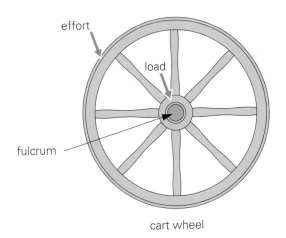

Figure 5.4

cart wheel

Axle or shaft

This is the part around which a wheel, gear or pulley will rotate. There will always be frictional loss between the wheel and axle but bearings will reduce this to a minimum. In addition, the mechanical advantage of the wheel leverage is so large that even on a wooden axle a wheel can be made to rotate.

Flywheel

The flywheel is a device for storing rotational energy. In most cases the storage time is extremely small; in a single cylinder engine the rotation of the crankshaft is only powered for half of the downward movements of the piston. The stored energy in the flywheel will carry the crankshaft round the remainder of

Figure 5.5 Flywheel on a steam engine

the rotation. Some railway locomotives have been fitted with flywheel boosters to carry them through gaps in the power rail. Flywheels used for storing energy have the advantage that they produce no harmful emissions but larger ones spinning at a high speed have been known to shatter. The steam engine in Fig. 5.5 was used for many years to operate Tower Bridge in London.

Motors

Mechanisms are often driven by electric motors, which can vary in size, power output

Figure 5.6 Lift motor and gearbox

and voltage requirement. Whatever type of motor is used, it will have to be coupled or joined to the mechanism in a way that allows the mechanism to rotate. The lift motor shown in Fig. 5.6 is coupled to the pulley through a worm gear; this does not allow the pulley to turn the motor shaft. For more information see Section 5.5 of this chapter.

Pulley

One useful method of linking a motor to a mechanism is by using a pulley and drive belt. This method is versatile and if a smooth rather than a toothed belt is used, the motor pulley can slip if the mechanism jams. The drive pulley is fully described in Section 5.4.

Lifting pulleys are used in a mechanism to assist in lifting heavy loads. In most pulley systems an extra pulley is used to reverse the direction of 'pull'. The two-pulley system has one to halve the effort and one to allow a downward pull. The length of rope that must be pulled down is doubled in this case.

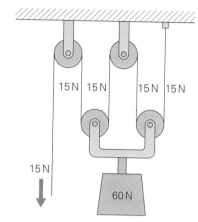

Figure 5.8 Three pulleys plus one to reverse the direction of pull

Figure 5.9 Small hoist for lifting car engines

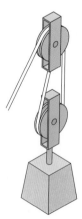

Figure 5.7 Using a pulley the effort is halved

Fixings

Fixings on mechanisms can be divided into those that are permanent or semi-permanent and those fixings that are temporary, meaning that they can easily be removed. The majority of fixings, particularly in prototype products, are temporary for maintenance reasons; it also allows easy dismantling and recycling at the end of a product's useful life.

Permanent fixings

Rivets of the solid type, although not often used now, can still be an effective means of joining parts together. It is possible, with careful use of spacers, to have a moving joint that has been riveted. It is also possible to have a totally rigid and extremely strong joint between two steel plates. In most cases the rivet head will be formed cold and possibly shaped, e.g. the snap head rivet. To form a joint, the rivet and joint have to be supported whilst the end of the rivet is formed into a head.

A useful type of rivet is the pop rivet; this can be fastened from one side. The hollow rivet body is expanded when a hard steel pin with a ball end is pulled through it. The hardened pin then snaps, leaving the joint complete.

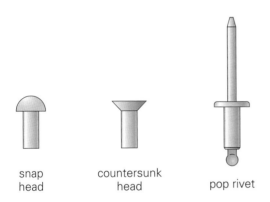

snap head

countersunk head

pop rivet

Figure 5.10

Adhesives are being used increasingly for joining parts together and also in the initial moulding of parts using composite materials. Epoxy resin has the strength and resistance to vibration to make it a suitable choice for a permanent fixing. In the aircraft industry the use of composite materials in their construction is becoming common. When moulded into an epoxy resin matrix materials such as carbon fibre and Kevlar will produce a tough material that is capable of replacing aluminium alloys.

Temporary fixings

By definition a fixing that can be taken apart is temporary. Threaded components such as nuts, bolts and screws fit into this category. Mechanisms will often involve vibration when they are operated; for this reason several ways of stopping threaded components from coming undone have been developed. Nyloc nuts and spring washers are the easiest to use in school projects, as they are low cost and easily obtainable. A nyloc nut includes an unthreaded portion of nylon which has a thread pressed into it as the nut is tightened. The nylon will try to go back to its uncompressed shape and so forms a tight seal on the thread. However, they can only be used once and should then be discarded. A similar nut is the 'aerotight', which is an all-metal locking nut. It is possible to make your own version of this by using a junior hacksaw to put a cut into the side of a nut and then closing the cut in a vice to distort the thread. Not ideal but it works.

Figure 5.11 Nyloc and aerotight nuts

Figure 5.12 Spring washers

Threads used now are normally metric and are known according to the diameter of the thread; an M10 thread being a Ø10 metric thread with a pitch of 1.5 mm. Useful bolt heads are hexagonal or cap head, tightened with a spanner or with a hexagon key.

Figure 5.13 Hexagon and cap head bolts

Washers should be used under a nut to spread the load on the parts being tightened and to give a good bearing surface to allow the nut to turn freely. For school projects, the most useful sizes will be M3, M4, M6 and M8.

Self-tapping screws are another excellent choice for project work. They are hardened and will cut their own thread as they are inserted. For fitting sheet materials to a frame they offer a good alternative to pop rivets.

Figure 5.14 A selection of small screws

▶ Modular components

Gearbox

For modelling a project it is useful to have a set of gears already in a frame that can be used to reduce the speed of a motor. There are a number of kits available that will allow this and provide enough parts to put together a range of different gear ratios.

Modelling mechanisms

Modelling systems such as Lego, Fischer Technic and Meccano have been around for many years and provide an easy way of modelling linkages, pulley systems and gearing systems. CAD software such as Crocodile Clips has mechanism features that allow electro-mechanical systems to be developed. 3D modelling software such as ProDesktop can be used for testing gears, linkages and cams although the parts have to be constructed first and then assembled into a working unit. For many linkage designs a simple 2D software package will allow the parts to be drawn accurately before cutting out and assembling. If your school has a laser cutter it is very quick to cut a simple mechanism out in acrylic and test it before final manufacture.

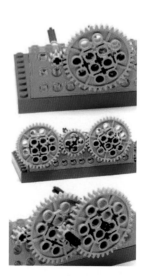

Figure 5.15 Models of a simple gear train, an idler gear and a compound gear train

5.3 BASIC MECHANISMS

Inclined plane

This is one of the most ancient simple machines, having no moving parts. It relies on the principle that a heavy load can be moved from one level to a higher level more easily by using a ramp or inclined plane rather than a direct vertical lift. The load has to travel further but the effort needed to move it is less. A road winding up a mountain rather than taking the shortest route to the top is an example of this. The mechanical advantage is given as the ratio of sloping distance travelled against vertical height moved. The inclined plane in Fig. 5.16 cut down the time taken for a canal boat to travel from one level to another.

Figure 5.16 Inclined plane

If an inclined plane is wrapped around a shaft, you have the principle of the screw thread; this is shown in Fig. 5.17.

Screw thread

This is one of the most commonly used simple mechanisms. It consists of a groove in the form of a helix cut either internally in the case of a nut, or externally for a bolt. Important features of a screw thread are the

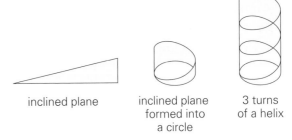

inclined plane   inclined plane   3 turns
                       formed into   of a helix
                        a circle

Figure 5.17

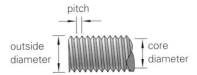

pitch

outside
diameter

core
diameter

Figure 5.18

outside diameter, the core diameter and the pitch. By using standard pitches and diameters, it is possible for screw threads to be specified in a design and then easily obtained. The thread will convert rotary movement to linear movement and as such is often used in actuators. In the last 50 years, worldwide acceptance of the ISO metric thread standard has meant that more equipment is interchangeable. However, a few alternative standards are still in use, the differences being in the profile of the thread and the angle of the thread.

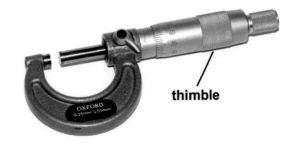

thimble

Figure 5.19 Micrometer

The buttress thread shown is used in quick release actions on a vice; the square thread, which is stronger than a vee thread, is used for clamping devices. Measuring devices such as the micrometer shown in Fig. 5.19 use threads with a 0.5 mm pitch; each rotation of the thimble will open or close it by 0.5 mm.

buttress thread　　　　square thread

Figure 5.20

Levers

The lever is one of the simplest mechanisms to make and use but it is also one of the most useful. It is also incidentally one of the oldest. First described by Archimedes in about 260BC, levers have almost certainly been in use since prehistoric times.

Levers can be split into three **classes** or **orders**. Each order has three common features: a position where effort is applied; a position where a load is moved; and a fulcrum or balance point.

A quick method of remembering the orders of lever is:

see-saw – wheelbarrow – tweezers

These three common items represent the first, second and third orders of lever.

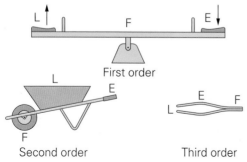

Figure 5.21 First, second and third order levers

Varying the distance between load and fulcrum or effort and fulcrum will alter the efficiency of the lever. The three orders are shown in Fig. 5.21.

First order lever

The fulcrum is between the load and effort. If there is to be a mechanical advantage, the distance from effort to fulcrum must be greater than load to fulcrum.

Second order lever

The fulcrum is at one end with the load between the fulcrum and effort.

Third order lever

This one will not give a mechanical advantage as the effort to fulcrum distance is always less than the load to fulcrum. It will however make some jobs easier to do because it allows more delicate handling of what is usually a small load.

Look around you at everyday items and you will see levers in action in many different roles. A spanner is a second order lever; a cycle brake lever is a second order lever.

Very often levers are used in pairs such as scissors, which are two first order levers; nut crackers, which are two second order levers; and salad tongs, which are a pair of third order levers.

When you see a lever, apply the rules to work out the order of lever:

• If the fulcrum is in the centre it is first order.

• If the load is in the centre it is second order.

• If the effort is in the centre it is third order.

5.4 MOTION

Types of motion

There are only four types of motion that can appear in any mechanism:

- **Rotary** – examples being a wheel, gear or cog
- **Oscillating** – moving through an arc or part of a circle
- **Linear** – straight line motion which is not constrained to return
- **Reciprocating** – forward and back in a straight line.

Most mechanisms involve more than one of these movements and it is normal for the type of motion to be converted in a mechanism.

The following are examples of everyday items involving conversion of motion:

- a door handle will convert oscillating movement into reciprocating movement
- in a desk stapler there is both oscillating and reciprocating movement as the head is pressed down
- in a foot pump the pedal will oscillate while the pistons reciprocate.

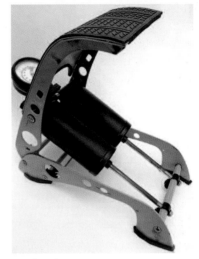

Figure 5.23 Car foot pump

These examples lead on to two standard mechanisms for converting motion.

The crank and the cam

Crank

A piston in a motorcycle engine is an example of reciprocating motion; this is converted into rotary motion by the crankshaft. The camshaft in the same engine will convert rotary motion into reciprocating motion.

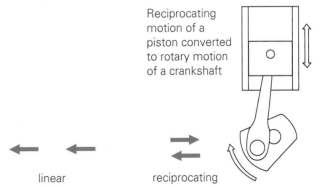

Reciprocating motion of a piston converted to rotary motion of a crankshaft

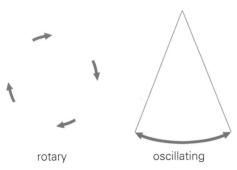

rotary   oscillating   linear   reciprocating

Figure 5.22 Types of motion

Figure 5.24 Cycle drive train

In the early days of cycling, the crank was attached directly to the wheel allowing no change in gear ratio; since then, the use of chain and sprockets has allowed multiple gear ratios.

Cam

The cam can be thought of as a wheel with the rim not concentric with the axle. That is simplifying it a lot but the result is there: as the wheel turns, the rim will move up and down – reciprocating motion. Cams are used for many purposes: for locking devices – tripod legs; knock down (KD) fittings, cycle quick release wheels; for adjustment – car brake shoes, cam nut, and for providing small reciprocating movements from a rotating shaft. A cam will require another part of the mechanism to rest on it or to follow the movement of the cam; this is called a cam follower. It can be a simple rod, a roller, a point or a knife shape. Each will be used in different situations. Followers can be offset to make them rotate, to ensure that any wear in the follower is even.

Cam design is quite complex but it can be brought down to a few basics:

- The number of times the follower lifts for each rotation of the cam.
- The distance the follower will move for each lift.
- The speed at which the follower moves.
- The amount of dwell or 'no movement' time during each rotation.

Cams are often found in automata projects in school and they can be cut from MDF or acrylic using a laser cutter for accuracy.

Figure 5.26 shows a constant velocity or heart-shaped cam with no dwell and continuous movement of the follower

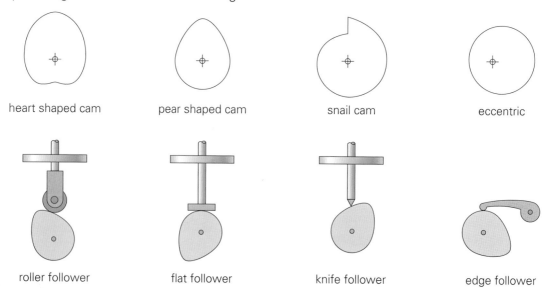

heart shaped cam   pear shaped cam   snail cam   eccentric

roller follower   flat follower   knife follower   edge follower

Figure 5.25 Cam profiles and followers

Figure 5.26 Constant velocity or heart-shaped cam

throughout 360°. This shape of cam was used on early sewing machines to wind thread evenly onto a bobbin.

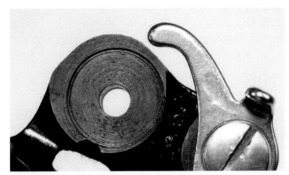

Figure 5.27 Heart-shaped cam and edge follower used on the bobbin winder of a sewing machine

Transmission of motion

Where movement or motion has to be taken from one part of a mechanism to another, there are three main approaches:

- gearing systems
- belt and pulley
- chain drive.

These can of course be 'mix and matched' when designing the system. Let's look at them in more detail.

Gears

Gears have teeth that mesh with other gear teeth to transmit motion. Depending on the number of teeth on each gear, the speed and torque of the second or driven gear can be changed.

The shape of the teeth is very important and good quality spur gears use teeth with what is known as an 'involute profile'. This means that the surfaces of mating teeth retain contact as the gears rotate. An involute is the path traced by the end of a piece of string that is wrapped around a circle. Teeth should be kept lubricated to minimise wear: grease in a slow moving system with steel teeth; an oil bath for rapidly rotating gears. Gears made from nylon will not require lubrication which is why nylon is used for geared equipment coming into contact with food.

When you are drawing gears, do not try to draw all of the teeth; use the symbol for a gear as shown in Fig. 5.28.

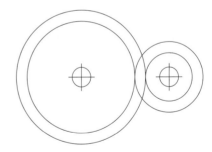

Figure 5.28

Gearing systems
Different arrangements and types of gear are available:

- A gear train has two or more gears meshed.

- A simple gear train has only one gear per shaft.

- A compound gear train has two gears locked onto the same shaft; this can

Figure 5.29 Compound gears in a servo motor

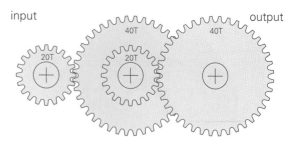

Figure 5.31 Compound gear train

reduce the size of the gear train for a particular reduction ratio.

- Unless a clutch is built in, there is no slip in a gear system.

Spur gears

These transmit motion in the same plane, reversing the direction of rotation from one gear to the next. In a simple gear train with an even number of spur gears, the output or driven gear will be rotating in the opposite direction to the input or driver. In a simple train with an odd number of gears, the output will rotate in the same direction as the input.

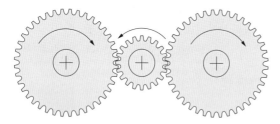

Figure 5.30 Idler gear used to keep input and output direction the same

An idler which does nothing but reverse the direction can be used; in this case the number of teeth on the gear does not matter.

In the compound gear train shown, each pair of gears gives a reduction of 2:1, the final

reduction is $(2:1) \times (2:1) = 4:1$. An input of 100 rpm will give an output of 25 rpm.

Pins or dowels are often used to hold a spur gear in place. This is a safety feature as the dowel can be made to shear before any damage occurs to the gear teeth. A similar method is to make one gear in a train from a softer material. This is known as a sacrificial gear, designed to fail before expensive damage takes place. Nylon gears are often

Figure 5.32

Figure 5.33 Replaceable wooden gear teeth in a watermill

used for this purpose. In the past, operators of watermills and windmills found that using wooden- and metal-toothed gears together resulted in the quieter operation of the mill machinery; it also reduced the wear on the metal-toothed gears. The wooden teeth, which could be replaced individually, would break if excessive force was applied, avoiding damage to the more expensive cast iron gears.

Bevel gears

The connection of shafts at an angle to each other, normally 90°, can be done using bevel gears. Gears with differing numbers of teeth will change the relative speeds of the shafts. One common use of bevel gears is in a differential gearbox. This will overcome the problem of an inner wheel in a corner needing to rotate more slowly than the outer one.

Figure 5.34 There are four bevel gears in the cage on the differential

Helical gears

These will connect parallel shafts but the teeth are cut at an angle to the axis of rotation.

Advantages

- They have teeth that are longer and stronger than straight cut gears, meaning a larger area of surface contact of the teeth.
- They can carry higher loads.

- Helical gears are quieter in operation and have less vibration than straight cut gears.
- They can be used to join two shafts at 90° to each other in a similar way to bevel gears.

Disadvantages

- Helical gears are more expensive to manufacture.
- The gears try to move sideways on the shaft; this is known as axial thrust.

Figure 5.35 Shaft from a car gearbox

Worm gear

This gear consists of a pinion and a worm gear: two shafts intersecting at 90° are used and the input gear is always the worm.

The worm gear is in the form of a screw thread and can be considered as a single-toothed gear. The pinion is a spur gear with helically cut teeth.

Figure 5.36 Worm gear

Figure 5.37 Further example of a worm gear

Advantages

- Large reduction in speed in a small space; the number of teeth on the pinion gear is the reduction ratio. For example, for the gearbox in Fig. 5.36, a 30T pinion will have a reduction ratio of 30:1.

- Very quiet and smooth in operation.

- Locking action – the worm will turn the pinion but the pinion cannot turn the worm.

Disadvantages

- Inefficient because of high frictional losses.

- High level of wear occurring on the gear surfaces.

- They must be well lubricated.

- High level of axial thrust on the worm gear shaft.

Rack and pinion

These gears are used to convert rotary motion to linear motion or the other way round. The rack can be thought of as a flat spur gear with a variable number of teeth cut into it. The pinion will mesh with the teeth in the rack. If the pinion is fixed, the rack will move from side to side or up and down; if the rack is fixed, the pinion will move along the rack as in a rack and pinion railway. The number of teeth in the pinion will affect the speed of the system; more teeth in the pinion means faster movement, less teeth means slower movement with higher torque.

Rack and pinion gears are used in vehicle steering systems, the steering wheel being attached to the pinion and the rack moving the track rods attached to the wheels. Pillar drills often use a rack and pinion to raise and lower the drill table. Canal locks use a rack and pinion to open and close the sluice gates controlling water flow.

Figure 5.38 Rack and pinion mechanism on a lock gate

Belt drive

On most occasions that a belt is used it will be necessary to have a means of tensioning the belt. This can be done using a separate tensioning wheel to apply pressure or by mounting one of the pulleys on a quadrant that will swing out, applying tension to the belt. Smaller belts can be tensioned by using the elasticity in the belt and stretching it over two pulleys.

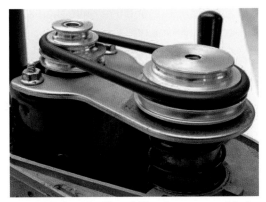

Figure 5.39 Small pillar drill using a round belt with stepped pulleys

Belt and pulley systems

This form of drive will transmit motion between parallel shafts.

Drive belts are often made from reinforced rubber and can be of round, flat, vee or toothed section. Round belts generally have some elasticity in them and can be stretched over a pulley to provide the tension.

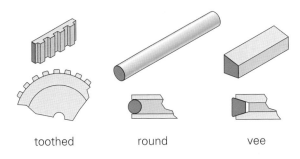

toothed   round   vee

Figure 5.40 Drive belts

Figure 5.41 Flat belt, notched vee belt and toothed camshaft belt

Vee belts are used where a higher torque is required and in some cases three or more vee belts will be used to ensure a high transfer of torque. This is often found in circular saws and planing machines. The vee belt does not fit right to the bottom of the vee on the pulley, and a tensioning method must be used to ensure that there is tension in the belt; adjustment may be required when the belt has stretched after use. To help the belt fit around a tight radius, notches can be cut out as shown in Fig. 5.41.

Where a lot of torque will be transmitted, a ribbed or toothed belt can be used, especially where belt slip must be avoided, such as a cam belt on a car engine.

Use of a belt is a less positive drive than a geared system and will generally take up more space in the mechanism. Friction between the belt and pulley is the driving force unless the belt is of the toothed type.

Advantages

- Output speed can be changed easily by using stepped pulleys.
- No lubrication required.
- Belt changing and maintenance is generally quick and easy.
- Very little vibration transmitted from one shaft to another so it can be quieter.
- Distance between shafts is not as critical as in a geared system.
- The belt can slip under a high load, providing a safety factor in the system.

Disadvantages

- A high maintenance method, belts must be checked on a regular basis for cracks and glazing caused by the belt slipping.

- Re-tensioning is required after a belt has been in use for some time.
- Providing a reversed direction of output is not as easy as with gears; a belt must be crossed over to do this.

Figure 5.42 This lawnmower uses a vee belt, a toothed belt and chain drives

Chain and sprocket system

This is another positive method of transmitting rotary motion between parallel shafts. Mention of a chain drive will make most people think of a cycle or motorcycle.

Figure 5.43 The derailleur mechanism tensions the chain as well as changing gear

The chain is a more positive drive than a belt and if correctly tensioned, it will not slip.

A tensioning method is normally required to allow adjustment of the distance between driver and driven sprockets. This can be in the form of a variable tension as in the derailleur gear on a cycle, allowing the effective length of the chain to be altered to accommodate different size cogs. The chain can also be tensioned by direct adjustment of the distance between axles. Chain size is specified by width of link, pitch and the number of links.

Advantages

- High torques can be transmitted.
- Will allow a certain amount of lateral (sideways) movement or distortion, e.g. derailleur gears moving across a block of sprockets, the chain is distorted in all but one of the available gear positions.

Disadvantages

- High maintenance, chains require regular lubrication to avoid wear.
- Can be noisier than a belt drive.
- Chains can stretch but not as much as a belt.

Drive systems

Attaching one of the previous drive methods to a shaft can be done in a number of ways.

Dowel or keyway

As mentioned with spur gears, the gear can be dowelled onto a shaft. Another positive method is to use a splined shaft to transmit the drive, with the spline on the shaft fitting into the spline on the gear or pulley. An advantage of this is that there can be some lateral movement of the gear or pulley.

Other methods of locking a gear to a shaft include the use of a key, half of which fits into the gear and the other half into the shaft. Once again, a safety factor can be built in as the key can be of a weaker material so that it will shear in the event of gears jamming.

Figure 5.44 Pulley keyed onto a shaft

Figure 5.45 Splined shaft

Plain couplings

These are simply a hollow rod that the ends of each shaft fit into, with a method of locking the coupling onto the shafts. Dowels can be used or a hexagon head grub screw will be used on smaller versions. Some couplings will have a spline on the outside to allow a gear to be attached to a shaft. Plastic couplings are available which will allow a

certain amount of misalignment in the shaft. Couplings should provide a positive drive with no backlash or unwanted movement, which can be a problem with geared systems.

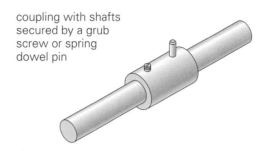

coupling with shafts secured by a grub screw or spring dowel pin

Figure 5.46 Plain coupling

Flexible couplings

As mentioned above, the material used for the coupling can provide a certain amount of flexibility but for any shafts that are designed to join at a slight angle, a universal joint will be needed. Rear wheel drive on cars was common until the transverse engine came in with the first Mini. In order to drive the rear wheels, a shaft with universal joints at both ends was used; the end nearest the engine also having a sliding spline to allow for slight forwards and backwards movements of the engine. The system is still in use in specialist cars, 4 × 4s and heavy vehicles. Universal joints can cope with up to 30° of misalignment in the shafts, although this

Figure 5.47 Universal joint from a socket set

amount is not common. Universal joints are also found in socket spanner sets.

Linkages

A linkage will be used to join parts of a mechanism together; it is also capable of changing speed, direction and timing in a mechanism.

To change direction, a **reverse motion linkage** will be used. A **bell crank linkage** will change horizontal reciprocating movement to vertical reciprocating movement. It was called a bell crank because it was used in large houses to operate the servants' bell.

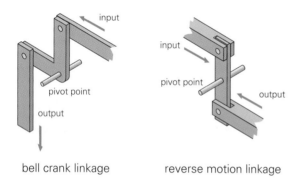

Figure 5.48 Bell crank and reverse motion linkages

A **parallel motion** or four bar linkage can be used to change direction and amplify movement; opposite sides will be parallel but the distance between them will change.

▶ Bearings and lubrication

General principles

In a mechanism any surfaces that move across each other are known as bearing surfaces. Over the years, new materials and production techniques have led to a range of bearings to suit all applications. There are two main functions of a bearing: to support a load and to reduce friction.

It is a fact that anything being moved will roll better than it will slide. There is less friction in two surfaces rolling across each other than there is if they are pushed across each other.

Each type of bearing has its merits and designers can now pick from a range of different sizes and types to suit most applications. Where an axle or shaft runs in a bearing, there are two loads to consider. The first is the radial load resulting from the weight of the item being supported by the axle; the second is the thrust resulting from forces such as cornering in a vehicle, where

Figure 5.49 Parallel motion linkage on a toolbox

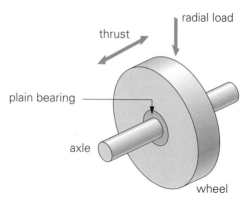

Figure 5.50

some of the load is coming from the side. Some bearings will only support load in one direction, while others provide support in both directions; this is illustrated in Fig. 5.50.

Types of bearing

Plain bearings rely on the materials used and effective lubrication to resist wear and reduce friction. In a car engine, plain bearings are used on the connecting rods joining the pistons to the crankshaft. Without a pressurised oil system the bearing would overheat and melt in a matter of seconds. The important point is that the bearing and shaft are kept apart by a film of oil. The material used for the bearings is softer than the crankshaft and allows any small particles to embed in it rather than scoring the crankshaft. The bearing is made in two halves to allow it to be fitted. Plain bearings in

positions where lubrication is difficult may use a material such as phosphor bronze which has had oil forced into it during manufacture. This type of bearing, known as self lubricating, is made using powdered metal technology or sintering.

Ball bearing

The ball bearing has a much smaller area of contact than a plain bearing. They can be used as separate bearings as in a cycle wheel or as a ball race where the balls are held in a cage. Ball bearings are capable of resisting both radial and thrust loading. Adjustment of a ball bearing race is not possible but loose bearings are adjusted by a cone and locknut system used to take up any play in the bearing.

Figure 5.53 Needle, roller and ball bearings

Roller bearings

These can be either taper, cylindrical or needle bearings. Taper bearings will resist radial and thrust load and can be adjusted accurately. Cylindrical bearings and needle bearings will only resist radial loading. Taper bearings are made to support immense loads such as in train or aircraft wheels.

Figure 5.51 Sintered bearing bushes

Figure 5.52 Combined radial and thrust bearing

Figure 5.54 Tapered roller bearing

Some odd bearings

Wooden bearings

Oil impregnated wooden bearings are commonly used for cart wheels in some parts of the world. Lignum Vitae, a tropical hardwood, is still used to manufacture plain bearings for the marine industry. In a ship propeller shaft, it will stay wet, retaining high strength and wear resistance. In some cases bearings made from Lignum Vitae have been giving trouble-free service for many years.

Self-aligning bearings

These bearings allow for slight misalignment of two shafts: the inner part of the bearing, which supports the shaft, is free to revolve inside the outer cage.

Figure 5.55 Self-aligning bearing

Lubrication of bearings

Bearing materials can be divided into the self-lubricating types and the type that require external lubrication. Silicon Nitride (ceramic) ball bearings can be used as an alternative to steel; they have high hardness, electrical insulation properties and continue to work even when lubrication is poor.

Polymers, such as nylon, HDPE and PTFE are often used for low speed applications where lubrication is difficult.

Cast iron, because of the free graphite in it, is able to provide a very good flat bearing surface. Machine parts that slide across each other, for example on a lathe, are normally made from cast iron.

Figure 5.56 Woodturning lathe with a cast iron bed

Bearings that require lubrication may be of the sealed for life type, where the grease that lubricates the bearing is sealed in with a rubber or plastic cover, or actively lubricated using a pressure system, gravity feed or an oil bath. An example is the car engine that has a pumped oil system. This will collect oil from a sump, feed it under pressure to the bearings and then deliver it back to the sump via a filter which removes any small particles.

Wear in the bearings will lower the pressure of the oil, eventually leading to failure of the bearing.

Grease is the lubricant that is normally packed around an open bearing, such as the ball bearings in a cycle wheel or pedal.

Figure 5.57 Pedal bearings packed in grease

Some machines will use a gravity feed system with the oil held in a reservoir. This can be seen in the case of the steam engine which was also shown earlier in the chapter.

Figure 5.58 Gravity fed oiling system

5.5 THE CONTROL OF MOTION

Motion can be defined as a physical movement or a change in position. Mechanisms all involve movement of some sort, sometimes rapid and sometimes very slow. In many cases the rate at which the movement takes place and when it takes place has to be controlled.

Brakes and clutches

The previous section looked at a situation where friction is to be avoided. In this section we look at situations where friction is essential: in the control of motion.

The clutch

A clutch is used to transfer drive from one part of a mechanism to another. It will rely either on a mechanical device such as a dog clutch or on a friction plate to control the motion.

Figure 5.59 Cable operated lawnmower clutch

A **dog clutch** will never slip as it relies on interference not friction for its operation. The dog clutch must be operated with the power off.

In a car, the engine is turning constantly once started and so there has to be a means of

Figure 5.60 Dog clutch on the lead screw of a metal turning lathe

stopping it from turning the road wheels; the solution is a **plate clutch**. A friction plate has pressure placed on either side of it, the pressure plate pushing the friction plate against a flywheel. When the pressure is removed, the flywheel can spin freely without turning the friction plate as well. With

Figure 5.61 Car clutch friction plate and pressure plate

Figure 5.62 On the sewing machine the clutch controls the drive to the needle or the bobbin winder

pressure applied, which is the normal position, the friction plate and the gearbox shaft attached to it will rotate. The plate clutch is designed to be operated by a pedal or lever when a machine is operating.

Other types of clutch include the **centrifugal clutch** used on chainsaws. This will allow an engine to idle with the output disengaged. When the engine speed increases, weights fly towards the outside of a housing causing the output shaft to be gripped. It will allow some slip, is automatic and maintenance is minimal.

The **viscous coupling** relies on the thickness or viscosity of a fluid to couple the input to the output. This type of coupling builds in 'slip' which gradually disappears as the output shaft catches up with the input. The principle is used on some car cooling systems, engaging the fan when the temperature is too high and stopping it when the engine is cool.

Brakes

The braking system in early cars was very similar to the horse-drawn coach, where a block of wood was forced down by a lever onto the surface of the tyre (See Fig. 5.63). This did have the effect of slowing the

Figure 5.63 Motor tricycle front brake pushing directly onto the tyre

vehicle but was inefficient and unreliable in wet conditions. The system was also used in the first motor vehicles.

Braking relies on friction between two surfaces: in a vehicle the friction appears on the brake itself and between the tyre and road surface. If the first is too effective, a skid will occur and the tyre will slide across the road.

Pressure is applied using a direct lever, a lever and cable, a hydraulic system or a pneumatic system. The cable, hydraulic or pneumatic components are simply transferring motion from the point of application, i.e. brake lever or pedal, to the brake mechanism.

Figure 5.64 Disc brake pads

Figure 5.65 Brake shoes from a hub brake

The brake itself will consist of a friction block or pad applying pressure to some part of the wheel.

Common types of brake in use today are the disc brake, which has recently been adapted for cycles, and the drum brake, known as a hub brake on cycles. These both operate on the centre of the wheel which is already rotating at a slower speed than the rim.

Figure 5.66 Cycle disc brake, hydraulically operated

Common types of cycle brake operating on the rim itself include cantilever, side pull and centre pull; all of which force brake blocks against both sides of the wheel rim. Applying

Figure 5.67 Side pull cycle brake using a first order lever

pressure is made easier by the brake lever operating the brake cable and the lever on the brake arm.

Figure 5.68 Cycle brake using a second order lever

Rim brakes are open to the elements and can lose efficiency in wet or icy conditions; hub brakes are enclosed and will remain efficient. Disc brakes, being partially open, can lose efficiency but being operated by a hydraulic system they will not suffer from stretch or friction in the cable.

To assist with the application of the brakes in a car, vacuum created by departing exhaust gases can be used to operate a servo.

This takes a lot of the effort out of heavy braking. An additional safety feature is the use of an ABS or anti-lock braking system. ABS was first developed in aircraft to reduce the length of runway needed when landing. ABS uses electronic wheel sensors to detect a locked wheel, releasing it and then re-applying the brake in quick sequence, thus cutting down the loss of control caused by skidding.

Ratchet and pawl

A standard mechanism to control the direction of rotary motion is the ratchet and

pawl. This will only allow movement in one direction; some uses will allow the direction to be reversed, though. A ratchet screwdriver or socket wrench will use a lever to control the direction of the ratchet. The movement in all cases is one tooth at a time, the spring loaded pawl dropping into the next tooth as the ratchet is turned. A clock movement will use this system to prevent the spring from unwinding.

Figure 5.69 Ratchet and pawl on a socket spanner

Figure 5.70 Ratchet and pawl on sewing machine

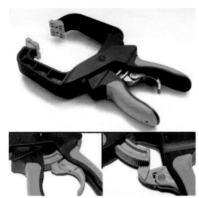

Figure 5.71 This clamp has a pawl that is operated by a finger to release the clamp

▶ Power sources – motors and actuators

The DC brushed motor

A motor will produce rotational movement; a linear actuator will produce linear movement from an available energy source. Most electric motors encountered in school projects are of the DC brushed type. They will rotate in a direction determined by the polarity of the supply and output can be controlled by using a change in voltage to alter speed or variation in current to control torque. In some cases speed is controlled by sending pulses to the motor instead of a constant supply. If the pulse 'on time' is the same as the 'off time', the result is that the motor is only powered for 50 per cent of the cycle, slowing it down. A big disadvantage of using a DC motor for controlling a mechanism is that there is no easy way of knowing where the motor shaft will stop or where it is at any given time.

The stepper motor

This will overcome the problem of knowing the position of the motor. A stepper is a brushless motor whose rotation is divided into a large number of steps. Each time the motor receives a pulse it will move forward one step or back one step, depending on the direction chosen. Mechanisms in a computer printer or scanner are controlled by stepper motors, full control being achieved by the system counting the number of pulses sent out. If the motor moves 7.5° for each step, it will need 48 steps for each revolution. By sending out 96 pulses you know that the motor shaft has completed two revolutions. Even finer control can be gained by using a gearbox on the output of the stepper motor.

The servo motor

These small motors are designed to hold a position and rotate when the pulse that is

Figure 5.72 Small DC motor

Figure 5.73 Stepper motor

being sent to the motor changes in duration. They are extremely useful in robotics, being small, suitable for radio control and quite powerful. Servos will normally not complete a full rotation, but move either side of a central position; they can however be modified to rotate fully, if the limit stops are removed.

Figure 5.75 The G cramp is a linear actuator

Figure 5.74 Servo motor

Actuators

A screw jack is a linear actuator; it will convert rotary movement from turning the handle to linear movement as the jack rises. Many actuators will use the principle of an inclined plane or screw thread to convert the motion. The photo of a G cramp in Fig. 5.75 is an example of this.

The lead screw of a lathe when rotated can engage with a nut in the lathe carriage in order to drive the carriage along. In this case the rotational force in the lead screw is quite small whereas the force in the linear movement is larger but moved over a smaller distance.

A wax motor actuator will use electric current to heat wax in a confined casing. As the wax melts it will expand and push a piston out, causing the linear movement. An example of the use of expanding wax is the thermostat in a car engine used to control the flow of coolant. It remains closed until the coolant in the engine has heated enough to melt the wax sealed into the thermostat; the wax then expands, opening the thermostat valve.

Figure 5.76 Thermostat from a car cooling system

5.6 POWER SOURCES

Provision of power

Mechanisms can be controlled by a number of different power sources; these can broadly be split into those using human or animal power as the energy source and those using an energy source such as electricity, or gas; included in gas will be steam and compressed air. Compressed air is often used to power a mechanism where electricity would be dangerous to use, e.g. near combustible materials or gases.

Figure 5.77 Compressed air tool

Electricity generation will in most cases involve the use of non-renewable energy sources; however as more wind farms and other alternative sources are introduced, the energy produced becomes more sustainable. Many parts of the world still rely on animal power in the form of horse or oxen for the operation of equipment.

Figure 5.78 Wind farm

Wind and solar energy are now becoming more widely used, particularly in remote areas where it is not easy to use mains power. Road signs of the type that illuminate only when needed are powered by a combination of wind generator and solar cells.

Figure 5.79 Illuminated road sign using wind and solar power

The cost of energy used to power equipment can be offset by re-using the heat produced and by limiting how much energy is required in the first place. In the motor industry continuous thought is being given to alternative power sources to fossil fuels. Bio-fuels obtained from plants are now common, and hybrid vehicles with electric motors for town use and various ways of harnessing the power of hydrogen are being tested. The biggest change in car energy consumption has really come about through the development of lighter materials and engines that burn more of the fuel that is put into them.

Energy in mechanisms should be considered in three ways:

- That used in order to produce the mechanism.
- That used during the working life of the mechanism.
- The energy used during disposal and recycling of parts.

5.7 CALCULATIONS AND ACTIVITIES

Calculations

Gears

In a gear train, the output speed of a shaft can be calculated if the input speed and gear ratio are known. A simple gear train with an 8T driver gear and a 40T driven will have a ratio of 5:1. Five turns of the driver will result in one turn of the driven gear. If the input speed is 100 rpm, the output will be 100/5 = 20 rpm.

A worm gear driving a 40T spur gear will have a ratio of 40:1 or 40 turns of driver = 1 turn of driven.

If the two systems were combined, the overall ratio would be (40 × 5):1 or 200:1

VR (gear ratio) = number of teeth on driven gear/number of teeth on driver gear.

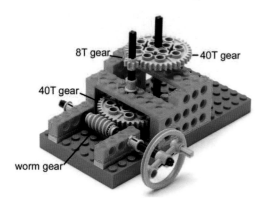

Figure 5.80 This illustrates the gear train described in the example

8T gear — *40T gear*
40T gear
worm gear

General formulae

Force = pressure × area

Force is in newtons; pressure is in newtons per mm^2; area is in mm^2.

$$\text{Mechanical advantage (MA)} = \frac{\text{load moved}}{\text{effort applied}}$$

$$\text{Velocity ratio (VR)} = \frac{\text{distance moved by effort}}{\text{distance moved by load}}$$

$$\text{Efficiency} = \frac{MA \times 100\%}{VR}$$

Pulley calculations

$$VR = \frac{\text{distance moved by driver pulley}}{\text{distance moved by driven pulley}}$$

$$\text{or} \quad \frac{\text{diameter of driver pulley}}{\text{diameter of driven pulley}}$$

Gear calculations

$$\text{Gear ratio (GR)} = \frac{\text{number of teeth on driven gear}}{\text{number of teeth on driver gear}}$$

In a compound gear train:

Final gear ratio = 1st ratio x 2nd ratio x 3rd ratio etc.

$$\text{Output speed} = \text{input speed} \times \frac{\text{product of driver teeth}}{\text{product of driven teeth}}$$

Lever Calculations

Moment = force(N) × distance
M_c = clockwise moment M_{ac} = anticlockwise moment
or $\mathbf{F_1 \times D_1 = F_2 \times D_2}$
In equilibrium $M_c = M_{ac}$

ACTIVITY

1. Look at Figs 5.81–5.83 closely and describe the mechanisms that can be seen.

Figure 5.81

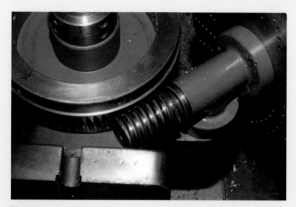

Figure 5.82

Figure 5.83

2. Carry out research on the mechanisms used in the following items:

- Watt governor
- Anchor escapement
- Archimedean screw
- Water meter
- Smoothing plane
- 3-jaw self-centring chuck
- Back gear
- Differential.

CHAPTER 6

ELECTRONICS

6.1 SELECTING AND MOUNTING AND FIXING COMPONENTS

LEARNING OUTCOMES

By the end of this chapter you should have developed a knowledge and understanding of:

- components used in electronics
- power sources and how to use them
- integrated circuits
- modular components
- circuit design using a systems approach
- calculations
- construction techniques
- quality control.

This chapter will take you through the content of the Electronics section of the course. Some parts of the chapter will be of use when you are completing the controlled assessments in units 1 and 3. For those candidates who are taking the Electronics unit 4 paper, it is important that you are familiar with the content of the chapter. The components and circuits that will be described are mainly those that are available in the school situation with the addition of industrial processes that you may be asked about in the written examination.

Constructing electronic circuits can be described as an assembly of a set of components to match a plan or circuit diagram. The difference between this area of designing and making and some of the others that you will have experienced is the need for complete accuracy; an electronic circuit that does not work is not very useful. It is rare however for a prototype circuit to function fully the first time that it is tested. The secret of successful circuit building can be brought down to the following:

- *an accurate circuit diagram*
- *high quality printed circuit board*
- *consistently good soldering*
- *knowing what should be happening in the circuit*
- *clear testing procedures, allowing faults to be identified quickly.*

Circuits in general should be broken down into small manageable sections or parts of a system. By doing this it makes both designing and building the circuit less of a daunting task. By carrying out tests on each part of the system, faults can be identified quickly and put right before continuing.

There are far too many devices available to give a full description of each but remember that each device will have a manufacturer's datasheet which can normally be accessed on a website. Many of these datasheets will give you typical circuits that can be the starting point for your own design.

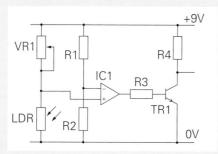

Figure 6.1

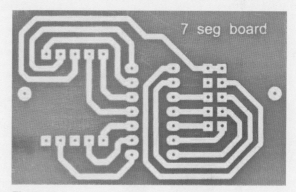

Figure 6.2

Figure 6.3 Quality of PCB and soldering are important

EXAMINER'S TIP

To find an integrated circuit (IC) datasheet do a search based on the number, e.g. searching for 4026B will bring up at least ten sites with the datasheet.

Components

The components that are used in electronics can be described as *discrete*, meaning they have a single function or *integrated circuits*, meaning a group of components in a single package. In addition to these two types,

Figure 6.4 **Integrated circuits**

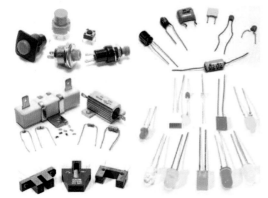

Figure 6.5 **A range of components**

hybrid circuits are used which are groups of discrete components, mounted on a PCB and possibly encapsulated in epoxy resin. The following section will provide detail on selection, mounting and fixing of components.

Selection of components

The circuit diagram will give many clues as to the nature of the component but there are still areas where decisions must be made. A circuit diagram may show a switch but not the type of switch. A relay may be required but it is left up to you, the circuit builder, to decide on the exact relay to use. Where there is a choice decisions are made based on:

• matching the needs of the circuit

• availability of the component

• price of the component

• size of the component.

In many cases you may have to compromise, using what is available in school. For some circuits, though, it may be better to buy the precise component that you need. This applies to the components that will be visible from the outside of the project casing, switches, LEDs, displays and output devices. To make a choice you will have to refer to catalogues and suppliers/manufacturers' websites.

Mounting components

Most of your components will be mounted on a PCB, but a few will need some thought as to how they can neatly be fitted in a casing. Potentiometers (variable resistors), switches and batteries are a few of the components that you will need to think about. In general, components in a prototype project should be fitted in a way that allows them to be removed, just in case you have got it wrong.

The majority of electrical connections will be soldered, but there remain a few that will need screw connectors, push fit connectors, spade connectors or plug and socket systems. When choosing your method it is a good idea to use connectors that will only fit one way round if possible, to avoid any incorrect connections.

ICs should be mounted in IC holders in a prototype circuit. The cost of these is minimal and it will ensure that there is no heat damage to the IC. If a replacement IC is required it is a simple job to fit one. IC holders have a notch at one end to match the notch in the IC. If you make a mistake when soldering in the IC holder it is often better to use a spot of white paint to indicate the pin 1 end as a reminder for when the IC is fitted.

When your circuit has been tested and is fully working, it is good practice to use cable ties to bundle cables together, if necessary adding stick-on pads to thread the cable ties through. Not only does this look neater it will also provide support to individual connecting wires and help to prevent breakages.

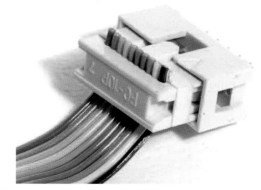

Figure 6.7 Plug and socket

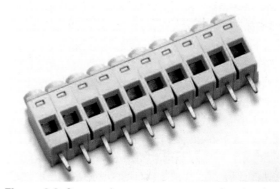

Figure 6.8 Connecting components to the circuit board

 EXAMINER'S TIP

Connecting wires that are likely to be moved should be multistrand while those that will have little or no movement can be single core.

Figure 6.6 IC holders

A final word on connecting wires:

- They are available in a choice of colours: use a colour coded system where possible, as fault tracing is much easier.
- Twist the connecting wires for a single component together, this will stop them getting tangled.

Fixing components

Care should be taken with any components that are visible when the project is completed. Screws, nuts and other fixing devices should be chosen for both functional and aesthetic reasons. A steel screw through a PCB can cause short circuiting, where a nylon screw will not. A chromed screw head will remain shiny where an unprotected steel screw will rust. A nyloc nut will remain tight but a plain steel nut can vibrate loose. A number of switches are of the push-in style which is very quick to fit; but they can be a problem if you need to remove them. Avoid making fixings that cannot be reversed if you need to take the project apart.

Figure 6.9 'Push-in' switch

▌ Power sources

All electronic projects will require a power source of some sort. The circuit diagram may only tell you the nominal voltage for the circuit; it probably will not give you an idea of the current drawn by the circuit. This important part of circuit design is often overlooked until too late, though it is quite easy to do if you have tested your circuit using simulation software such as *Circuit Wizard* or *Crocodile Clips*. Multimeter tests can readily be carried out on parts of the circuit that are constructed on a prototyping board, more commonly known as a breadboard. The calculation method is more suitable for individual components rather than a complete circuit; for example if the resistance of a solenoid coil is known, the operating current can easily be calculated. Once the current is known a suitable power source can be chosen. Power packs or bench supplies are an accurate source for testing but they are, in most cases, unsuitable for the final circuit. When setting up a power pack for use it is important to check the actual voltage with a voltmeter rather than relying on the marking on the power pack. Bench supplies will often have a dual rail supply available for use with op-amps along with a fixed +5V supply for use with integrated circuits.

Batteries

Battery capacity will be rated according to output voltage and mAh. To use this figure you will need to divide the battery rating by the expected current draw and that will give the battery life in hours.

For example, an LED circuit with an expected current draw of 10 mA connected to a PP3 battery rated at 500 mAh would operate for 50 hours. A small solenoid rated at 1.5W continuous coil use in a 9V circuit will have a current draw calculated using P(watts) $= V \times I$ or $I = P/V = 166$ mA.

In this case the same 9V battery would only operate the solenoid for 3 hours, and that figure does not include the current drawn by the operating circuit.

Rechargeable batteries are an option though the popular NiMH type has slightly lower nominal voltages than an equivalent disposable battery; for example, a NiMH AA cell will be 1.2V compared to the 1.5V of an alkaline cell. Environmentally they are a better option though. Most school projects will use either a mains adaptor or disposable battery for operating the prototype circuit. It is when developing the circuit for production that further thought needs to be given to the effect on the environment of the energy requirements of the project.

For most purposes a single rail supply, +V and 0V will be required. If a dual rail battery supply is needed, it will require two batteries connected in series, giving 0V at the connection point as shown in Fig. 6.10.

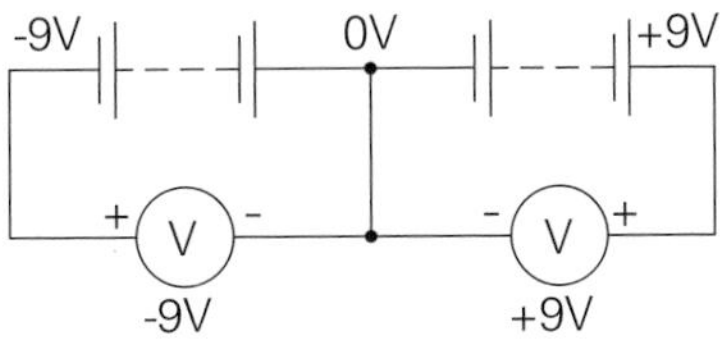

Figure 6.10

Solar cells

Solar power or photovoltaic cells are an option for some circuits. They are commonly used in garden lighting systems and for providing power to illuminate road signs. Another common use of these devices is in powering calculators, where they can supplement the power provided by a battery. Cells for projects are available as 0.45V with output current ranging from 100 mA to

800 mA. As a power source they will, in most cases, need to be connected in series to give sufficient operating voltage and this can lead to quite a bulky package.

Figure 6.11 Photovoltaic or solar cells

The capacitor

Large value capacitors or supercapacitors are now available that can be put to practical use; their capacitance is measured in farads rather than microfarads. They will charge in a short time, about 10 seconds, and can be effectively used as memory back-up to overcome interruptions to power, e.g. when changing main batteries. Supercapacitors can be charged and discharged any number of times without reduction in their capacity. If higher voltage is required they can be connected in series. As a sole power source they are not really suitable because the available voltage will drop fairly quickly as they discharge.

Mains adaptors

For school-based projects these can be extremely useful. Adaptors are readily available as new items or they are often left in working order when original items such as mobile phones have been disposed of. A range of output voltages is available with different styles of connector which can easily be replaced if necessary.

Figure 6.12 Power adaptor with low voltage output

Safety note

One vital note of caution is that a mains adaptor should never be dismantled and a suitable connector should be found to allow the low voltage output cable to be attached to a project.

The polarity of the output connector centre pin can vary so before use it should be checked with a voltmeter. Another problem with some adaptors is that the DC voltage is not smoothed. The ripple in the output will cause problems and needs to be removed with a suitable electrolytic capacitor (1000 μF) before it is connected to the main circuit. To make certain that the supply is suitable, an oscilloscope should be used to view the output of the adaptor.

Discrete components

Resistors

This section will concentrate on those components that are designed to cause resistance in a circuit. Resistance is an essential part of all circuits and will appear in most components in a circuit. Put simply it is the opposition that is shown by an object to an electrical current passing through it. The SI unit of resistance is the ohm, often shown by its symbol, Ω. Larger values are known by initials, k or M, standing for kilo and Mega. 1000Ω becomes 1kΩ; 1,000,000Ω becomes 1MΩ. In addition to this notation, you will often see resistor shorthand used on circuit diagrams. This is done to avoid confusion over decimal points, capitals R, K and M being used to show the higher values; 1000 ohms is 1K and 1,000,000 ohms is 1M. Any decimal values use the appropriate letter as the decimal point; 4.7ohms becoming 4R7, 47 ohms is shown as 47R and 4700 ohms as 4K7. If you are using a range of different circuit diagrams you will have to get used to the different ways that values are written.

To sum up, 10,000 ohms resistance could be written as 10kΩ or 10K. Resistors can be connected in series, in which case the values are added together:

$$R_{total} = R_1 + R_2 + R_3 \text{etc.}$$

or in parallel where the total resistance is shown by the formula

$$\frac{1}{R_{total}} = \frac{1}{R_1} + \frac{1}{R_2} + \frac{1}{R_3} \text{ etc.}$$

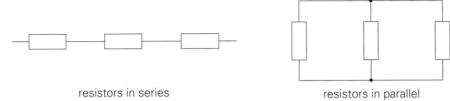

resistors in series   resistors in parallel

Figure 6.13

Fixed resistors

In schools these will normally be of the carbon film type. They have the value marked as a colour code and will usually be 5 per cent tolerance and from the E12 series. To explain why this is so, consider the problems facing the resistor manufacturer; if they threw away every resistor that was not precisely the correct value they would have very few left.

E12 series resistors are therefore made using 12 set values:

10, 12, 15, 18, 22, 27, 33, 39, 47, 56, 68, 82

These values will cover the full range for most requirements, a 10Ω, 5 per cent tolerance resistor will have a value between 9Ω and 11Ω; a 12Ω resistor between 10.8Ω and 13.2Ω, meaning that all values are covered. In most cases the precise value makes little difference to the working of the circuit. 0Ω resistors can be used as link wires in a circuit board.

Surface mount resistors are made in the same values as carbon film but are of course much smaller. To calculate the power rating, use the formula $P = V^2/R$. For example, in a 9V circuit, a 680Ω resistor will require a power rating of 81/680 or 0.119W. In this case, a 0.25W resistor will do the job: if the voltage were increased to 15V the formula

gives $15^2/680 = 0.33$W. Looking in a catalogue you would find that 0.5W is the most suitable. If you are designing a PCB and need to use a 0.5W resistor, remember that the body of the resistor is longer and it will require 0.5" spacing rather than the usual 0.4".

High power resistors

Fixed resistors will also come with different power ratings, to allow those with a larger current passing through them to withstand the heating that occurs. These may be of the ceramic body wirewound or aluminium clad wirewound type. They are rarely used in school projects but if required can handle much higher power loads, typically up to 50W for the aluminium wirewound.

Resistor networks

Available as either SIL (single in line) or DIL (dual in line), these are multiple resistors in a single body. The DIL network is particularly useful when using 7 segment displays or groups of LEDs.

Surface mount resistors

These are very small devices, typically less than 2 mm long. Although used extensively in commercial applications, they are not easy to use in school projects. Values and tolerances are similar to the normal 'through hole' resistor.

Figure 6.14 A range of fixed resistors are shown here

Potentiometers

These are sometimes known as variable resistors and are marked on circuit diagrams as VR1, VR2, etc. The low cost commercial type will normally have quite a high tolerance on the nominal value, so a potentiometer marked 10K could actually be between 9K and 12K; this is of course the highest value that the resistance can be set to; because of the construction method the lowest value will never quite go down to zero. Larger types of potentiometer have a long spindle that will need cutting down to suit the casing; a control knob is then fitted to allow easy setting. If the resistance is not going to

require change once it has been initially set, a type known as a preset is used. These are not normally visible from the outside of a casing and if necessary they can be fixed on a setting with a small amount of glue. For precision setting of values, multiturn presets are available with up to 10 turns required to cover the full range of resistance. All presets will have three solder tags.

Larger potentiometers are easy to use: the outer tags cover the full range of resistance and the centre tag or wiper is the adjustment. If a 100K potentiometer is set to give 15K between an outer contact and the wiper, the resistance between the wiper and the other outer contact will be 100 − 15 = 85K. The photo of the inside shows the 'horseshoe' carbon track and the moving contact or 'wiper'.

Figure 6.16 Potentiometer

Figure 6.15 Resistor networks and presets

Figure 6.17 Inside the potentiometer

Capacitors

Capacitors consist of two conductive plates and a dielectric as an insulator between the plates. The capacitor can be thought of as a storage device, much like a battery; it will store a charge, normally for as long as the circuit supply is connected. The charge will then drain away taking a varying time depending on the resistance that is encountered as it drains. A variety of materials are used for their construction depending on the value of capacitance required. For larger values electrolytic capacitors are normally used; these are of the polarised type, meaning they must be fitted the correct way round in the circuit and they are also marked with the safe working voltage; this is the maximum voltage that should be applied to them. Capacitors can be used in timing circuits, to smooth power supply circuits, to filter or remove unwanted signals and as sensing devices.

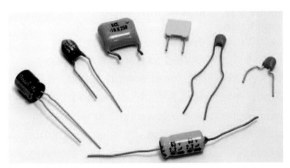

Figure 6.18 Capacitor types with a range of values

Safety note

Capacitors can store high voltages for a long time after the power source is disconnected. Camera flash gun capacitors powered by a single AA battery are quite capable of being charged up to 300V, giving the potential for a nasty shock.

Electrolytic capacitors connected the wrong way round can literally explode, causing electrolyte to be sprayed from the casing. The 'cross' indented in the top electrolytic capacitors is a weak area that will dictate where the casing splits if there is a problem

Figure 6.19 Electrolytic capacitor – note the weak area on the top

Values

The unit of capacitance is a farad. This is an extremely large amount so for most capacitors the value will be measured using the microfarad μF, nanofarad, nF or picofarad pF.

$$1F = 1,000,000 \ \mu F = 1,000,000,000nF$$
$$= 1,000,000,000,000pF.$$

It is a lot simpler to use the notation 10^{-6} for μF, 10^{-9} for nF and 10^{-12} for pF.

For school projects, the most commonly found capacitors will be electrolytic for larger values, 1 μF to 2000 μF; ceramic, which have values in the pF and nF ranges; polyester for the nF range; and ceramic for the surface mount ranges. The value can be found printed on capacitors.

Connection of capacitors

Electrolytic capacitors are available as axial, where the leads run through the axis of the body, or radial where the leads both exit the body at the same end. For most purposes, the radial version is easier and neater to fit in a circuit board. For industrial production snap-in capacitors are available which have sprung pins to hold the capacitor in place on a PCB whilst it is soldered.

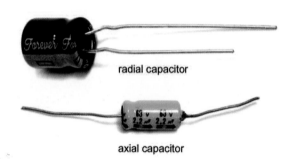

radial capacitor

axial capacitor

Figure 6.20 Radial and axial style electrolytic capacitors

▶ Semiconductors

The diode

This is the first of the 'semiconductor' components which are commonly used in circuits. It is in essence a one-way valve which will allow current to flow in one direction but not the other. Diodes are used to convert AC to DC and to block signals from certain parts of a circuit. A common use is to block back electromotive force (emf) occurring in inductor circuits; an example is a circuit with a relay using a diode to protect the driving transistor from back emf.

A diode can also be used to protect a circuit from the power supply being connected the wrong way round. Examples of diodes that you may use in a project are the 1N4001, which is a rectifier diode or the 1N4148,

which is a signal diode. Rectifier diodes are also available in a package known as a bridge rectifier which can be used to change an AC signal to DC.

Figure 6.21 A rectifier diode and a signal diode

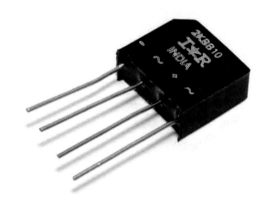

Figure 6.22 Bridge rectifier – note the AC and DC connections

The voltage needed to operate the diode, known as the forward voltage, is about 0.7V. When reverse biased or connected the wrong way round, the diode will resist almost all current flow. If the voltage is increased the diode will eventually break down, allowing current to flow more freely. This breakdown of a diode in reverse bias is used in infrared sensing circuits.

The transistor

This component is probably the most important development of the twentieth century in electronic terms. It was developed in the 1940s and since then has revolutionised electronic circuitry. Many different types of transistor are available but the ones most commonly encountered in school will be dealt with here; these are the bipolar transistors, NPN and PNP type and the field effect transistor or FET.

The NPN transistor is a semiconductor with three legs: base, emitter and collector. When a small current is passed through the base/emitter circuit, a larger current can pass through the collector/emitter circuit giving an amplifying action. The amount of amplification is known as the gain of the transistor, shortened to h_{FE}. This is shown by the formula h_{FE} = collector current/base current = Ic/Ib. In order to operate, the NPN transistor will require an input voltage of about +0.7V at the base. The base of the transistor must be protected from too high a current by using a resistor at the input.

Transistor legs are not in the same position for each type. The pin diagram must be found in a catalogue and used to identify pin positions.

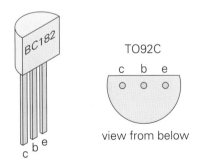

Figure 6.23 NPN transistor with pin details

The transistor can also be used to create an electronic switching action that will operate many thousands of times faster than a conventional switch. An NPN transistor is said to be switched on when the base is at a higher potential than the emitter. A PNP

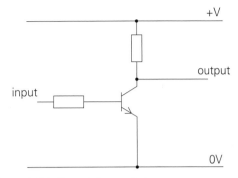

Figure 6.24 Transistor switch

transistor is switched on when the base is at a lower potential than the emitter.

To use the transistor as a switch, the collector should be connected to positive by a resistor when the transistor is switched off; this resistor is known as a 'pull up' resistor.

A special arrangement of transistors to provide high gain is called a Darlington pair; the total gain of the pair is the product of the two separate transistor gains. It can be made from two separate transistors such as the BC108 and BFY51 (which at one time was a standard way of doing the job), or a single Darlington transistor can be used. This has both transistors built into a single package, costing far less than the two separate transistors. The symbol for this is the same as a single transistor symbol.

The most common FET to be used is the MOSFET, or *metal oxide semiconductor* FET. They are likely to be used for providing power to output devices such as relays, solenoids or motors. Details on suitable types and circuits are given in the section on circuit design.

Transistors are available either singly or in transistor arrays as a DIL package.

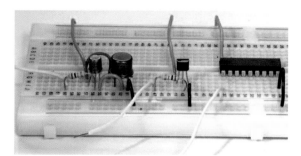

Figure 6.25 Three methods for a Darlington Driver; discrete transistors, one in a single package and an IC array

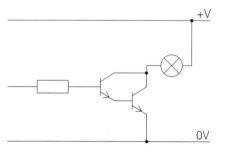

Figure 6.26 Circuit diagram for Darlington pair

▶ Sensor

Sensors are a vital part of the input to many circuits so a thorough understanding of what is available is needed before any designing can go ahead; this section gives a brief outline of the most useful.

Light sensors

These include LDRs (light dependent resistors), photodiodes and phototransistors. Each of these will detect a change in the level of light falling on it, but the results are returned in different ways.

The LDR has a changing resistance that will decrease as the light increases and increase as less light falls on it. The change is relatively slow but for many circuits that does not make any difference. The LDR is normally

set up as one half of a potential divider, the centre point providing a changing voltage level that can be input to a transistor or op-amp.

The photodiode can convert light into either current or voltage. The response time is quite rapid which makes it suitable for digital circuits. Photodiodes are used in reverse bias, conducting very little in the dark but as light falls onto the diode it will begin to conduct. They are often used with an infra-red source which will avoid many of the problems caused by stray visible light hitting the sensor.

Figure 6.27 LDRs

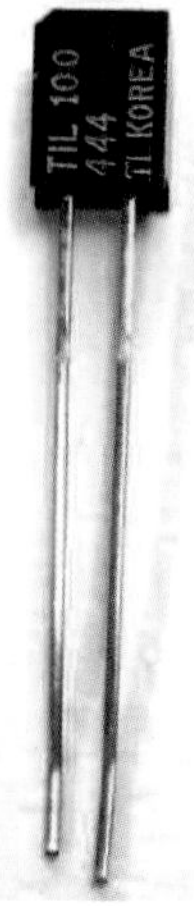

Figure 6.28 Photodiode

The phototransistor has a higher light sensitivity than the photodiode or LDR. It can have either two or three legs, the optical window being attached to the base leg through a photodiode. When the photodiode conducts, the transistor is switched on.

Figure 6.29 Phototransistor

Heat sensors

The NTC (Negative Temperature Coefficient) thermistor is basically a resistor that reacts to heat; resistance moving in the opposite direction to the temperature. As temperature rises resistance goes down, as temperature falls resistance goes up. They are available in a range of resistance values at 25°C so a suitable one can be chosen for the temperature being measured.

Other sensors are available such as the LM35, which can give a reading directly in °C; the LM 334 with an output of 10mV per °C; and the Dallas 18B20, which will interface directly with a PIC chip, giving output in °C. This last one is possibly the most worthwhile to consider in a temperature-based project because of the accuracy of the temperature and the ease of gaining the reading.

Figure 6.30 NTC thermistor and Dallas 18B20, two of the most useful heat sensors

Sound sensors

This will normally be a microphone although it is possible to use a small loudspeaker or a piezo sounder. The piezo sounder will react to fairly loud, sharp sounds and it can easily be used to trigger a 555 timer. If a microphone is used to sense sound in an alarm project, the resulting signal can be input to a comparator where it will be compared to a reference voltage.

Smart cable

This material uses the piezoelectric principle to converting mechanical energy into electrical energy. It can convert stress, strain, vibration, impact, sound or pressure change into small electrical signals.

Motion sensors

Very useful in an alarm circuit, these small

Figure 6.31 Vibration sensor and tilt switches

devices can have a rolling ball inside or the more sensitive ones will send a signal on the smallest vibration. They are all basically a simple single-pole, single-throw (SPST, or on-off) switch.

Optical sensors

Slotted opto switches can operate at high speed in detecting an item passing across or blocking the infrared (IR) source. A slotted wheel or disc can be used and rapid movement will be detected. The reflective opto switch will reflect an IR light back onto the sensing diode. Discrete components can be used but in most cases it is easier to buy the complete package which has both source and sensor.

Figure 6.32 Optical sensors using an IR LED and either a PIN diode or phototransistor

Pressure sensors

In industry an increase in pressure in a gas or liquid can be measured using a wide variety of methods but in the school situation there are more limited methods available. Industrial methods include capacitive technology where a pressure diaphragm is one plate of a capacitor, changing shape as pressure is applied, resulting in a changing value of the capacitor.

The strain gauge can be used either singly or as a pair in a circuit called a Wheatstone bridge.

A smart material that has a use in detecting pressure is the material known as QTC

(quantum tunnelling compound); it is available in sheet form or as small rectangular or square pellets. In the normal, unstressed position it is an insulator but as pressure is applied, resistance falls and it will begin to conduct. For further details on QTC, see Section 2.6 on page 55.

Some pressure switches use a diaphragm to operate micro switch contacts when air pressure on the diaphragm increases. These are useful in positions where direct electrical connection could be dangerous.

In school projects the pressure mat will often form part of the input to an alarm system, detecting the pressure of a person standing on it. This type of sensor is available ready made or it can be modelled using aluminium foil with a sponge separator.

The commercially produced pressure mat will usually include a continuity loop which can either be used as an additional sensor or tied off and ignored. This type of pressure mat can also find a use in projects involving games and interactive toys.

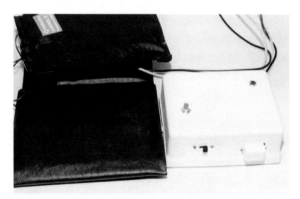

Figure 6.33 Pressure mat

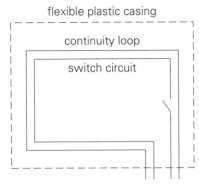

flexible plastic casing

continuity loop

switch circuit

Figure 6.34 Pressure mat circuit

Integrated circuits

When a number of components are built into a small circuit and encapsulated, the result is an integrated circuit. Package types vary but the most common will be the DIL or dual in line and the 3-pin package similar to a transistor. Another approach that you may come across is the COB or chip on board where the integrated circuit is permanently attached or bonded to the PCB. This has the advantage that it is smaller and has a much lower profile. It does mean, though, that if there is a problem with the board it cannot be repaired.

All DIL ICs are numbered anticlockwise starting with pin 1 at the top left. To indicate pin 1 there is either a small indented circle next to it or a notch at the pin 1 end of the IC. (See Fig. 6.38.)

Voltage regulator

The first integrated circuit to consider is the voltage regulator. In many circuits the voltage level is not critical and a range of different batteries can be used. There are circuits, though, that require a specific voltage that does not fluctuate. An example of this is the PIC microcontroller that has an input voltage of $5V \pm 0.25V$. In order to supply this accurately, a voltage regulator can be used. It is a simple device to build into a circuit, having only three connections: input voltage, common or 0V and output voltage. The 7805 can be obtained in several versions, each having a steady +5V output and varying power ratings from 100mA to 1A. If the regulator is going to be powered by a mains adaptor, it is usual to use capacitors to take out any ripples in the supply (see Fig. 6.97). Output voltages other than +5V are available; the 7812 gives a +12V output and the 7815 +15V. Devices starting with 79 have minus voltage outputs, for example the 7905 provides −5V.

Figure 6.35 COB or chip on board technology, popular with disposable circuits

Figure 6.36 Three versions of the 7805 regulator, each having a different power rating

6.2 SIGNAL PROCESSING

Digital electronics and logic

The following section will give a basic understanding of logic circuits used to make decisions and carry out actions. In terms of a system, they form the control or process part of the system. Because the majority of the processing takes place inside integrated circuits, a full understanding of how the process works is not essential – the

KEY TERMS

DIGITAL ELECTRONICS – Signals with only two states, on/off, commonly referred to as high/low. A voltage near to the supply represents high and 0V represents low. High refers to logic 1 and low refers to logic 0

IC – Integrated circuit, with no external components needed

LOGIC – The use of reasoning to solve problems

LOGIC GATE – A means of making a decision or reasoning within a circuit. The available types are AND, NAND, OR, NOR, XOR and NOT

PULL UP RESISTOR – Digital systems require a signal to be either high or low, a resistor is often used to ensure that a signal is always either high or low, never disconnected or floating. Figure 6.37 shows the arrangement used to give a digital signal from a push switch

BINARY SYSTEM – A counting system using only two numbers or digits, 0 and 1. These numbers can easily be represented using electronics

CLOCK – A method of providing a series of on/off pulses. Can be irregular as in the case of a switch input or regular, e.g. 555 astable output

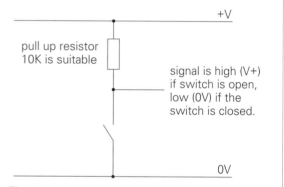

Figure 6.37

Figure 6.38 A dual in line or DIL IC

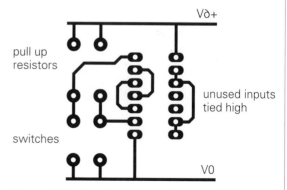

Figure 6.39 Pin diagram for the quad NAND gate IC

important thing is the result, what happens at the output of the system.

The photo in Fig. 6.38 shows a typical integrated logic circuit IC; it is a 14-pin DIL package. The number on the top indicates what the IC will do and there is a key to how it works in the form of a pinout diagram. This diagram shows what each pin will do and gives the information needed to use the IC in a circuit. Each IC has a pinout diagram that should be used when designing circuits. To make it easy, the layout of the basic logic ICs are the same. The ICs are made with four logic gates for the main types. Each gate has two inputs, hence the description, **quad 2 input gate**. For special uses it is possible to get 3, 4 or 8 input ICs.

Designing a logic system

A	B	Q
0	0	1
0	1	1
1	0	1
1	1	0

Figure 6.40 Truth table

It is best not to think in terms of electronics when first designing the system; for example, if A represents 'drinking', B represents 'driving' and Q represents 'allowed by law', draw a truth table to show 'if you drink you must not drive'. The truth table in Fig. 6.40 shows that doing neither is allowed, drinking is allowed, driving is allowed but doing both is not allowed.

By checking against the truth tables for all gates, it is possible to see that a NAND gate would represent the system.

Types of logic: NOR   OR   AND   NAND   NOT   XOR

For each type of logic, a truth table can be constructed which will give the state of the output. For any 2 input gate, there are 4 possible combinations of the 2 inputs. In a truth table the inputs are normally called A and B, the output is Q. In the case of the AND gate, if both inputs are logic 1, the output will be at logic 1. There is a gap in the NOT column because if inputs are *tied* or joined they must both be at the same value (Fig. 6.41).

The NAND and NOR gates are particularly useful because any other type of gate can be

	OR	NOR	XOR	AND	NAND	NOT (INVERTER)

A	B	OR Q	NOR Q	AND Q	NAND Q	NOT Q	XOR Q
0	0	0	1	0	1	1	0
0	1	1	0	0	1	-	1
1	0	1	0	0	1	-	1
1	1	1	0	1	0	0	0

SCHMITT NAND

SCHMITT INVERTER

Figure 6.41

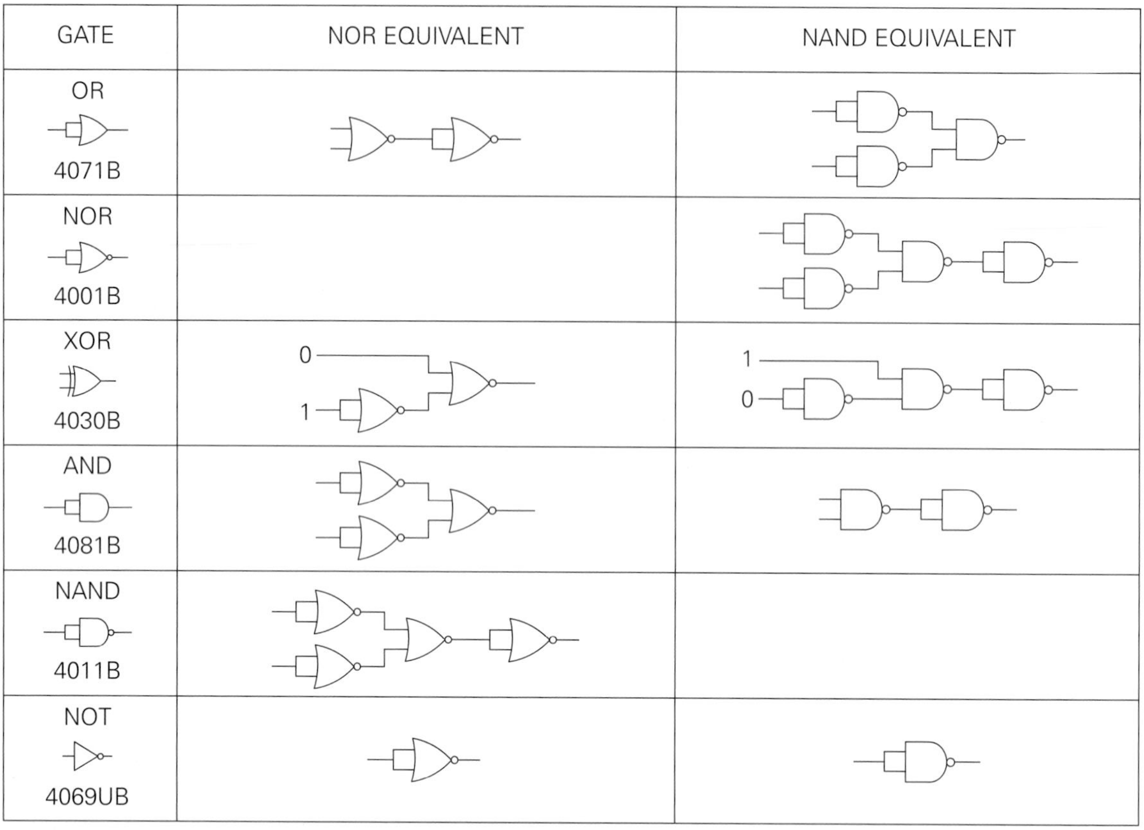

GATE	NOR EQUIVALENT	NAND EQUIVALENT
OR 4071B		
NOR 4001B		
XOR 4030B	0 / 1	1 / 0
AND 4081B		
NAND 4011B		
NOT 4069UB		

Figure 6.42 Using NAND and NOR gates to make any other gate

made from them. It is common in electronic systems to only use NAND or NOR gates for this reason. It is important to note that if the two inputs on a NAND or a NOR gate are connected, the gate becomes a NOT gate.

Electronic logic circuits

Different types of circuit can be used to construct logic gates, but the ones that are used today are mainly of either the TTL or CMOS families. The TTL circuit (transistor–transistor–logic) is based on bipolar transistors. The CMOS (complementary–metal–oxide–semiconductor) circuit is based on field effect transistors (FETs).

TTL ICs started as the 7400 series, CMOS as the 4000 series, e.g. 4001B, 4011B. There are now a number of variations such as 74LS, 74HC and 74HCT series.

The 74HC series are high speed CMOS ICs with pin layout compatible with the older 7400 series. For school project work, the 4000 series is useful as they operate between +3V and +15V. Both types are normally in the form of 14 or 16-pin DIL packages.

The two types are not compatible so should not normally be mixed in one circuit. They differ in the following ways:

- **Power supply** – TTL requires a stabilised 5V supply, CMOS requires 3–15V.

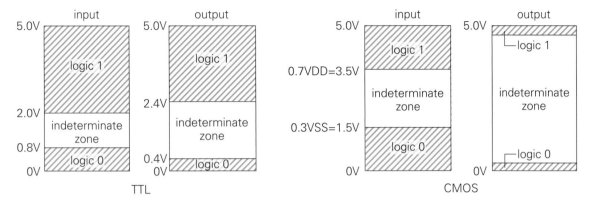

Figure 6.43 Logic levels for CMOS and TTL

- **Current** – TTL requires milli-amps, CMOS requires micro-amps (1000 times less).

- **Input impedance** – CMOS circuits have very high input impedance which can lead to possible damage from static charges on input pins. For this reason they are supplied in anti-static or conductive carriers. TTL chips do not suffer from this because of the low input impedance of the bipolar transistors used in them.

- **Switching speed** – Much faster for TTL, 10 nanoseconds against 300ns for CMOS (1ns = 0.000000001s).

- **Fan out** – This means the number of gates that can take their input from the output of the first gate, 10 for TTL, and 50 for CMOS.

- **Unused inputs** – Floating (unconnected) inputs on TTL assume logic 1, although it is safer to tie, or connect them either high or low. Unused CMOS inputs **must not** be left to float. They must be tied either high or low.

- **Logic levels** – Ideally should be 0V or supply (5V for TTL). In practice, these values are not often achieved. TTL input low can be from 0–0.8V, CMOS low can be from 0–1.5V. TTL high is 2V–5V, CMOS high is 3.5V–5V (on a 5V supply). Outputs from TTL are similar to input; CMOS outputs are much closer to 0V or supply. As can be seen in Fig. 6.43, the lowest value for TTL logic 1 output is 2.4V; this is below the lowest value for CMOS logic 1 input. The result would be impossible to predict. If the two types have to be used in one circuit, a transistor switch should be used as a buffer between them.

- **Pinouts** – The pinout of TTL and CMOS ICs can vary; this is another reason it is not possible to substitute one family for another.

Logic circuits can be tested in a number of ways. Using simulation software is an easy way (but make sure that the logic family and supply voltages are set). Breadboarding can also be carried out before making a PCB.

A number of points should be considered when designing a digital circuit:

- Unused inputs should be tied (joined) to either high or low.

- Test points at suitable outputs should be built in using an LED and resistor. This will show when the circuit is working.

- Inputs from sensors should be taken through a Schmitt inverter to give a reliable signal.
- A 100n capacitor should be used across the supply rails to smooth out any electrical noise.
- ICs should be placed in an IC holder and not soldered direct into the circuit.

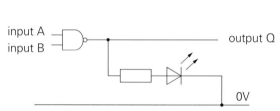

Figure 6.44 Test point

Useful circuits

SR bistable

The basic SR bistable or latch can be used for debouncing a counter input, or latching an alarm system. It can be made from either NAND gates or NOR gates. It is also made as a quad SR chip with four latches on one chip. The basic PCB layout is also shown below

This circuit is useful for counting systems as it is more reliable and uses fewer

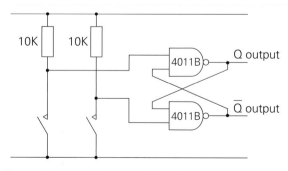

Figure 6.45 NAND gate latch or bistable

components than the 555. There are six inverters on one chip so four are left free for use.

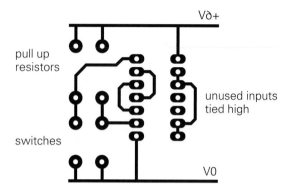

Figure 6.46 PCB layout for the NAND gate latch

$$frequency = \frac{1}{2RC}$$

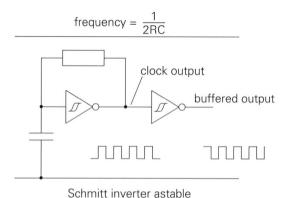

Schmitt inverter astable

Figure 6.47 A useful astable circuit using the Schmitt inverter

Schmitt trigger ICs

This type of device will give a fast rise and fall between logic states and are often used to 'clean up' a signal. The most useful is perhaps the Hex Schmitt trigger IC with six inverters on it. The astable circuit in Fig. 6.47 can be used as a clock input to counter circuits.

Counter ICs

These are a specialised type of logic IC. They will count the number of input pulses entering and then output the result in a standard format. The easiest to understand is probably the decade counter which will output a high signal at 1 of 10 output pins, depending on the state of the count. The binary counter outputs a 4-bit binary count either as full binary or as binary coded decimal (BCD). This is hard to understand so a decoder can be used to change the binary into either a decade count or a seven segment display output.

There are several features that are commonly found in counter ICs:

- a reset pin that will take the count back to zero
- a carry output that allows two or more counters to be linked to increase the maximum count
- a pin to set the direction of the count.

A useful counter IC for project work is the CMOS 4026B which has seven decoded outputs for a display.

All counter ICs require a 'clean' input pulse. When the input comes from a push switch, it will have contact bounce which will cause the count to jump and be generally unpredictable. The solution to this is to use a debouncing circuit after the switch.

▶ The PIC® microcontroller

The Peripheral Interface Controller (PIC) microcontroller is a group of devices that can be easily programmed to carry out a task and reprogrammed if there is an alteration needed. PICs will have a number of input and output pins in addition to the pins used for programming. While they can look daunting, they are in fact quite easy to set up and far more versatile than a logic circuit. PICs are available in a number of different sizes of DIL package, each having its own configuration of inputs and outputs; the method of programming is however quite similar. Programs in school are usually written as flowcharts or in a computer language known as 'Basic'. Either version can be tried out or simulated before sending it to the PIC. (See Section 4.8, pages 113–114 for more information on PICs.)

▶ Operational amplifier

One of the earliest types of integrated circuit, this can be set up in number of different ways. In essence it is a high gain voltage amplifier which will amplify the difference in voltage between the two inputs and send the result to the single output. Because the gain of the op-amp is normally extremely high, negative feedback is often used to control the

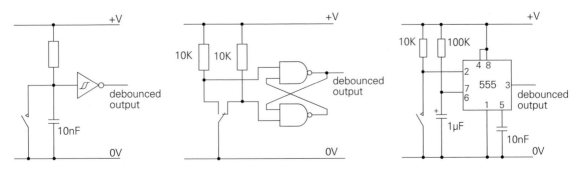

Figure 6.48 Debouncing circuits

level of output. Apart from the inverting and non-inverting amplifier which can be constructed from the op-amp, it can be used as a comparator which will compare two voltage levels, changing the output according to which is greater. Many standard op-amp circuits will use dual rail voltage supplies, but it is quite possible to use them with a single rail power source.

The most common op-amp is the 741 which has been in existence for about 40 years. Since that time, many improved versions have been designed, along with some that have multiple op-amps on a single IC. The CA3140 is a single MOSFET op-amp that can directly replace a 741. If more than one op-amp is required, dual or quad versions are available.

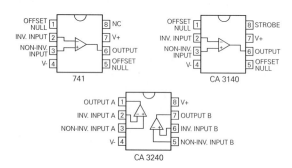

Figure 6.49 Op-amp pinout diagrams

555 timer IC

One of the best known of all integrated circuits is the 555 timer. It has been around since the early 1970s and can be set up to carry out a number of timing tasks. The better known uses of the 555 are as a monostable or as an astable. The monostable will send a single pulse to the output, whereas the astable sends a continuous stream of pulses. Setting up the device is comparatively simple with a minimum of

external components required; it is also very reliable and able to stand up to quite rough treatment.

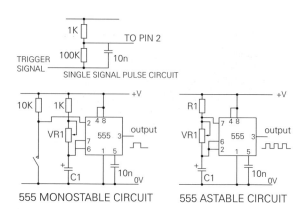

Figure 6.50 555 monostable and astable circuits

Driver ICs

Darlington Driver

The Darlington Driver array is an easy way to overcome the problem of boosting output power from either a logic system or a PIC circuit. In most cases, the economics of designing are quite simple to work out and the winner will normally be the Darlington Driver array. If you have a single output that will draw a current of 200mA, this is way above that supplied by most ICs, so a transistor will be needed. The Darlington Driver configuration, as mentioned earlier, can be made from two separate transistors or a single Darlington transistor. If more than one Darlington Driver is needed in a circuit, it is more economical to use an array such as the ULN2803 which has eight Darlington pairs on it. In addition it also has current limiting resistors on each pair and a protective or clamping diode on each for inductive loads such as a relay or motor. A single array will cost slightly less than two separate Darlington transistors, giving four times the value. To drive high current loads, the separate inputs of an array can be connected in parallel.

Figure 6.51 Darlington Driver IC with 8 Darlington pairs

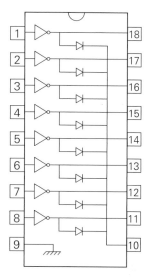

Figure 6.52 Darlington driver pinout

Bar/dot display driver LM3914

This useful device will sense an input voltage and will light a series of LEDs proportionate to the level of the voltage. It can be set to display either single LEDs in the dot mode or a group of LEDs in the bar mode.

6.3 SWITCHING AND OUTPUTS

Switches

The purpose of a switch is to either connect or disconnect conductors in a circuit. Switches can differ according to contact arrangement, voltage and current rating and how the switch is operated.

The first of these to examine is the contact arrangement. The simplest form of switch has two contacts that can be brought together or moved apart. This is known as single pole, single throw or SPST: single pole because there is only one set of contacts; single throw because there are only two contacts involved. Two switches of this type in a single body would be called double pole, single throw or DPST. A switch with two outer contacts, one of which is always joined to a centre or common contact, is known as double throw or DT; a pair of these in a single body would be DPDT. If you are not sure of the contact arrangements of a switch, first see if there are three or six contacts; that will indicate double throw. Only two contacts indicates single throw. In a double throw switch, the two contacts that can be isolated are known as normally open, NO and normally closed, NC; the third contact is the common, C, which is connected either to NO or NC. This type of switch is sometimes known as a changeover switch.

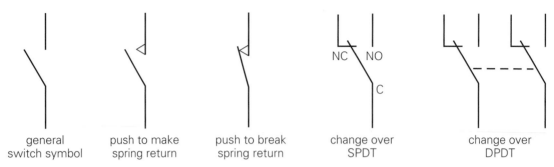

general switch symbol | push to make spring return | push to break spring return | change over SPDT | change over DPDT

Figure 6.53 Switch symbols

A catalogue or datasheet will give details on the voltage and current rating of the switch; many will also give details of the guaranteed number of times the switch can be operated. For most school electronic projects, this will not be a problem and the current in a circuit will not even approach the maximum.

Knowledge of switch action is quite important when making a choice. A main on/off switch in a circuit will almost certainly have to be of the type that will stay in position when set; a toggle switch, rocker switch, slide switch or latching switch will be suitable. If a single pole switch is used for the on/off switch, it should be placed in the live wire; if a double pole switch is used, both power connections can be isolated.

For controlling an action in a circuit, very often a quick or momentary connection is needed; this will be supplied by a push to make, push to break switch or microswitch. The microswitch is a particularly useful device, using a very small, light movement to operate the contacts. Often a lever or roller is attached to move the actual switch.

Special types of switch are available, for example, when sensing in an alarm circuit – the reed switch, operated by a magnet, the tilt switch operated by a rolling ball or conducting liquid and the vibration sensor, which can be very sensitive.

Figure 6.54 Push to make switches

Figure 6.55 Microswitches

Multipole rotary switches giving up to 12 switch positions can be useful, for example in a timing circuit where different capacitor/resistor networks can be connected to give differing time intervals.

PCB mounted switches such as the dual in line parallel (or DIP) switch can be fitted for initial setting up of a circuit. These are up to eight pole, single throw switches and are standard DIL spacing.

Figure 6.56 PCB mounted DIP switches

Figure 6.58 The speech recording unit is a low cost way of adding sound to a project

For a reset switch on a PIC circuit, the miniature tactile switch is ideal. This is a SPST switch where feedback is given when the switch has been pressed. Although there are only two connections needed, the connections are like a staple with both ends visible; this can make routing tracks on a PCB easier.

Figure 6.59 PIR units from a domestic alarm can be used in projects

Passive infrared units are available as sensors for alarm circuits and these only require power connections in order to give a digital on/off output. In the photo in Fig. 6.59, alternative mounting positions for the PCB can be seen to allow pets to go undetected.

Figure 6.57 Tactile switch giving feedback through the finger when it has been pressed

▶ Modular components

There are occasions when it is easier to use a ready-made sub-assembly rather than designing and making your own. Examples of this are speech recording or playback units that are readily available and can be added to your own circuit, as shown in Fig. 6.58.

Small circuit boards with sounds stored using chip on board (COB) technology are low cost and can be added to an amplifier that has been designed as a project. Liquid crystal display (LCD) units can add an interesting output to a PIC project but designing and making the driving circuit would be a project in itself. These units, although quite expensive, are easy to use requiring power plus serial input and output connections.

Output components

Relays

The relay is an isolating component that is fitted between a control circuit and an output device.

It has output contacts that are closed by an electromagnet on the control circuit side. When choosing a relay, the following points must be considered:

- Coil voltage – This is determined by the operating voltage of the control circuit. An exact match is not essential as many relays will have quite a large tolerance on the operating voltage.

- Contact arrangement – SPST or DPDT are the most common.

- Power rating of the contacts – normally given in amps.

- Physical size and pin layout – needed for designing a PCB.

Most catalogues will give details and accurate dimensions of the pin layout.

You can work out a relay pin layout using a multimeter on resistance setting. Find the coil pins first; they will be the two pins with a low value resistance between them. The pins with no resistance will be common and normally closed.

Figure 6.61 A relay

The solenoid

This is an electromagnet with a centre pin that is moved in or out as current is passed or blocked. They are useful for converting electrical energy into mechanical movement but it should be remembered that they can consume a lot of power. To overcome this, latching versions are available which require a short pulse to move the centre pin to the set position and then they consume no power.

Figure 6.62 Small solenoid with spade connector terminals

The DC motor

This has two useful features for school projects that can be used when designing.

- The motor direction can be reversed by reversing the polarity of the supply.

Figure 6.60 A larger DPDT relay shown along with the two most used in school projects

- If the shaft of the motor is rotated fast enough, the motor will generate electricity.

A DC motor can easily be reversed using a DPDT relay or a DPDT slide switch.

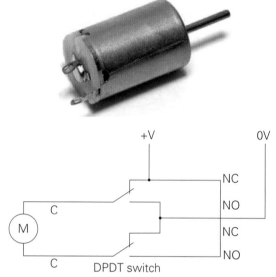

Figure 6.63 A small DC motor and reversing circuit

LED

This is one of the most common components in use today and is growing in popularity because of its long service life, rugged nature, low running cost and small size.

The range of colours, sizes and shapes available make them a popular choice for a range of lighting needs. Cycle lamps have for some years used flashing LEDs as their light

Figure 6.64 A standard 5 mm LED

source; traffic lights and car tail lights can now be found using LEDs.

An LED has two legs – a positive leg, sometimes called the anode, and a negative leg or cathode. Current through the LED must be controlled with a resistor to avoid damage, with the normal operating current being in the range of 10–20mA.

Seven segment display

These are available with one, two, three or four digits. The one digit display consists of seven LEDs for the segments plus one for the decimal point. The LEDs have either the anodes or the cathodes connected internally. When you buy a display for a project, you need to know whether the signals to switch on the LEDs will be high or low. If the signals are high, you will need a common cathode display; if they are low, you need a common anode. A counter IC driving the display directly will require a common cathode. A PIC chip sending its output to a Darlington Driver array will produce a high output that switches on the transistor. The transistor output is low so the signal to the display is low and a common anode display is needed. You must remember to use a current-limiting resistor for each LED on the display.

Seven segment displays are available in different sizes and different colours. The manufacturer's data sheet will give the pin diagram. Pin arrangements can be very different so it is important to know which display you will be using before designing a PCB. In some cases, the common connection, either anode or cathode, will have two available pins which are connected internally; only connect the most convenient on your PCB layout.

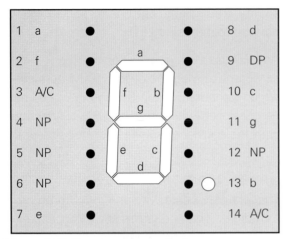

1	a	●	●	8	d
2	f	●	●	9	DP
3	A/C	●	●	10	c
4	NP	●	●	11	g
5	NP	●	●	12	NP
6	NP	●	● 〇	13	b
7	e	●	●	14	A/C

Figure 6.65 Seven-segment display

Figure 6.66 Each of these displays has a different pin layout so an accurate pin diagram is essential

In many cases it is better to build the display on a separate PCB attached with a ribbon cable. This will cut down the number of link wires and gives flexibility when mounting the display in a case.

Figure 6.67 Display separated from the main PCB

Liquid crystal display (LCD)

These displays have a number of advantages over LEDs. They operate on a tiny current and have a large range of characters available for the display.

The easiest way to use an LCD display is to buy the complete module: driver circuit plus display. This type of module is easily interfaced with a PIC project and allows a range of messages to be displayed, giving much greater flexibility when designing display outputs. The one shown in Fig. 6.68 has two lines of display, each line having 16 characters.

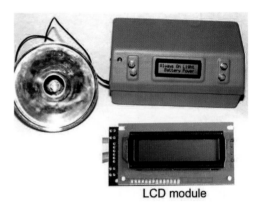

LCD module

Figure 6.68 Two line display with a total of 32 characters

Loudspeaker

For projects requiring a sound output, two options are a loudspeaker or a piezo sounder. The loudspeaker is an electro-mechanical device that uses an electromagnet to move a cone at the frequency of the sound being generated. For school projects, the smaller type of speaker covering the full range of sounds will generally be sufficient.
Impedance of the speaker will normally be specified in a circuit diagram and will be 4, 8 or 16 ohms.

Piezo sounder

The sound source in a piezo-electric sounder is a piezo-electric diaphragm. When an AC sound signal is connected to the sounder, the diaphragm distorts and then goes back to its normal position at the same rate as the sound frequency; this rapid change of direction causes the sound to be output.

Figure 6.69 Speakers and piezo sounders

Buzzer or sounder

As well as the older style buzzer with flying leads, there are a number of PCB mounted devices now available. Low cost musical buzzers are also available that can add interest to the output of a project; these have a number of tunes stored in them

Figure 6.70 PCB mounted buzzers with an alarm siren and a buzzer with flying leads

6.4 CIRCUIT DESIGN

Circuit design

Designing a circuit can be a complex task unless a strict routine is followed. Until quite recently the best method of testing a circuit was to make it up on a breadboard using real components.

Simulation software that is now available can take far less time and gives accurate test results before the circuit is finalised. There are still occasions though where it is better to use real components to test your ideas.

The following approach to circuit design has been used for many years and it has been found to work.

Figure 6.71 Breadboard circuit

Use a system approach, break the task into input–process–output sections and look carefully for the points where feedback will be used if it is a closed loop system that you are designing.

During your course you will have used a number of small sub-circuits that can be added together to make a complete system. Consider the following before you start:

- Power supply – Will any voltage regulation be needed?

- Inputs – How many, what form will they take, what signal will be passed onto the processing circuit?

- Process – What is the nature of the processing: logic, counting, timing, comparison?

- Output – Light, sound, motor, movement, a combination?

- Feedback – Manual or automatic? Is an override needed?

When the above questions have been answered, you can start to think about the type of circuit needed – logic, analogue, digital or PIC.

You should already have part of your circuit diagram from your research; it will now need to be tested using simulation software if this is available. If not, go straight to the breadboard circuit.

When drawing a known circuit on screen, it is vital to use correct component values, particularly resistors and capacitors. If you do not change them they will default to something like 1K for resistors and 100μF for capacitors. When you actually make the circuit, if these values are used you can expect some strange results.

It should be possible to simulate or test each part of the circuit so that faults can quickly be identified and corrected. Try to remember to build the test features into your early design that will remain in the final version, for

example an LED can give visual confirmation that an output is high or low. Test points for attaching a multimeter or oscilloscope can be designed in. If you use a test point in the simulation, it is a good idea to build one into the final circuit.

Figure 6.72 Two test point LEDs – access for a logic probe and a plug socket can be seen here

It is good practice to keep a full record of your designing; with CAD this is quite easy. Every five minutes or so save the design with a different version number so that it can be printed later. If you are using a breadboard, take photos of what you have done at the end of each session.

PCB manufacture

The approach here should be:

- Draw the circuit diagram.

- Use the software conversion feature.

- Evaluate the design that is produced, cutting out flying leads and links where possible.

- Either develop the auto-routed design or design the board yourself.

- Place components.

- Add positive and 0V rails.

- Add power connections to ICs.
- Add signal connections.
- Add power and on/off switch pads.
- Add any links.
- Check the finished layout by on-screen testing or matching to the circuit design.

Both auto routing and manual design have benefits and drawbacks. The main benefit of doing your own design is that you can decide exactly where each component will be placed and you should know what each track is doing. With a converted circuit you may need to trace the path of a track to see exactly what it is doing.

Benefits of your own design

- Logical orientation of components.
- Better understanding of layout.
- Schematic has to be checked and followed precisely.
- More versatile in terms of shape.
- Precise placing of components.
- Can build in plans for resolving errors.

Benefits of auto-routed design

- Design follows circuit precisely.
- Component sizes will be chosen for you.
- Faster.
- Good degree of control with most software.
- Many attempts can be made in short time.
- Allows real world view to be checked.

KEY TERMS

TRACK – a connection between two or more pads

PAD – position of a hole for a component leg

SCREEN LAYER – outlines of component position/value printed on the component side

COMPONENT SIDE – side of the board that components are fitted from

SOLDER SIDE – copper side of the board where pads and tracks are

RAIL – either the positive or 0V rail in a single rail design

LEGEND – written information either on screen layer or copper layer

LINK WIRE – where pads are placed either side of a track allowing a connector to go over a track without touching it

VIA – a plated connector between the two sides on a double sided board

SUBSTRATE – the insulating base of the PCB which the copper layer is attached to

TEST POINT – a pin or loop that a test instrument can be attached to

SHORT CIRCUIT – a direct connection between the positive and 0V rails

GERBER FILE – file format used to export from the PCB software to a PCB manufacturer

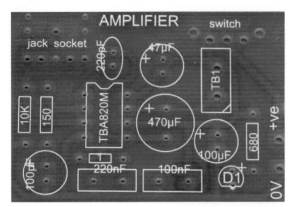

Figure 6.73 Screen layer on the component side of the board

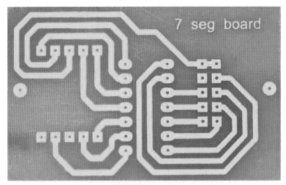

Figure 6.74 The copper or solder side of the board

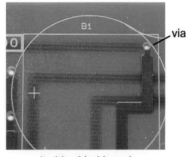

Figure 6.75 Double sided boards use a VIA to connect the two sides of the board

Points to bear in mind when designing PCB layouts

- Reduce links to a minimum; where they are needed, a 0Ω resistor can be used.
- Use connectors or terminal blocks for connecting to the PCB.
- Do not take tracks between narrow gaps in IC pads.
- Keep ICs the same way up as far as possible.
- Add spare pads to the positive and 0V rails to allow for missed connections.
- Use ribbon cable and connectors to join two or more PCBs together.

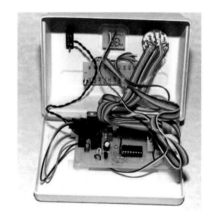

Figure 6.76 Ribbon cable used to connect separate parts of a circuit

PCB design uses the Imperial system for measurements, spacing normally being on a 0.1 inch grid. There are a few components that are given with metric dimensions but they will normally also have the Imperial equivalent alongside them. Spacing of components is important but much of it is taken care of with CAD layout software. If the method you use has no 'real world' view, the layout should be printed to allow real components to be checked for fit.

In general, the following points should be observed:

- Tracks and pads should be as large as possible; this will not only allow higher current to pass safely but it does give a margin of error if the drill is not lined up.
- Tracks run horizontally or vertically as far as possible, with corners chamfered to avoid undercut when etching.
- Always check that IC power tracks have been added.
- Always have some reversed text on the layout so that the layout cannot accidentally be reversed during exposure.
- Holes for mounting the PCB on a base should be included.

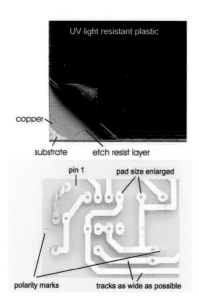

Figure 6.77 Photo-etch board and a completed PCB

Manufacturing the PCB should follow the sequence below for the photo etch process:

- exposure of PCB through artwork with UV light
- developing to remove background resist

- washing to remove developer
- etching to remove unprotected copper
- washing to remove etching chemicals
- remove remaining resist using abrasive rubber or re-expose and re-develop
- tinning – optional, the alternative is to solder through the resist or use a protective flux.

Safety note

Safety precautions should be observed fully during the process. The main dangers are looking directly at the UV light source, spillage or splashing of developer or etchant. Accurate timing is needed for each part of

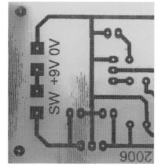

Figure 6.78 Under-developed board with some copper remaining

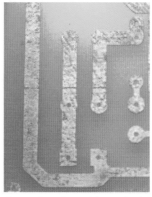

Figure 6.79 Over-developed board with porous tracks and cracks showing

the process, especially the developing where very short development times may be experienced. Use the off-cuts of circuit board to test the strength of the chemicals. Switch the tank heaters off after use.

Potential problems and solutions during PCB manufacture

Hairline cracks in artwork causing breaks in the copper when board is etched:

- Before exposure: repair with black fine line pen if noticed, use a light box to pick up mistakes.
- After exposure and development: use a spirit based pen (OHP pen) direct onto the resist on the board.
- After manufacture: repair with solder.

Missing resist on board, too much copper etched:

- Check the board carefully before use, look particularly for scratches that have come through the plastic protective coating.
- Spirit pen to repair small areas.

Over exposure, resulting in thin or porous tracks:

- Make a test strip when using either a new or untried light source or a new batch of board.
- Printing of artwork can be done on clear acetate but more control is possible if good quality tracing paper is used.

Over development, resulting in thin or porous tracks:

- Resist will go purple/black at the edges and the outline of tracks is ragged when etched.
- Use fresh developer and test the strength with off-cuts of board.

- A development time of about 20–25 seconds will give good control of the image.

Over etching, leading to very thin or missing tracks and pads:

- Symptoms: porous tracks, missing sections.
- Know the strength and age of etchant.
- Any areas that remain un-etched can be scratched with a scalpel to ensure clean copper is exposed.
- Turn the board after half of the etching time; this will ensure consistent results and prevent the top half from being over etched.

Tracks in the wrong place or missing:

- Cut with a scalpel to remove incorrect connection.
- New connection can be added to solder side – telephone wire is good for this.
- Adhesive copper track is another possibility for repairs.

The finished board is now ready for drilling. The following should be noted:

- A good general purpose size for the drill bit is Ø0.8 mm; this will be correct for resistors, capacitors and IC legs.
- For terminal blocks and preset potentiometers use Ø1.0 mm.
- For relay pins Ø1.2 mm
- When drilling, tape your circuit onto a fresh piece of MDF or ply; this will prevent the drill from slipping into existing holes on a used piece of backing.

Safety note

Wear goggles or a visor for drilling or

watching somebody else drill. It is very easy to break a small PCB drill. If the holes appear ragged at the edges, it usually means that the tip of the drill has been snapped off. Do not carry on drilling with a broken drill bit!

6.5 COUNTING SYSTEMS

Binary counting

Full binary

In normal counting (the **decimal system**), there are 10 distinct symbols or numbers used: 0, 1, 2, 3, 4, 5, 6, 7, 8, 9. When there are no more numbers to use (after 9), a new column is started to the left of the first one, and the first column goes back to 0.

This continues until 99 has been reached, then a third column is started.

Binary counting uses only two numbers, 0 and 1. For this reason it is ideal for use in electronics. Two voltages are used: one to represent a binary 1, the other to represent binary 0. In binary, the first column can only have two values, 0 or 1. After this a second column is needed to give a different number. As in decimal, a second column is added to the left of the first one. This column represents blocks of 2, where the decimal second column represents blocks of 10.

For example:

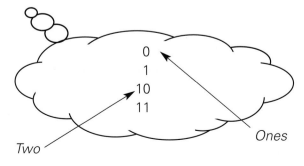

As columns are added, each one doubles in value, so the columns are 1s, 2s, 4s, 8s etc. The binary count, up to four columns, is shown below with the decimal equivalent next to it.

Look carefully at the pattern in the binary count: the 1s column is alternately 01 01; the 2s column is alternately 00 11 00 11; the 4s column is 0000 1111 etc. This pattern can be used to write the sequence of binary numbers if you find it easier.

Try to predict what the next column will be and the pattern it will show.

8s	4s	2s	1s	Decimal
0	0	0	0	0
0	0	0	1	1
0	0	1	0	2
0	0	1	1	3
0	1	0	0	4
0	1	0	1	5
0	1	1	0	6
0	1	1	1	7
1	0	0	0	8
1	0	0	1	9
1	0	1	0	10
1	0	1	1	11
1	1	0	0	12
1	1	0	1	13
1	1	1	0	14
1	1	1	1	15

What is the point of counting in binary?

It is the basic language of electronic counters and of computers. It may seem complicated to start with, but it is far easier to build an electronic system that has only two voltage levels to recognise rather than to build one that recognises ten, which would be the case if we used the decimal system.

Binary coded decimal

It is very confusing if a human has to convert a large decimal number to binary, so a simpler system has been devised. Each single decimal digit is converted to a four column binary number; for example, **123** (one hundred and twenty-three) would be **0001 0010 0011**.

If binary coded decimal is being used it is not allowable to have a binary number greater than 1001. The reason is that each block of four binary digits (bits) has to convert to a single decimal digit; if you had 1010, this would convert to 10 (ten) in decimal.

8 bits = 1 byte   1024 bytes = 1 Kilobyte (kb)
    1048576 bytes = 1 Megabyte (Mb)

ACTIVITY

Number exercises

1. Convert the following numbers to binary:

7	9	3	13	6
15	1	5	8	16

2. Convert the binary numbers to decimal:

0111	1010	0101	1110	1000
00010101	1100	0000	0100	11111111

3. Convert the decimal numbers into binary coded decimal (BCD):

1234	13	1876	1999	8634

4. Convert the BCD numbers into decimal:

0111 0111	1001 1000	0011 0101	0010 1001	0001 0001

5. Which of the following numbers cannot be used in BCD:

0011	1010	0111	1111	0101

Research task

Another counting system used in electronics and computing is based on **16**; it is called hexadecimal. See if you can find out how it works and how the numbers between **9** and **15** can be represented.

Useful ICs for counting systems

IC	Function	Description
4001B	Quad 2 input NOR gate	Logic IC – 4 NOR gates
4011B	Quad 2 input NAND gate	Logic IC – 4 NAND gates
4017B	Decade counter/divider	Count to 10 and reset
4024B	7 stage binary counter	Maximum count 127
4026B	Decade counter with decoded 7 segment output	Outputs direct to 7 segment display
4027B	Dual JK flip-flop	Can be set as RS bistable, or 2 bit binary counter
4060B	12 stage binary counter	Maximum count 4095
4093B	Quad 2 input NAND Schmitt	Logic IC with Schmitt output
4510B	BCD up/down counter	Counts to 9 in binary and resets
4516B	Binary up/down counter	Counts to 16 in binary and resets
4585B	4 bit magnitude counter	Compares two 4 bit binary numbers
40106B	Hex Schmitt trigger	6 Schmitt inverters

Table 6.1

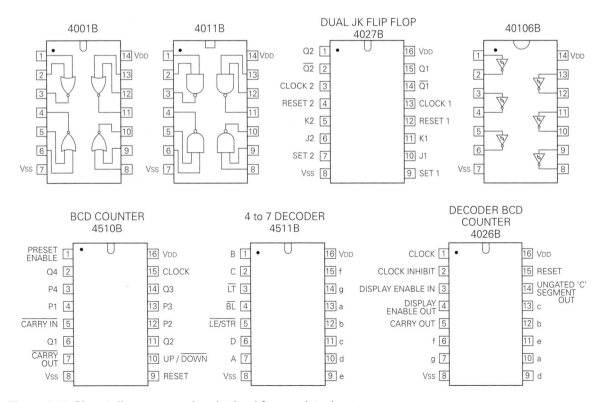

Figure 6.80 Pinout diagrams can be obtained from a datasheet

IC pinout diagrams can be found from catalogues or datasheets. A few examples are shown in Fig. 6.80. Remember that an over score or a small circle on an input means that it is active when low.

6.6 CALCULATIONS

The main formulae to remember are given below in **bold**; the others are rearrangements of the two main formulae.

V = voltage in volts
I = current in amps
R = resistance in ohms
P = power in watts

$V = I \times R$	$I = V/R$	$R = V/I$
$P = V \times I$	$V = P/I$	$I = P/V$
$P = I^2 \times R$	$P = V^2/R$	$I = \sqrt{(P/R)}$
$R = V^2/P$	$R = P/I^2$	$V = \sqrt{(P \times R)}$

Resistors in series $\quad R_{total} = R_1 + R_2 + R_3$ etc.

Resistors in parallel $\quad \dfrac{1}{R_{total}} = \dfrac{1}{R_1} + \dfrac{1}{R_2} + \dfrac{1}{R_3}$ etc.

Potential divider $\quad$ Voltage out $= \dfrac{R_2}{R_1 + R_2} \times$ supply voltage

Transistor formulae $\quad I_c$ = collector current in amps
$\qquad I_b$ = base current in amps

Current gain $H_{fe} = \dfrac{I_c}{I_b}$

Emitter current $= I_b + I_c$

Voltage gain $= \dfrac{V_{out}}{V_{in}}$

Capacitors in series	$\dfrac{1}{C_{total}}$	$=$	$\dfrac{1}{C_1}$	$+$	$\dfrac{1}{C_2}$	$+$	$\dfrac{1}{C_3}$ etc.
Capacitors in parallel	C_{total}	$=$	C_1	$+$	C_2	$+$	C_3 etc.

Op-amps R_f = feedback resistor in ohms, R_{in} = input resistor in ohms

Inverting amplifier   voltage gain $= \dfrac{-R_f}{R_{in}}$

Non-inverting amplifier   voltage gain $= \dfrac{R_f + R_{in}}{R_{in}}$

When carrying out any calculations it is vital to have all parts of the formula in the correct units. For reference the main units are laid out below:

Voltage $1V = 1000\ mV = 1{,}000{,}000\ \mu V$ or $1V = 10^3 mV = 10^6\ \mu V$

Current $1A = 1000\ mA = 1{,}000{,}000\ \mu A$ or $1A = 10^3 mA = 10^6\ \mu A$

Capacitance   1 Farad $= 1000\ mF = 1{,}000{,}000\ \mu F = 1{,}000{,}000{,}000\ nF = 1{,}000{,}000{,}000{,}000\ pF$

Timing

Time constant $-$ t(seconds) = R(resistance in ohms) $\times$ C(capacitance in farads)

555 timer monostable t(seconds) = 1.1 $\times$ R(ohms) $\times$ C(farads)

e.g. using a 10K resistor and a 100 μF capacitor $t = 1.1 \times 10{,}000 \times \dfrac{100}{1{,}000{,}000} = 1.1 \times 1$
= 1.1 seconds.

555 timer astable frequency $f = \dfrac{1.44}{(R_1 + 2R_2)C}$ R_1 is from pin 7 to positive
R_2 is from pin 6 to pin 7

If large value electrolytic capacitors are used, the time will be approximate because of the high tolerance in them.

Resistor colour code

Band 1 1st Digit		Band 2 2nd Digit		Band 3 No of Zeros (multiplier		Band 4 Tolerance	
Black	0	Black	0	Black	–	Silver	0.01
Brown	1	Brown	1	Brown	0	Gold	0.1
Red	2	Red	2	Red	00	Gold	0.05
Orange	3	Orange	3	Orange	000	Brown	0.01
Yellow	4	Yellow	4	Yellow	0000	Red	0.02
Green	5	Green	5	Green	00000		
Blue	6	Blue	6	Blue	000000		
Violet	7	Violet	7				
Grey	8	Grey	8				
White	9	White	9				

Figure 6.81

6.7 QUALITY CONTROL IN ELECTRONICS

The sheet in Fig. 6.82 is an example of how you can check your practical work in a methodical way to give the greatest chance of success. This chart assumes that you have already checked the PCB carefully before adding any components. Quality control is something that you should be responsible for yourself: aim for perfection – you may not always get there but you will know that you have done your best.

In industry quality control is often carried out by specialists who have not actually carried out the construction. It is a good idea in the school situation to get another member of your group to carry out the tests for you as they may quickly spot a problem that has been missed.

Quality assurance is a step further than simple control of the circuit quality; it covers the whole operation, from purchase of components and materials through to after-sales service. Components used must be of a suitable quality and in many cases they have to be traceable, so that if a fault develops involving a single component all other circuits using the same batch of that component can be identified and recalled.

Possible faults

- Faulty PCB design.
- Faulty PCB manufacture.
- Faulty soldering/construction.
- Logic ICs – are all CMOS inputs tied?
- Open collector outputs – no pull-up resistor.
- Components damaged by heat.
- Missed/incorrect connections on counter or logic ICs.
- Faulty components.

General checks to be carried out	Pass	Fail	Work needed
Battery lead orientation			
Board fully populated			
Polarised capacitor orientation			
Polarised capacitor value			
Non-polarised capacitor values			
LED orientation			
LED lead colour coding			
LED shrink sleeving			
Diodes type			
Diodes orientation			
Transistor type			
Transistor orientation			
Resistor values			
Potentiometer value			
Connecting leads secure			
IC holders correctly fitted			
Soldered joints visual inspection			
Dry joints			
Bridged joints			

Voltage check before and after on/off switch			
Voltage check on IC positions			
Inputs working			
Outputs working			

ICs correctly fitted			
Powered test with ICs in place			

Additional checks for PIC circuit

Voltage at +5V			
Digital input signals			
Analogue input signals			
Outputs from PIC			
Outputs from driver IC or transistor			
Accepts test program			
Check on inputs			
Check on outputs			
Full check on program function			

Figure 6.82

Strategies for finding faults

- Use known circuits.
- Simulation and/or breadboarding of circuits.
- Design-in the facility to repair – extra pads on 0V and power rails for missed connections.
- Indicate outputs at each stage within the circuit – LEDs, test points.

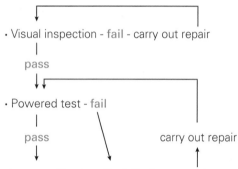

· Visual inspection - fail - carry out repair

pass

· Powered test - fail

pass   carry out repair

Test against specification   Fault finding procedure

Figure 6.83 Test procedure

Problems with the PCB

- Porous tracks.
- Fine cuts in the track resulting from scratches on artwork.
- Inverted artwork.
- Tracks joined together.
- Text information joining two tracks.
- Tracks too thin for current in circuit.

▶ Test equipment

The multimeter is probably the most important item of test equipment; it can either be digital or analogue, the latter having a moving needle to indicate values. Some of the more expensive meters are auto-ranging and no setting of scale is required. Most of them however will require a scale and the

correct reading to be set. In some cases current reading on the mA setting will require one of the test leads to be moved.

Figure 6.84 Digital multimeter and analogue multimeter

A logic probe will save a lot of time when checking digital circuits. Once connected to the power rails, it has a needle probe which can be touched onto the circuit, lighting a low or high LED where the value falls into those ranges. Many probes will also have the ability to send a pulse into the circuit which can be quite a useful feature.

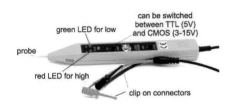

Figure 6.85 Logic probe

▶ Construction techniques

Soldering is the main technique that has to be learned for constructing electronic circuits. Once learned it is an easy technique to use but it is perhaps the most important aspect of construction and the most frequent cause of problems with circuits.

The main requirements for effective soldering are:

Correct equipment

- Soldering iron with a clean tip of the correct size.
- Stand to hold the soldering iron when not in use.
- Damp sponge to clean the tip of the iron.
- Tip cleaner for initial cleaning and tinning.

Figure 6.86 Using tip cleaner and a damp sponge to clean the tip

- Method of holding PCB in position.
- Desoldering tool.
- Solder – normally multicore with flux included.

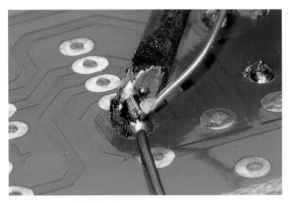

Figure 6.87 Soldering iron and solder are at opposite sides of the joint

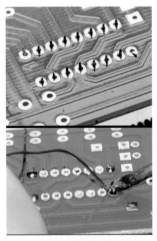

Figure 6.88 Diagonally opposite pins on socket are bent before soldering other diagonal pins; bent pins are then straightened and soldered

Correct technique

- All parts of the joint must be hot enough.
- All parts of the joint must be clean, with no oxide, oil or grease on the joint.
- Close enough – solder works by capillary action and it will not jump large gaps.

Fault	Cause	Remedy
Dry joint	Iron not touching one part of joint	Reheat, making sure that both parts are hot
Solder will not flow	Dirt on one or both parts of joint	Clean with glass fibre pen or abrasive rubber
Solder on both parts but joint not made	Gap too large	Bend component leg to touch pad
Tip of iron will not tin	Contamination on tip	Use tinning compound
Iron not hot enough	Tip has moved along the element or tip not tightly screwed on	Wait for iron to cool and tighten tip
Solder has dull appearance	Joint has moved during cooling	Reheat, making sure that both parts are hot
Solder has 'blobbed'	Too much solder fed in	Use desoldering tool to remover excess and resolder
Bridged joint	Too much solder fed in	Wipe dry iron across joint or use desoldering tool

Table 6.2

When soldering, you are heating the two parts to be joined to a temperature above the melting point of the solder, feeding solder into the joint and then allowing it to cool without any movement. The main faults will occur because one of the correct technique items is missing. If the iron is not held against both parts of the joint, uneven heating will result and the solder is attracted to the hottest part, often not attaching to the cool part. This is known as a 'dry' joint. On a PCB it can typically be seen as a dark ring around the component leg.

Figure 6.89 A dry joint can be seen, as well as a burnt track at the top of the photo

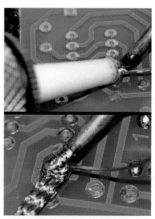

Figure 6.90 Two methods of desoldering: a desoldering tool and copper braid used to 'soak up' the solder

Figure 6.91 Adding a forgotten track

Forgotten tracks can be added either by using wire connections between two points or by using adhesive copper tape to make a new section of track. When positioned, the adhesive will hold the tape while solder is dropped onto the joint. The tinned section of tape is then as strong as a normal track. To break a connection between tracks, two parallel cuts should be made with a scalpel or craft knife before the centre section is scratched away. This sequence can be seen in Fig. 6.91.

Safety note

It is stating the obvious but soldering irons get hot and so does the work you are soldering. The temperature on the iron approaches 200°C; think of boiling water – it is twice as hot as that. Do not forget that large components and terminals will take a lot longer to cool down.

Some fluxes can be an irritant, try not to breathe any flux fumes in.

Lead-free solder is now compulsory in industry, but not in schools. If you are using leaded solder make sure that hands are washed at the end of the lesson.

◗ Off-board components

These can include batteries, speakers, motors and other quite heavy items. Any connecting wires should be attached to the board through terminal blocks, or if soldered direct, use strain relief loops.

Wires for any component involving movement should be stranded not single core.

Figure 6.92 A tidy circuit with the strain relief on the battery wires

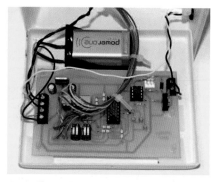

Figure 6.93 Test LEDS for the IC outputs can be seen and wires are neatly tied

Connection between boards

The simplest way of doing this, if your circuit involves two or more boards, is to use ribbon cable and connectors. One connector can be fixed; the other should be a plug and socket so that it can be removed. Edge connectors are also available but these do not give the flexibility in positioning that you can get with a ribbon cable.

Figure 6.95 A variety of PCB mounting methods are available, some are shown here

Figure 6.94 Ribbon cable connector with one fixed end and one plug and socket

▶ Fitting the PCB to a casing

You can use any of the following:

- Self-adhesive pillars – a quick and easy method using 4 mm holes that can be designed into the PCB.
- Threaded pillars – more expensive but easier if you have to take the PCB out of the case.
- Screws – can be fiddly to fit and get the PCB level.
- Mounting strip – no hole needed in PCB.
- Support posts – good for inter-board connection.

KEY TERMS

AC – alternating current
ANODE – LED/diode positive leg
CATHODE – LED/diode negative leg
CMOS – complementary metal oxide semiconductor
COB – chip on board
DC – direct current
DIL – dual in line
DPDT – double pole double throw
DPST – double pole single throw
emf – electromotive force
FET – field effect transistor
IC – integrated circuit
IR – infrared
LCD – liquid crystal display
LED – light emitting diode
mAh – milli-amp hours, a measure of battery capacity
MOSFET – metal oxide semiconductor field effect transistor
NYLOC – locking nut with an unthreaded nylon insert
PCB – printed circuit board
PIR – passive infra red

SIL – single in line
SMT – surface mount technology
SPDT – single pole, double throw
SPST – single pole, single throw
TTL – transistor–transistor logic
UV – ultraviolet

6.8 USEFUL CIRCUITS

The following circuits can be adapted for a variety of different projects.

Process circuits will vary according to what you are doing in your project. The ones in Fig. 6.98 are only a small example of what may be needed. When looking for a process circuit, it is important to use information from a datasheet where this is available. A web search will normally find a number of sources

for the sheet that you are looking for. The search should include the device number and possibly a brief description. For example, a search for '3140 op amp' will produce a range of datasheet sources. Many of the sheets give example circuits which can be tried either on a breadboard or using simulation software before the design is finalised.

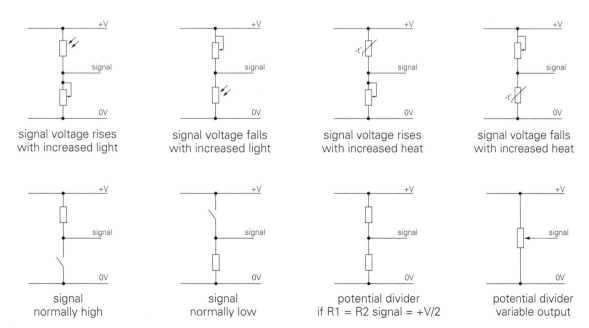

Figure 6.96 A range of input circuits are given here

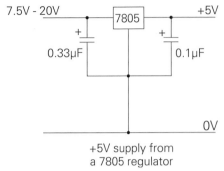

Figure 6.97 This circuit will provide a regulated 5V supply

To understand counting circuits it is a good idea to build a JK flip-flop circuit (as shown in Fig. 6.99). This will output at half the speed of the input. As the IC has two flip-flops, the first output can be fed into the clock input of the second, dividing the first input by four. If you build this circuit with LEDs on the outputs, you should see that the device is counting in binary.

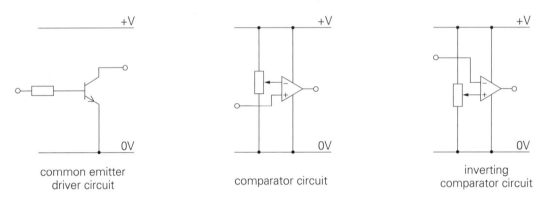

Figure 6.98 Process circuits

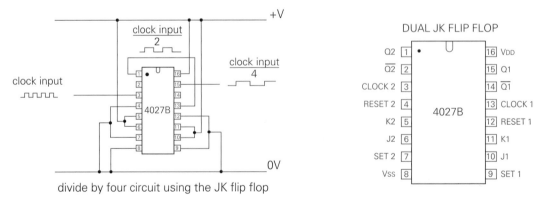

Figure 6.99 JK flip-flop set up as a 2 bit binary counter

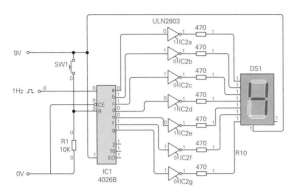

Figure 6.100 4026 decoded counter circuit constructed using simulation software

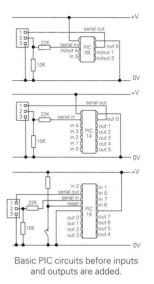

Basic PIC circuits before inputs
and outputs are added.

Figure 6.103 There are an increasing range of PIC devices available, a few are shown here

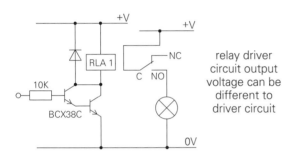

relay driver circuit output voltage can be different to driver circuit

Figure 6.101 A relay driver circuit can be used to isolate the input from the output

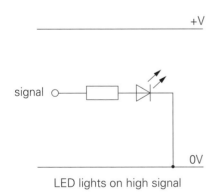

LED lights on high signal

Figure 6.102 LED outputs

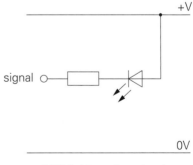

LED lights on low signal

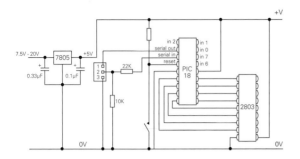

18 pin PIC with regulated input and buffered outputs

Figure 6.104 The full 18 pin PIC circuit with each output capable of sinking 500mA

Circuit symbols

Circuit symbols will be essential in your design work. The ones shown in Fig. 6.105 are the standard ones that are used in examination papers. Many symbols used in books and software will differ slightly from these and from each other.

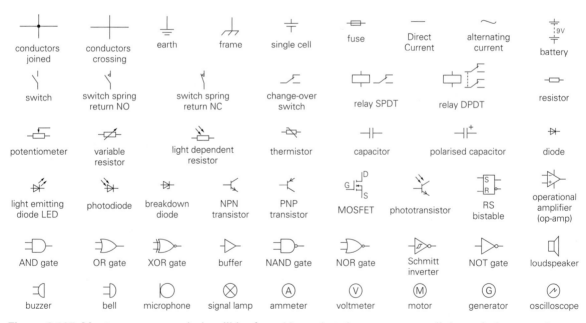

Figure 6.105 Most common symbols will be found here, but there are many slight variations used

CHAPTER 7

CONTROL SYSTEMS – PNEUMATICS

7.1 MATERIALS AND COMPONENTS

By the end of this chapter you should have developed a knowledge and understanding of:

- the use of the pneumatic components, their application within existing systems and how they interact to provide a required function
- the use of calculations to determine reasons for component selection
- the use of common formulae.

Pneumatics is using compressed air to do useful work. Compressed air has many uses, from keeping footballs and tyres inflated to powering machinery for industrial production lines. A bicycle pump compresses air into a tyre, but in the pneumatic systems used in industry the arrangement would be the other way round – compressed air moves a cylinder which would be doing useful work. With the use of various types of cylinders, valves and other associated components, many different types of circuits can be designed to perform a variety of control functions.

▶ Air supply

The movement of cylinders and other pneumatic components relies on compressed air. Air is compressed in a compressor, which is a pump usually driven by an electric motor. The compressed air is forced into a strong storage tank called a receiver, or sometimes a reservoir, which supplies the pneumatic circuit.

The receiver is important because it supplies a constant operating pressure which can be set by the regulator and displayed by the pressure gauge.

The safety valve will open and release the

pressure if for any reason the safe working pressure is exceeded.

The drain valve is attached to the lowest point of the receiver and should be regularly opened to release any water which is produced when air is pressurised.

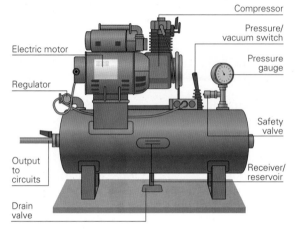

Figure 7.1 The main components used to safely supply air under pressure

▶ Cylinders

Cylinders are the main components used as output devices in pneumatics. A cylinder has a piston which is moved by air pressure entering either end. Fig. 7.2 shows the commonly used cylinders.

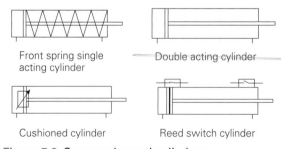

Figure 7.2 Commonly used cylinders

In a single acting cylinder, air pressure forces the piston out and the internal spring returns it.

In a double acting cylinder, air pressure forces

the piston out and air pressure at the other end returns it.

In a cushioned cylinder, the final part of the movement is slowed down to prevent an abrupt stop.

In a reed switch cylinder, air pressure forces the piston out and air pressure at the other end returns it, but there are reed switches fixed each end to detect the position of the piston.

A single acting cylinder

Fig. 7.3 shows a simple circuit diagram using a three-port two-way (3/2) valve to activate a single acting cylinder; this cylinder is suitable for applications where only a limited force is required. When the push button is pressed, main air sends the piston out against the spring where it stays until the button is released. When the button is released the spring expands and the piston returns.

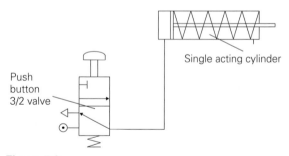

Figure 7.3

An example where this type of circuit could be used is on a date stamping machine.

A double acting cylinder

The double acting cylinder has a port at each end. Compressed air entering the rear port will outstroke the piston causing air in front of the piston to exhaust through the front port. If compressed air enters the front port the piston will instroke and air is exhausted through the back port. As a double acting cylinder requires air pressure to both outstroke and instroke the piston, it is necessary to use a five-port two-way valve (5/2). A useful circuit can be built by combining the valves to produce an automatically reciprocating sawing machine, as shown in Fig. 7.12.

A cushioned cylinder

Sliding doors are often operated using cushioned pneumatic cylinders because the cushioning at the end of each stroke prevents the door from slamming open and shut. The cushioning of each stroke is brought about by trapping a small amount of air, a cushion, at the end of the cylinder and allowing it to exhaust much more slowly than the rest of the air. Or, in the case of sophisticated applications, a separation piston with a regulated bleed orifice.

A reed switch cylinder

A reed switch cylinder differs from a normal cylinder. It has a magnetic disc built into the piston which causes the reed switches to close when the piston comes close, and the switch opens when it moves away. The closing and opening of the switches can

complete an electrical circuit which can then be fed into a microcontroller.

▶ Valves

Valves connect the outside world to the circuit. A pneumatic circuit uses valves which can be operated in various ways to cause an input. The basic internal structure of these valves is similar, and as a general rule they are activated and cause a change in the direction of the air flow. Fig. 7.4 shows the two states of a valve which has three ports. These are known as three-port two-way, or 3/2, push button, spring return valves. Also shown is a shuttle valve which is a non-return valve allowing flow from only one end at a time to be directed to the next section of the circuit.

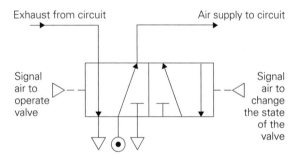

Figure 7.6 The two states of a five-port valve

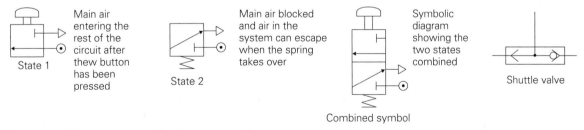

Figure 7.4 The two states of a three-port valve

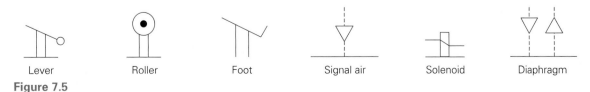

Lever   Roller   Foot   Signal air   Solenoid   Diaphragm

Figure 7.5

Valve control

Valves can be operated in various ways. Fig. 7.5 shows some of those alternatives.

Fig. 7.6 shows the two states of a valve which has five ports. These are known as five-port two-way, or 5/2.

Valve port identification

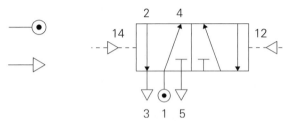

Figure 7.7

The ports on the valves are identified by numbers as shown in Fig. 7.7.

- **1** is the main air with the symbol 1.
- **2** and **4** can be either input or return from the circuit.
- **3** and **5** are exhausts with the symbol 3 or 5.
- 12 and 14 are pronounced 'one two' or 'one four', referring to the fact that main air 1 is applied to output 2 (12) or output 4 (14).
- Main air is a solid line; signal and exhaust lines are broken.
- An extended piston rod is outstroked.
- A retracted piston rod is instroked.

Restrictors or flow control valves (FCV)

Another pneumatic component used in sliding doors and many other circuits is the restrictor or flow control valve. It comes in two varieties: bi-directional and uni-directional.

Fig. 7.8 shows the symbols, and as the name implies, a bi-directional restrictor restricts the air flow in both directions but a uni-directional restricts flow in one direction and allows full flow in the other. As in the shuttle valve, there is a component which blocks the flow of air in one direction.

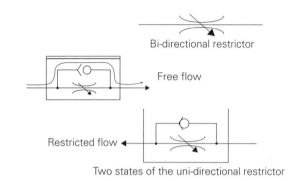

Bi-directional restrictor

Free flow

Restricted flow

Two states of the uni-directional restrictor

Figure 7.8 Restrictors

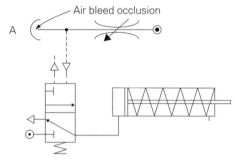

Air bleed occlusion

A

Figure 7.9 Air bleed occlusion circuit

▶ Circuits

Air bleed occlusion

A useful way of detecting movement or the covering of a small air hole is by using an air bleed occlusion circuit. The circuit makes use of low pressure air venting through a small hole, and if the hole becomes covered the low pressure change is detected by a diaphragm valve. The diaphragm valve has a large surface area on which the low pressure acts, and the valve changes state in the usual way. Fig. 7.9 shows an air bleed occlusion circuit and the small hole at A being open. If the hole at A is covered then air will be directed to the diaphragm operated two-way three-port valve which will change state, directing the main air supply to the single acting cylinder, causing it to outstroke.

An application for this could be on a conveyor belt where the product arrives in the correct place and covers the escaping air and sends out the cylinder to stamp the date or punch a hole.

Automatic return with time delay

The circuit in Fig. 7.10 uses a reservoir, a container which fills with compressed air, to create a time delay.

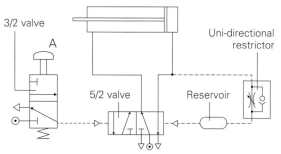

Figure 7.10 Automatic return with time delay circuit

When A is pressed and released, a signal is sent to the 5/2 valve to change state and send main air to outstroke the cylinder. At the same time, air is sent to the uni-directional restrictor and on to the reservoir; the restrictor will control the flow into the reservoir. Eventually the reservoir will pressurise sufficiently to cause the 5/2 valve to change state and cause the cylinder to instroke.

A delay has been caused while the reservoir was being pressurised and this delay can be adjusted by adjusting the uni-directional restrictor.

Circuits often need a time delay, for example in operating a sliding door.

Pressure decay

The circuit in Fig. 7.11 uses a diaphragm valve to sense the change in pressure.

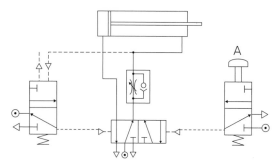

Figure 7.11 Pressure decay sensing circuit

Pressure decay sensing is achieved by taking some of the exhaust from the moving piston and feeding it to the diaphragm valve, and feeding the rest through the restricted path of the uni-directional restrictor.

In this circuit the diaphragm valve is connected in a different way: the main air and exhaust are reversed to create a normally open valve.

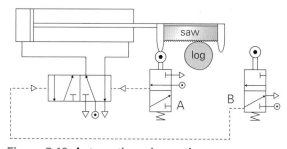

Figure 7.12 Automatic reciprocation

The exhaust from the moving piston holds the diaphragm valve in the exhausting state, but when the cylinder is fully outstroked, the exhaust decays away and the valve changes state. Main air is then sent to the five-port valve, and that changes state, causing the cylinder to instroke.

Automatic reciprocation

Figure 7.12 shows an example of automatic reciprocation of a cylinder.

When valve A is operated by the end of the saw it switches the five-port two-way valve over and main air enters the opposite end of the double acting cylinder, causing it to outstroke and move the saw across the log to cut it. When it gets to the end of the stroke, valve B is operated and the cylinder instrokes and the saw returns to start again.

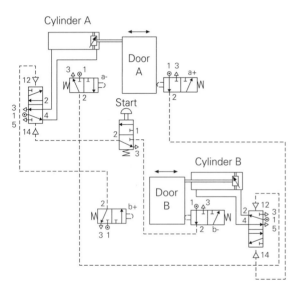

Figure 7.13 Sequential control circuit

Sequential control

In many pneumatic circuits it is necessary to combine the operation of more than one cylinder. When describing the sequence the following convention is used: cylinders are shown with capital letters with an A+ for outstroke or an A− for instroke. Values are shown with lower case letters. This is called a sequential control circuit. Fig. 7.13 shows the movement of two doors A and B controlled by cylinders A and B in a sequence of:

cylinder A instroking (A−) / cylinder B outstroking (B+) / cylinder A outstroking (A+) / cylinder B instroking (B−)

The circuit in Fig. 7.13 will cause door A to move left, then door B to move left, then door A to move right and finally door B to move right.

The circuit works as follows:

The start button is pressed and released then a signal is sent to port 14 of the 5/2 valve controlling cylinder A.

Main air out of port 4 is sent to cylinder A, causing it to instroke and door A to move to the left.

Door A hits 3/2 valve a− and a signal is sent to port 12 of the 5/2 valve controlling cylinder B.

Main air out of port 2 is sent to cylinder B, causing it to outstroke and door B to move to the left.

Door B hits 3/2 valve b+ and a signal is sent to port 12 of the 5/2 valve controlling cylinder A.

Main air out of port 2 is sent to cylinder A, causing it to outstroke and door A to move to the right.

Door A hits 3/2 valve a+ and a signal is sent to port 14 of the 5/2 valve controlling cylinder B.

Main air out of port 4 is sent to cylinder B, causing it to instroke and door B to move to the right.

The circuit will now wait until the start button is pressed again and the sequence A− B+ A+ B− will start again.

Signal amplification

The circuit in Fig. 7.14 has been used as an air bleed occlusion, but can also be used for signal amplification.

The low pressure at point A is amplified by acting on a diaphragm which causes the 3/2 valve to change state and can then switch main air pressure to enter the circuit at B.

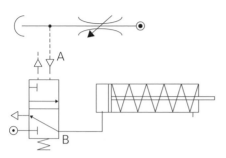

Figure 7.14

▶ Logic functions

The 'OR' function

Fig. 7.15 shows the arrangement which can be used to produce an 'OR' function. This circuit uses 3/2 valves and a shuttle valve. The shuttle valve allows a signal from A to pass through to C and also blocks the line from B. The shuttle valve will remain in this state until B is pressed, causing the line from A to be blocked. A **OR** B can be pressed to send main air to the rest of the circuit.

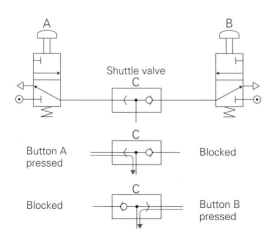

Figure 7.15

The 'AND' function

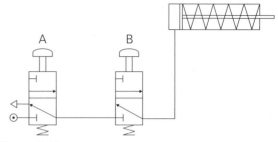

Figure 7.16

Fig. 7.16 shows the arrangement which can be used to produce an 'AND' function. The two 3/2 valves A and B must both be pressed before the single acting cylinder will outstroke. If only one is pressed nothing will happen. A **AND** B must be pressed to send main air to the rest of the circuit.

The 'NOT' function

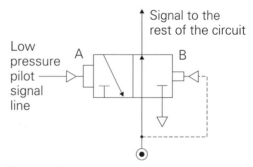

Figure 7.17

Fig. 7.17 shows the arrangement which can be used to produce a 'NOT' function. In the resting state, the valve allows air to the rest of the circuit, the higher pressure at B holding it in that state.

The low pressure pilot signal at A acts on a larger surface area than B and will switch the valve and stop the signal to the rest of the circuit. This valve acts as an inverter or a NOT valve.

Group air system

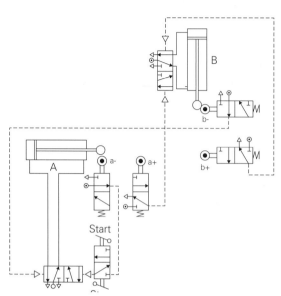

Figure 7.18

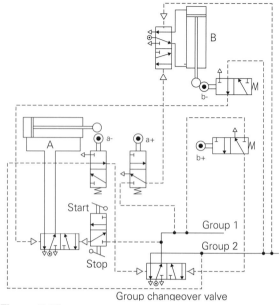

Figure 7.19

Fig. 7.18 shows a circuit in which two cylinders are controlling each other in a sequence. An example of this circuit is where cylinder A pushes a component in place and cylinder B drills a hole and retracts for cylinder A to remove the component.

This sequence should be cylinder A outstroking (A+), cylinder B outstroking (B+), cylinder B instroking (B−) and cylinder A instroking (A−).

The sequence is shortened to A+, B+, B−, A−.

There is a problem with Fig. 7.18 which causes an inoperable circuit. This problem occurs when the signal from the B+ 3/2 valve tries to change the cylinder B 5/2 valve over to make the cylinder B instroke.

The cylinder B 5/2 valve is still receiving a signal from the A+ 3/2 valve which was operated when cylinder A outstroked.

The cylinder B 5/2 valve has a dual signal on it.

To overcome this problem another 5/2 valve is used which acts to switch from one group of air outputs to another. This is known as group air system.

Fig. 7.19 shows how a solution can be found with an additional 5/2 valve that changes state when the 3/2 b+ is activated and returns again with the 3/2 a− valve. This gives the circuit two air supplies and removes the dual signal problem.

Calculations

The theory of force, pressure and area

Cylinders are available in various piston diameters and stroke lengths, and the correct type must be chosen for the particular application. The supply pressure is another variable, as is the required force that the cylinder must produce. All these variables can be calculated using the equation:

FORCE = PRESSURE × AREA

or: F = P × A

AREA = πr^2

The area of the piston on which the air pressure is acting is measured in mm^2. The force produced by the cylinder is measured in Newtons (N). The air pressure acting on the piston can be expressed as N/mm^2.

Fig. 7.20 shows the cylinder dimensions.

If the pressure supplied by the compressor was 0.1 N/mm^2 and the diameter of the piston was 25 mm, then the force produced by the piston rod can be calculated using the formula F = P × A.

F = 0.1 × π × 12.5^2 N
F = 49.09 N

This calculation is for an outstroking piston. If the calculation is for an instroking piston, then the area of the piston will differ because the

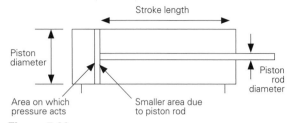

Figure 7.20

piston rod takes up some of that area. To compare the previous example and give the piston rod a diameter of 8 mm:

F = P × (Area of piston − Area of piston rod)
F = 0.1 × (π × 12.5^2 − (π x 4^2)) N
F = 0.1 × (490.87 − 50.26)
F = 44.06 N

If the piston is outstroking, it can exert a force of 49.08 N but on the instroke it is only 44.06 N, so if the cylinder is doing the same work in both directions the calculations must be based on the instroking piston.

7.2 SYSTEMS AND CONTROL

LEARNING OUTCOMES

By the end of this section you should have developed a knowledge and understanding of:

- the use of flowcharts to plan a system
- the use of microcontrollers to control and operate a circuit
- the integration of pneumatics with electronics and mechanisms
- the design of fittings and fixtures to components to enable them to carry out their function
- the use of syringes to model a circuit
- the importance of working safely with components.

Using flowcharts

The simple drawings that the flowchart uses are symbols which define a function, and there are only a small set of them needed, as

shown in Fig. 7.21. The names used may vary from user to user. There are other symbols but at this level these are sufficient. The standard used is ISO 5807.

The Terminator is usually found at the beginning and end of a flowchart, also known as the Entry or Exit symbol. Other words which are often used are 'Start' and 'End', 'Start Prog' and 'End Prog' or 'Return'.

The Process symbol is used to describe a single action or sequence. An example could be 'Send signal to instroke cylinder A' or 'Time = 10 seconds'.

The Decision symbol is used where a branch may occur within a program. An example could be 'Has the reed switch A− closed?' or 'Have 10 seconds passed?' There is an exit point that can continue the program if the decision has been satisfied, but there is also an exit point that can be fed back into the program before the question, if the answer is No, and will continue being fed back until the answer is Yes.

The data symbol is used to display an input or output when an interaction has taken place. An example could be 'Display the state of reed switch A−' or 'Display the countdown of the 10 seconds'.

The Predefined process symbol is a subroutine which indicates a call to a procedure or function. An example could be a subroutine which causes a delay, 'Delay 10 seconds'. At school level this is not seen often but is used where there are a number of embedded subroutines.

The Flowline joins the symbols together and indicates the direction and order of execution.

There are other symbols which are rarely used in schools but are available and can be found on many drawing programs.

An example of a flow chart is shown in the next section.

Computer/microcontroller

Many manually operated valves and other components can be replaced by an electrical/electronic version. Fig. 7.22 shows the circuit of a reed switch cylinder controlled by a solenoid-operated 3/2 valve.

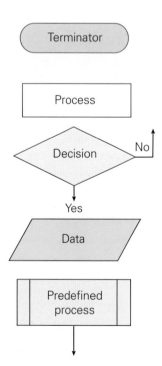

Figure 7.21

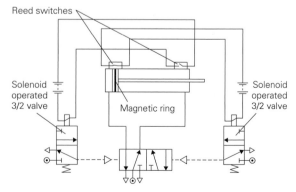

Figure 7.22

A reed switch cylinder differs from a normal cylinder. It has a magnetic ring built into the piston which causes the reed switches to close when the piston comes close, and the switch opens when it moves away. The closing and opening of the switches can complete an electrical circuit which can then operate a solenoid 3/2 valve. The 3/2 solenoid valves, as with all solenoid valves, have a coil inside which, when energised, causes the valve to switch states. When the solenoid valve changes state, it reverses the direction of movement of the piston until the magnetic ring on the piston influences the other reed switch, which again reverses the direction of movement of the piston.

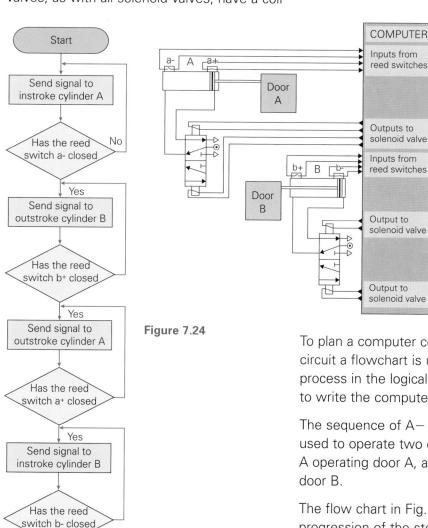

Figure 7.24

Figure 7.23

To plan a computer controlled pneumatic circuit a flowchart is used. This puts the process in the logical order, which is required to write the computer control program.

The sequence of A− / B+ / A+ / B− could be used to operate two doors A and B, cylinder A operating door A, and cylinder B operating door B.

The flow chart in Fig. 7.23 is a logical progression of the steps which need to be planned in the computer program.

Fig. 7.24 shows the implementation of the plan shown in the flowchart. The computer or

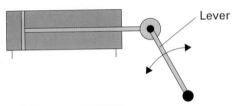

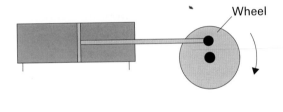

Figure 7.25

microprocessor reads the state of the reed switches and sends a signal to the 5/2 solenoid-operated valves at the correct time.

Computer control also gives more flexibility. It would be easy to program in a delay before a cylinder made any movement. As a safety precaution the program could make a warning sound before there was any door movement, or even speech synthesise the words 'Beware door closing'.

With a computer program running the sequence, it is quick and easy to go back in and change the order of the cylinder operations, so that if the circuit is a prototype then alternatives can be explored. To change a piped up mechanical sequence significantly more time would be needed.

Pneumatics are often used in hazardous industrial situations and with computer control, the operation can be monitored remotely from a safe distance.

Integrating pneumatics

Fig. 7.24 shows how pneumatic components can be integrated with electronics. They can also be integrated with mechanisms by attaching the moving piston rod to a lever or wheel, as shown in Fig. 7.25.

Design

It is necessary to design fittings that will allow the correct movement and fixing of

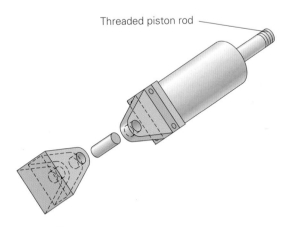

Figure 7.26

pneumatic components. As an example, the cylinders in the lever and wheel systems in Fig. 7.25 must have a fixing that will allow the cylinder to move as required. One possible answer is shown in Fig. 7.26.

Another possible question could ask to design a possible component to attach the threaded piston rod end to the lever or the wheel.

Vacuum principles

It is possible to use another output from the compressor to provide a vacuum. This could be used to lift and move large flat sheets of material, as shown in Fig. 7.27.

Hydraulics

Hydraulics are used where high precision of piston positional control and more force are

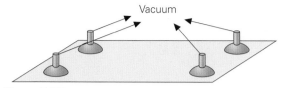

Figure 7.27

required. There are many similarities between pneumatics and hydraulics. The obvious one is that pneumatics use air pressure and hydraulics use a liquid pressurised in place of air. Similar valves can be used but the main difference is that in pneumatics the exhaust air can be vented into the atmosphere, but in hydraulics the liquid must be retained and sealed within the system for continuous use. This continuous use and the fact that it is a sealed system has the advantage that a hydraulic piston can be stopped anywhere along the stroke and held there, giving the advantage of positional control. The fact that the hydraulic oil will not compress gives another advantage over pneumatics, because air can be compressed.

Modelling

The modelling of a pneumatic circuit can be carried out using syringes connected to tubes and the air pressure provided by a bicycle pump or an inflated balloon. For a simple circuit just connect two syringes together with one outstroked and the other instroked; the instroking one will outstroke the other.

If the syringes and tubes connecting them together are filled with water, it is possible to see that the movement is more positive, and can be stopped more precisely.

There are also computer programs which allow the circuit to be modelled on the screen and simulated to check if it is workable.

Safety

Safety precautions to be taken when working with pneumatics:

- Receiver tanks have to be maintained according to Pressure Systems Safety Regulations 2000 or PSSR. This involves having a written scheme of examination that certifies the system is suitable for its intended use. A regular inspection of the equipment is a legal requirement.

- Pressure should be set accurately and not be too high.

- Never allow compressed air to be directed onto the skin.

- Disturbance of dust due to high pressure air can cause eye hazards.

- Always check for good connections, and be ready to shut off the air if a leak appears.

- Beware of pipes 'snaking' or 'whiplash' when an air line is switched on.

- There is a risk of moving mechanical parts trapping fingers. High forces can be involved.

CHAPTER 8

QUALITY

By the end of this chapter you should have developed a knowledge and understanding of:

- the difference between quality of design and quality of manufacture
- how the quality of the product can be affected by the selection of materials and manufacturing processes
- the importance of dimensional accuracy
- what 'tolerance' is and how it is used to ensure component parts of products work
- simple quality control checks that can be carried out to ensure accuracy and quality of finish.

Industry takes quality very seriously and devotes time to building quality attitudes amongst staff. When a company undertakes product manufacture they will put in place procedures to ensure that the products that are produced are of a consistently high quality. This is known as 'quality control'.

Quality is not just a consideration during manufacture. Quality will influence the design of products through the selection of materials and production methods.

In your controlled assessment tasks you will have to show consideration of quality in both design and manufacture.

Why is quality important?

The reputation of manufacturing companies is very important. Building 'brand' loyalty to ensure repeat business and product recommendation is a key factor to business success. There would be little point in a manufacturer producing low quality goods as

people would very quickly learn that the product does not perform well and would not purchase it. It is important for a manufacturer to understand who their target user for a product is. This allows them to anticipate and respond to the target user needs. Failure to meet the customer needs will result in poor sales as the product will either not sell because:

- the product quality is too low and it is regarded by users as poor
- the product quality is high but because of the quality of components and manufacturing methods used, it is too expensive for the target user to purchase.

Faults occur sometimes in products after they have been in use for a period of time. Manufacturers need to respond to these faults to ensure that they are able to maintain customer satisfaction levels. In some cases products may be recalled for repair or replacement.

Faults that may lead to product recall can be caused by poor construction, the use of inappropriate materials, or simply poor initial design of the product.

8.1 QUALITY OF DESIGN

Quality of design is an issue for both the manufacturer and the user of the product. Ensuring that products meet the needs of users whilst maintaining value for money is of paramount importance. Repairing or replacing faulty equipment can have substantial cost implications for manufacturing companies. Ensuring quality of design will help reduce the number of products that have to be repaired or replaced and will help achieve product sales.

Quality of design will be judged by different user groups in different ways. This will depend upon the type of product, its target market and its cost. Aesthetics (how the product looks), method of operation and function may all affect how people judge a design.

Quality of design is an issue for the manufacturer as well as the user. To be successful in a competitive market, a design must be reliable but not 'over engineered'. A balance between material cost, quantity of materials used and meeting the needs of users needs to be maintained.

Quality of design will result in products that are:

- right first time
- delivered on time
- manufactured within budget
- innovative for the benefit of the client
- not 'over engineered' – material and component usage will have been carefully considered to strip out wastage.

To achieve quality of design in your own work you will need to:

- evaluate similar products
- carry out targeted research and investigation with user groups
- design the product to be 'right first time'. Changes required to correct faults after manufacture are expensive
- simplify the design to achieve the lowest number of parts, components and stages in manufacture
- not compromise – do not use cheap parts or subsystems to save time and costs
- reuse proven designs, parts, modules and processes to minimise risk and assure quality.

8.2 QUALITY OF MANUFACTURE

There are four main features that define quality of manufacture:

- Selection of appropriate materials and components.
- Selection of appropriate manufacturing methods.
- Components made within appropriate tolerances.
- Quality of finish of individual components and the overall product.

The aim of quality in manufacture is to achieve quality by organising every process to get the product 'right first time' and prevent mistakes ever happening. This is also known as a 'zero defect' approach.

Selection of materials and components

High quality manufacture may not be achieved unless the material or components selected are the most appropriate for the product. The selection of materials or component will be affected by their cost, availability, working properties and associated environmental issues. The selection of inappropriate materials or compromising on material quality may lead to early product failure and increased costs. Further information on materials can be found in Chapter 2.

Selection of manufacturing method

To achieve quality in manufacture it is essential to select the most appropriate manufacturing method for the shaping, joining and finishing of materials and components. The type of manufacturing method selected will be dictated by the quantity of products to be made, availability of tooling/specialist equipment, environmental considerations and health and safety issues.

School-based manufacturing methods

The products you make in school will usually use wood, metal or plastics to produce the outer casing and possibly other component parts. It is essential that you choose the most appropriate manufacturing method to achieve a quality outcome.

8.3 QUALITY ASSURANCE

Quality assurance is carried out by the manufacturer to ensure that the product meets the minimum quality standards that have been set. The product will be checked at pre-determined points during the manufacturing process. These checks will take place before, during and after manufacturing.

The aim of quality assurance is to make sure the product is 'right first time and every time'. Quality assurance is seen to be the responsibility of everyone involved in the manufacturing process. It has an emphasis on 'self-checking'. Advantages include:

- Reduced costs because there is less wastage and re-working of faulty products as the product is checked at every stage.

- Improved motivation as workers have more ownership and recognition for their work.

- It can help break down 'us and them' barriers between workers and managers as it eliminates the feeling of being checked up on.

- With all staff responsible for quality, this can help the firm gain market advantage arising from a consistent level of quality.

Figure 8.1 Linkages organised for the suspension of TrackNav vehicle

EXAMINER'S TIPS

In your own design and make activities, you should always aim to achieve the highest possible quality. If a PCB is poorly made, you will spend lots of time correcting faults and chasing defects. Quality checks should be built into your manufacturing process and the results of these checks should be included in your work report.

Figure 8.2 Drive system for eco marathon vehicle

'Testability' is important in systems – can each stage be proved to work? In electronics extra LEDs may be added to show the correct function of a stage.

To achieve quality of manufacture in your own work you will need to:

- Select the highest quality manufacturing process possible. Use of hand processes tends to produce lower levels of consistent quality; use of machine tools helps to make accurate parts.

- Raise and resolve issues early. Carry out research, experiments and modelling.

Generate alternative manufacturing contingency plans.

- Optimise tolerances by cutting down on the variables which would lead to failure of parts fitting together. A design is robust if it can be manufactured predictably with consistently high quality.

- Do not use cheap parts or subsystems to save time and costs. Manage the time well to fully finish the product. Do not rush and accept lower quality just for speed of production.

- Reuse proven designs, parts, modules and processes to minimise risk and assure quality, especially on critical aspects of the design.

- Document thoroughly and completely. In the rush to develop products, many designers fail to document every aspect of the design thoroughly. Drawings, manufacturing instructions and cutting lists need to convey the design unambiguously for manufacture. Imprecise drawings invite misunderstandings and interpretation, which add cost, waste time and may compromise quality.

8.4 QUALITY CONTROL

Quality control checks to ensure accuracy, correct function and quality of finish are used in the manufacturing industry. Depending upon the type of product being made and the volume of production, quality inspectors will measure or test:

- every product
- samples from each batch; or
- random samples.

Advantages of quality control checks

Inspection is intended to prevent faulty products reaching the customer. This approach means having specially trained inspectors. It is thought that inspectors may be better placed to find widespread problems across an organisation.

Disadvantages of quality control checks

Individuals are not encouraged to take responsibility for the quality of their own work. Other approaches to quality (such as Total Quality Management) mean that there is much less need for quality control if the whole manufacturing process is geared towards 'zero defects' or getting it right first time.

Rejecting products at the quality control stage is expensive for a manufacturer. The manufacturer has incurred the full costs of production but the product cannot be sold. The manufacturer does not want to be associated with substandard products. If defect levels are very high, the company's profitability will suffer unless steps are taken to tackle the causes of the failures.

 EXAMINER'S TIPS

In your work at school quality checks can be made at various points such as:

- at the very beginning of the making activity with choice of materials
- checking that selected tools to shape materials are fit for purpose
- ensuring that PCB masks are complete and have dark lines
- checking for successful ultra-violet exposure and development
- ensuring copper etch produces a good quality board
- ensuring all holes are correctly drilled and aligned

- ensuring correct insertion and soldering of components
- insulating legs and components
- testing of the circuit board for each sub-section
- assembly of components in casing
- full product function testing.

Although this list may not fit your project exactly it does indicate many of the quality checks that you could make. In your record of making it would be a good idea to record many of these stages and any action you took to correct any faults. The recording of fault finding and your corrections, modifications and improvements will demonstrate your making ability. It would be good to list the quality checks.

8.5 DIMENSIONAL ACCURACY IN COMPONENT PARTS FOR ASSEMBLY

The variability in materials and forming processes can cause problems when trying to fit parts together. These variations must be controlled in order to achieve a high quality product.

Using wood to build structures accurate to dimensions from your drawings will rarely lead to exactly fitting parts. You will need to adopt a different strategy of making the parts then trial fit the parts together with trimming and adjusting until you get the fit required. Wood fibre does not always cut easily or smoothly, causing variations in size and surface finish.

When forming plastics there is a problem with 'relaxation'. As the plastic cools after forming, it will shrink and angled parts will tend to 'open up'. When injection moulding plastics, fillers are used to stiffen the material to stop these changes occurring. The draft angle on vacuum-forming moulds ensures that the mould can be released once the plastic has cooled.

Metals are the most stable material for dimensional accuracy when forming. When wasting material by hand or by machine processing, parts can be made accurately to the sizes on the working drawings. This means parts should fit accurately together first time.

Bought-in components and sub-assemblies are made to critical dimensions. This means that you can expect them to fit the holes that you have provided on your chassis or case.

Using CAM tooling ensures repeatable accuracy when making multiple parts. The only variable tends to be wearing on the cutting tools.

Tolerances for assembly and manufacture

You will use measurements all the time when constructing your product. Some of these measurements are critical for parts to work correctly.

Figure 8.3 CAM tooling the parts, sizes are repeatable for this SnakeBot

Example

A 6 mm shaft needs to spin in a metal frame. However, a 6 mm shaft will not necessarily run in the 6 mm drilled hole.

When you start looking in detail at the shape of rods from which the shaft would be made, you may find that they may not be round or smooth from the manufacturing process. You have to allow for these inaccuracies when you want parts to run together. It would be better to drill an oversize 6.20 mm hole to ensure the rod will spin.

For an interference or press fit where parts are to fix together, a 5.9 mm hole would be better. If making wood models, the size difference will need to be greater: if the 6 mm dowel is to rotate in the wood frame, the hole would need to be 6.5 mm, to allow for non-roundness of the dowel and the wood fibre not clearing the inside of the hole.

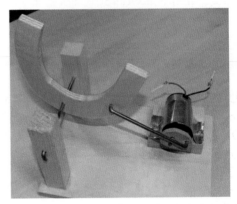

Figure 8.4 Modelling with wood can cause fitting problems

8.6 QUALITY CONTROL METHODS IN INDUSTRY

Quality circle

A Quality Circle is a group of workers who meet to talk about improvement in their workplace and to show management their ideas regarding the quality of the work completed in the factory. They also discuss ideas on how to improve organisation within the work area and how to effectively motivate employees by making them feel valued in the organisation. Areas considered in these discussions include improving occupational safety and health, improving product design and ways to improve the manufacturing process. To ensure everybody's voice is heard, the best size for a quality circle is between eight and ten members.

Kaizen (continuous improvement)

Kaizen forms part of the 'Japanese' approach to management, or 'Lean Production'.

Kaizen, or 'continuous **improvement**', involves the continual introduction of small incremental changes in a company in order to improve quality and/or efficiency. Employees are best placed to identify areas for improvement, since they see the company and production line in action on a day-to-day basis. Industries that use this method of quality control have a culture that encourages and rewards employees for their contribution.

Total quality management (TQM)

This is a specific approach to quality assurance that aims to develop a quality culture throughout the company. In TQM, manufacturing organisations consist of 'quality chains' in which each person or team treats the receiver of their work as if they were an external customer and adopts a target of 'right first time' or zero defects.

In the controlled assessment tasks, you are the manufacturer. Your work will involve the use of parts and product assembly. You should operate TQM where everything is made 'right first time'.

KEY TERMS

QUALITY CIRCLE – a small group of people meeting to make improvements in the work of a company

TOTAL QUALITY MANAGEMENT (TQM) – a culture in a company, where everyone accepts responsibility for the quality of products

'RIGHT FIRST TIME' – part of TQM where everyone is working together to produce products or sub-assemblies that are 'right first time'

QUALITY OF MANUFACTURE – taking care to organise all the processes to ensure each part contributes to the quality process

QUALITY CHECK – the checks made by quality inspectors; could be every item or a sample of a batch

TOLERANCES – use of measurements to ensure parts fit together or fix together with interference fit

QUALITY CONTROL – a system adopted to ensure a finished product is correctly assembled and finished for the customer

CHAPTER 9

HEALTH AND SAFETY

LEARNING OUTCOMES

By the end of this chapter you should have developed a knowledge and understanding of:

- the health and safety responsibilities of designers and manufacturers to the workforce, the consumer and the general public
- the importance of personal safety when designing and making products in school workshops
- basic risk assessment procedures
- COSHH
- how safety signs and symbols are used in workshops
- identification of design modifications needed to make products safer to use.

Designers and manufacturers have obligations to ensure the health and safety of both production staff and the end user of products. This chapter will examine the issues around health and safety and how these affect the work of designers and manufacturers. It will also examine the steps that you need to take in your own work to ensure that you work safely and do not put others at risk by using unsafe working practices.

9.1 DESIGNERS' AND MANUFACTURERS' RESPONSIBILITIES

The Health and Safety at Work Act is the basis of safety law in the UK. Employers have a duty to ensure, as far as reasonably practicable, that employees and visitors to places of employment are safe at work.

There are two organisations involved with enforcing the regulations on health and safety

law and which provide advice on health and safety issues:

- Health and Safety Commission (HSC) which develops health and safety policy for the government
- Health and Safety Executive (HSE) which implements and checks the working of the

policy and would be involved with the investigation of reportable incidents.

When products are designed and manufactured, it is important that they are both safe to manufacture and safe to use. Designers and manufacturers must consider the following issues:

- Product misuse – what would happen if the product was misused? Would it be a danger to the public?
- The safety and health implications of the manufacturing processes, components and materials that are used in their products.
- The safety standards that apply in the countries where the product will be sold.
- Product maintenance – where this is to be carried out by the product users, it must be safe for them to do so. Clear instructions would have to be given with the product.
- Instructions for safe use – products should include detailed instructions on use.
- Labelling of hazards such as electrical connections or high temperature components.

In addition to the above points, manufacturers would also need to consider:

- The working environment in which the products are manufactured and the working conditions of the workforce.
- The organisation of the workplace so that manufacturing/assembly processes may be carried out safely.

- Risk assessments for each process involved in the product manufacture.
- Clear workspaces and routes around production areas.
- Designated storage areas for tools, components and completed products.
- Safe storage and clear handling instructions for chemicals, solvents, flammable and toxic substances. Employers are required by law to carry out 'risk assessments' for these substances.
- Clear procedures for evacuation in the event of a fire or other incident.
- Clear procedures for the reporting of accidents.
- Adequate lighting to enable processes to be carried out safely.
- Correct workplace temperatures.
- Use of machine tools:
  - regular maintenance at correct maintenance intervals
  - fault reporting process with faulty equipment being taken out of use
  - instructions for use clearly displayed close to the machine
  - safety signage and instructions relating to personal protective equipment (PPE) should be provided
  - machine operators should receive adequate training for safe use
  - emergency 'stop' buttons and safety interlocks are provided and operational.

9.2 SAFETY STANDARDS

The BSI Kitemark®

Figure 9.1 The Kitemark symbol

When you see a product with a Kitemark this means that the British Standards Institution (BSI) has independently tested it, has confirmed that the product conforms to the relevant British Standard, and has issued a BSI licence to the company to use the Kitemark. The manufacturer pays for this service. Their product is tested, and the manufacturing process is assessed, at regular intervals.

The British Standards Institution and the Kitemark are the guardians of quality standards and the safety of products in the UK. Information on standards can be obtained from the BSI Education website. For more information on Kitemark visit www.kitemark.com.

Figure 9.2 The CE mark symbol

In the European Union there is an extra standard covering products. This is known as the CE mark and it is used on all products that are to be used within the EU.

What is CE marking?

Many products such as toys must meet legal requirements before they can be sold within the European Community, and must carry CE marking. CE marking is designed to remove European trade barriers. It indicates that the product complies with the European Directive.

The CE mark is not a safety or a quality mark. It is a declaration of conformity stating that the product has been made following any relevant directives and is compatible with 'norms' or 'standards'. It states the intended use of the product and any restrictions for its usage.

9.3 PERSONAL SAFETY

When you are in the workshop manufacturing area you must not endanger other people, cause a hazard or put yourself in danger. You must wear appropriate personal protective equipment (PPE).

Personal protective equipment (PPE)

Personal protection is about you and the environment you are working in. You must keep yourself clear from hazards and use sufficient equipment to ensure your safety.

The Health and Safety at Work Regulations (1992) dictate the type of equipment that should be used. The equipment should be assessed before use to ensure:

- it is suitable
- it is maintained and stored properly
- it is provided with instructions on how to use it safely
- it is used correctly.

Hazards and types of PPE

Eyes

Type of hazard – chemical or metal splash, dust, projectiles, gas and vapour, radiation.

Methods of protection – safety spectacles, goggles, faceshields/facemasks, visors.

Head

Type of hazard – impact from falling or flying objects, head bumping on objects, hair entanglement.

Methods of protection – a range of helmets and bump caps.

Breathing

Type of hazard – dust, vapour, gas.

Methods of protection – disposable filtering facemask or respirator.

Protecting the body

Type of hazard – temperature extremes, chemical or metal splash, spray from pressure leaks or spray guns, impact or penetration, contaminated dust, entanglement of own clothing.

Methods of protection – conventional or disposable overalls, boiler suits, specialist protective clothing

Hands and arms

Type of hazard – abrasion, temperature extremes, cuts and punctures, impact, chemicals, electric shock, skin infection, contamination.

Methods of protection – gloves, gauntlets, mitts.

Feet and legs

Type of hazard – wet, slipping, cuts and punctures, falling objects, metal and chemical splash, abrasion.

Methods of protection – safety boots and shoes, gaiters, leggings, spats.

Ears

Type of hazard – high frequency noise from cutting machines, low frequency noise from air extraction systems and impact-forming of materials.

Methods of protection – disposable ear plugs, ear defenders.

Training should be provided to make sure you are aware of why PPE is needed and how it is used properly. In risk assessment, PPE is the last resort because the risk cannot be controlled in any other way.

Eye protection is one of the most difficult hazard areas. Goggles vary in the amount of protection they give for particular types of hazard. Goggles can be purchased for dust, impact or chemical protection. Safety spectacles are rarely sufficient in workshop activity.

Machine guards

Machine guards are designed to protect you from a variety of dangers by enclosing the tool behind impact-resistant clear plastic shielding. Guards are designed to protect you from rotating parts, cutting tools and the swarf that is produced during machining operations.

There is extra risk with computer-operated tools which may move or operate without warning. Most machines have interlock mechanisms. If guards are open the cutters cannot run. Laser cutters have extra protection to prevent damage from the light energy source.

Most injuries occur from the misuse of guards and protection systems. In schools where machines are usually used for 'individual' tasks guarding methods may need adjusting to accommodate the machining operation that is to take place.

▶ Dust and fume extraction

Whenever cutting takes place, dust and swarf are produced. Particles can be large, visible and easy to remove with vacuum systems at the point of cutting. Vacuum systems can also remove debris as it builds up. Finer dust is generated from tools such as jigsaws and requires more focused extraction as near to the cutting blade as possible to stop dust rising into the air. Drilling machine tables and work benches should be cleaned with vacuum hoses to reduce the dust getting in the air and on the floor.

Fume extraction systems have to be used where toxic fumes are produced during manufacture. The use of laser cutters, welding processes and spray painting are typical school workshop activities which require fume extraction.

▶ Waste disposal

In all cutting and wasting processes debris is produced. This needs to be controlled in order to ensure the work area is safe. Chemicals such as those used in making printed circuit boards (PCBs) have to be used and disposed of in line with the instructions provided on the manufacturer's data sheets. Specialist waste companies may need to collect certain types of chemical waste from the manufacturing plant or school.

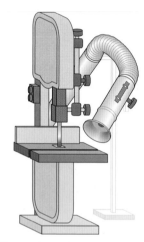

Figure 9.3 Extraction of wood dust from a bandsaw

Figure 9.4 Use of fume extract when welding

9.4 RISK ASSESSMENT

Risk assessment is the process, required by law, to be undertaken by companies, including schools, to identify potentially dangerous situations in their workplace and to explain how the risks may be reduced or eliminated so that everyone connected with the company or school can operate in a safe and healthy environment.

You will need to undertake risk assessments as part of your practical work during this course. When thinking about your risk assessment, remember:

- A hazard is anything that may cause harm, such as chemicals, electricity, heat, dust, fumes, sharp edges, an open drawer, a parcel left on the floor, etc.
- The risk is the chance, high or low, that somebody could be harmed by these and other hazards, together with an indication of how serious the harm could be.

There are five stages in carrying out a risk assessment:

1. Identify the process, operation or substance.
2. Identify the possible hazard.
3. Consider the risk, that is, how likely it is that the hazard will occur.
4. Explain the control measures you need to carry out to provide protection.
5. Explain what emergency measures you need to carry out in the event of personal injury.

Risk assessments relating to all processes and tools in the workshop and design studio should be made regularly. Risk assessment does not mean all risks are eliminated; the aim of risk assessment is to ensure that all reasonable and practical measures have been taken to minimise risk.

Accident procedures

It is important to record and document all accidents, even small cuts, as well as major injuries. Your school will have procedures set up for these situations. After an accident, learning should take place to remedy the problem which caused the accident and prevent a repeat of the incident.

Control of Substances Hazardous to Health Regulations 2002 (COSHH)

Using chemicals or other hazardous substances at work can put people's health at risk, so the law requires employers to control exposure to hazardous substances to prevent ill health. They have to protect both employees and others who may be exposed.

Hazardous substances include:

- substances used directly in work activities (e.g. adhesives, paints, cleaning agents)
- substances generated during work activities (e.g. fumes from soldering and welding)
- naturally occurring substances (e.g. grain dust)
- biological agents such as bacteria and other micro-organisms.

Examples of the effects of hazardous substances include:

- skin irritation or dermatitis as a result of skin contact
- asthma as a result of developing allergy to substances used at work
- losing consciousness as a result of being overcome by toxic fumes
- cancer, which may appear long after the exposure to the chemical that caused it
- infection from bacteria and other micro-organisms (biological agents).

Table 9.1 shows an example of a student's hazard analysis for the use of Tensol cement. This is a common plastic adhesive that you may use in your own making activities.

▌ Manufacturers' data sheets

For each chemical used in making your product there is a data sheet showing the risks when using the chemicals. Each manufacturer of chemicals must provide a data hazard sheet. In workshops these should be filed and available for consultation.

Process or operation	Hazards	Risk assessment	Control measures
Joining acrylic	Tensol cement is an irritant to the skin, eyes and lungs. It is highly flammable.	In a large workshop environment the fumes from Tensol cement would not cause a problem with normal usage. A large spillage may however result in a hazard. Using Tensol cement in a confined space would also present a hazard. Tensol cement would need to be kept away from eyes and skin. Vapour from Tensol could be ignited by flames or other heat sources.	1. Use in well-ventilated areas. 2. Apply barrier cream and/or wear protective gloves. 3. Eye protection must be worn. 4. A suitable dispenser should be used to minimise the risk of spillage. 5. Tensol should not be used close to sources of flame or heat.

Table 9.1

Fig. 9.5 shows a data sheet for WD40 lubricant spray – there are sections which deal with the oil, propellant and the spray can. This is one of four pages of the safety data sheet.

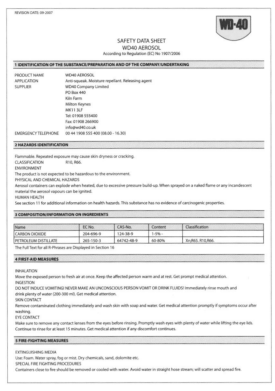

REVISION DATE: 09-2007

WD-40

SAFETY DATA SHEET
WD40 AEROSOL
According to Regulation (EC) No 1907/2006

1 IDENTIFICATION OF THE SUBSTANCE/PREPARATION AND OF THE COMPANY/UNDERTAKING

PRODUCT NAME   WD40 AEROSOL
APPLICATION   Anti-squeak. Moisture repellant. Releasing agent
SUPPLIER   WD40 Company Limited
                    PO Box 440
                    Kiln Farm
                    Milton Keynes
                    MK11 3LF
                    Tel: 01908 555400
                    Fax: 01908 266900
                    info@wd40.co.uk
EMERGENCY TELEPHONE 00 44 1908 555 400 (08.00 - 16.30)

2 HAZARDS IDENTIFICATION

Flammable. Repeated exposure may cause skin dryness or cracking.
CLASSIFICATION   R10, R66.
ENVIRONMENT
The product is not expected to be hazardous to the environment.
PHYSICAL AND CHEMICAL HAZARDS
Aerosol containers can explode when heated, due to excessive pressure build-up. When sprayed on a naked flame or any incandescent material the aerosol vapours can be ignited.
HUMAN HEALTH
See section 11 for additional information on health hazards. This substance has no evidence of carcinogenic properties.

3 COMPOSITION/INFORMATION ON INGREDIENTS

Name	EC No.	CAS-No.	Content	Classification
CARBON DIOXIDE	204-696-9	124-38-9	1-5% -	
PETROLEUM DISTILLATE	265-150-3	64742-48-9	60-80%	Xn;R65. R10,R66.

The Full Text for all R-Phrases are Displayed in Section 16

4 FIRST-AID MEASURES

INHALATION
Move the exposed person to fresh air at once. Keep the affected person warm and at rest. Get prompt medical attention.
INGESTION
DO NOT INDUCE VOMITING! NEVER MAKE AN UNCONSCIOUS PERSON VOMIT OR DRINK FLUIDS! Immediately rinse mouth and drink plenty of water (200-300 ml). Get medical attention.
SKIN CONTACT
Remove contaminated clothing immediately and wash skin with soap and water. Get medical attention promptly if symptoms occur after washing.
EYE CONTACT
Make sure to remove any contact lenses from the eyes before rinsing. Promptly wash eyes with plenty of water while lifting the eye lids. Continue to rinse for at least 15 minutes. Get medical attention if any discomfort continues.

5 FIRE-FIGHTING MEASURES

EXTINGUISHING MEDIA
Use: Foam. Water spray, fog or mist. Dry chemicals, sand, dolomite etc.
SPECIAL FIRE FIGHTING PROCEDURES
Containers close to fire should be removed or cooled with water. Avoid water in straight hose stream; will scatter and spread fire.

Figure 9.5 Safety data sheet for WD 40

9.5 SAFETY SYMBOLS

To help recognise where PPE should be used and to state the dangers of equipment, safety signs are used.

Blue signs are mandatory, that is, you MUST do what they say.
Black and yellow signs are warnings.
Red diamonds are warnings of hazards.

ACTIVITY

1. Identify all the safety signs in your technology rooms.

2. Draw them and explain what each means.

Figure 9.8 Signs displayed in areas of work

Figure 9.6 Advisory signs for PPE

Figure 9.7 Sign warning of danger

9.6 MODIFYING PRODUCTS TO MAKE THEM SAFER

When evaluating products to make improvements and modifications, the safety of the user needs to be of prime importance. Designers need to consider any feedback that has been received about the product from the target user groups and other interested parties such as production teams. The aim of the designer must be to create the safest possible product design before full production begins. Failure to do so could result in product recalls which will result in loss of earnings to the manufacturing company.

KEY TERMS

RISK ASSESSMENT – the process, required by law, to be undertaken by companies, including schools, to identify potentially dangerous situations in the workplace and to explain how the risks may be reduced or eliminated so that everyone connected with the company or school can operate in a safe and healthy environment

COSHH – the Control of Substances Hazardous to Health. COSHH is the way that employers assess the risks from using substances that could be very dangerous to our health and is one part of risk assessment

CHAPTER 10

UNIT A511: INTRODUCTION TO DESIGNING AND MAKING

By the end of this chapter you should have developed a knowledge and understanding of:

- what you are required to do to satisfy the assessment criteria for this unit
- how to structure your work and folio evidence for this unit.

This unit of work will involve you in researching, designing, modelling, making a prototype product and evaluating your work. If you are taking the full GCSE qualification this work will be 30 per cent of your total marks. If you are taking the GCSE short course, the work will be 60 per cent of your total marks. In both cases this work will take 20 hours. The prototype product you will make will be finished sufficiently for you to show the function of the product. The prototype does not necessarily need to be a fully finished product.

10.1 SUBMISSION OF CONTROLLED ASSESSMENT WORK

Your work can be submitted on paper or in electronic format but not a mixture of both.

Work submitted on paper

A contents page with a numbering system should be included to aid organisation. All your work should be on the same size paper but it does not matter what size paper you use. You can produce your work by hand or by using ICT.

Work submitted electronically

Your work will need to be organised in folders so that the evidence can be accessed easily by a teacher or moderator. This structure is commonly known as a folder tree. There should be a top level folder detailing your centre number, candidate number, surname and forename, together with the unit code A511. The next folder down should be called 'Home page', which will be an index of all your work. The evidence for each section of the work should then be contained in a separate folder, containing appropriately named files. These files can be from the Microsoft Office® suite: movie, audio, graphics, animation, structured mark-up or text formats. PowerPoint® is an ideal platform for producing electronic portfolios.

10.2 RULES FOR CONTROLLED ASSESSMENT

The work associated with this unit must be completed under your teacher's supervision. However, some of your research work and testing of the product, by its very nature, may take place outside school under limited supervision. You must clearly reference the source of any information you use at the appropriate point in your portfolio.

10.3 ASSESSMENT

A maximum of 60 marks is available for this work. The 60 marks will be divided into six sections:

1. Creativity 10 marks
2. Designing 14 marks
3. Planning and making your prototype product safely 20 marks
4. Solving technical problems 4 marks
5. Recording the making of your prototype product 4 marks
6. Evaluation of the processes involved in the designing, modelling and making of the prototype product 8 marks

KEY POINT

- You will need to think about how you use the time you have available and make sure that you spend longer on the sections which can be awarded more marks and less time on those sections with fewer marks.

10.4 STARTING POINTS

The examination board, OCR, will publish a list of themes which are to be used as the starting points for your controlled assessment task. The themes will change periodically so it is important that you check with your teacher that you are using the correct themes. You will choose one of the themes provided and then identify a specific existing product or starting point that is associated with the theme. You will then undertake research associated with the specific product before establishing a design brief and detailed specification for an improved or similarly functioning prototype product. For example, if the chosen theme is 'Travel' you may decide to design and model a hand-held game which can be used 'on the move'. You are not allowed to use the same theme for this unit as submitted or intended for submission for unit A513.

WHAT YOU NEED TO DO

You should clearly state the design problem you are going to work on. You should demonstrate that you fully understand the target user/customer group and the design problem.

Having considered the information you have gained about the problem and user, you will write a clear and precise design brief. A design brief states what you are trying to do, as a simple statement.

You should then identify a similar product to that which you intend to design. You should carry out a detailed product analysis activity that is focused on your selected product. You should use the methods shown in Chapter 1 in order to successfully complete the product analysis. In your investigation of the product you should examine the control system, quality of construction and how the product meets user needs. As part of your research you should establish relevant data that will help with your designing, for example the size of tubing used on a bike if you are to design an alarm which will be fitted to a bike.

The marking criteria shown in the table below will be used to assess your work in this section.

Basic ability	Demonstrates ability	Works competently with independence
• Make simple/limited links between principles of good design and technological knowledge, showing limited awareness of the user. • Identify one or two trends in existing solutions and use this understanding in a design context. [0–3 marks]	• Identify associations linking principles of good design and technological knowledge, relating products to users' needs. • Demonstrate the significance of research that identifies trends in existing solutions; interpret and apply this understanding in a design context. [4–7 marks]	• Identify complex associations linking principles of good design and technological knowledge, relating products to users' needs and wants. (AO1) • Demonstrate and understand the significance of trends in existing solutions; reinterpret and apply this understanding in imaginative ways. (AO1) [8–10 marks]

Table 10.1 Mark scheme – Creativity

Let's look at three sample projects to see how the connections to the mark scheme are made.

> *A primary school is collecting aluminium drink cans for recycling but cans can take up a lot of space. To reduce storage space, it is necessary to crush the cans flat.*
>
> *The target audience, therefore, will be schools. However, in my opinion various other areas could also use a can crusher, depending on the demand. I believe that offices, restaurants, public places and maybe even the family home could all be within the possible market for buying a can crusher.*
>
> *I am going to design and produce a prototype of an electro-pneumatic system that could be used in the can crusher. I have decided to use an electro-pneumatic system so the user will find it a lot easier to crush the can, as all the effort is done by the pneumatics, NOT the user, as all they have to do is press a button and start up the system.*

Examiner's comments

It is clear who the user of the product is, now and in the future. The design brief clearly states what the product will be. The opportunities for research would be more open if the electro-pneumatic system had not been specified as part of the design brief.

Fig. 10.1 shows a product analysis with photographs of products known to the student. *Primary* product analysis, where you handle the product and are able to disassemble it, will result in better quality work than *secondary* product analysis, where you rely purely on pictures from web pages or magazines.

Examiner's comments

The photographs (in Fig. 10.1) show products which are suitable for product analysis. The top paragraphs on the page are simply descriptive. The second half of the page is about a future model. There is an absence of system notes, information relating to how the

On the left is an existing model working crossing that was also designed for learning purposes when a new method of sensing was being introduced. Radio-based operation is demonstrated, which is a new operational concept of the Deutsche Bahn AG. The train controls track elements directly.

This means that junctions and level crossings are not controlled by the signal box but directly by the train, which is shown by the model on the left. The model process is a divided automating system which consists of a network of three computer knots. These computers only communicate through radio signals. Radio communication is visualised by special hardware. Each computer knot controls the train and the level crossing at a time. A third computer simulates the centre which observes the whole track.

For my use the model would not be completely practical for a few reasons:

- There is a large amount of equipment required for this system which means a lot to transport, the only way to do this would be to dismantle the electronics for the system for transportation but if it is to educate someone they are likely to have trouble setting it up.

- Also the large amount of wiring means so the models look messy, and this would take lots of work to hide rather than just creating a system with a lot less wiring.

- The way the model uses radio control may over complicate things as for the learner it will be important for them to be able to have all the individual track circuits in real life and this will be less accurate compared to actually using track circuits.

- The model doesn't include any of the signals like the white driver's light. I will have to include this as it is an important part of the system.

- As it us designed around a German crossing it doesn't include boom lights or the flashing red and flashing yellow lights, which I will have to include as they are key parts in the flow chart.

Figure 10.1 Student's work showing the investigation of an existing model

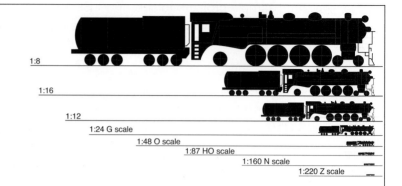

There is a massive variation in possible sizes for model railways, the largest ridable engines at 1:8 going all the way down to matchbox size at 1:220. Some of the more popular scales are G Scale, Gauge 1, O Scale, H0 Scale (in Britain, the similarly sized 00 is used).

TT scale, and N scale. The single most popular scale used is H0 Scale or 00 Gauge. 00 Gauge is the United Kingdom's version of H0 Scale which is slightly larger. This size may be because it is a good size that is compact but still allows great amounts of detail to be applied. It is also very easy to get hold of 00 Gauge railway as it is one of several 4mm scale standards (4mm to the foot, or 1:76.2) in use, and the only one served by mass market manufacturers.

1:8
1:16
1:12
1:24 G scale
1:48 O scale
1:87 HO scale
1:160 N scale
1:220 Z scale

00 Gauge is likely to be one of the better sizes to use for my project. As it is so readily available it will be easy to purchase parts in batch production and they won't be too expensive. Another good thing about it being so popular is that there will be a variety of types of locomotives to choose from and they won't be too expensive. Also the size isn't too excessive so it won't be too big and yet is not too small to be able to build a good quality detailed model.

Being so popular, this type of train must be relatively easy to use; in batch production it only needs to be assembled and no extra parts need to be made which makes it better for the end user.

Figure 10.2 Collection of data

product meets user needs, details about materials or construction methods. Although it is only a model there is function detail to note.

There are some technology connections where the work examines radio systems, networks and control by train.

In Fig. 10.2 data has been collected relating to the sizes of the model which could be used on the rail system.

Examiner's comments on Fig. 10.2

Some 'real' information has been gathered. This relates to track sizes. More information is needed about the operating method, sizes of fingers for switches and the components which are to be triggered by the model train.

Marking

Look at the evidence provided in the three samples of work above. Many aspects of research are missing which would lead to difficulty when designing. These sheets fall in to the middle band of attainment.

▶ Designing

Your first task in this section is to produce your design specification. It is good practice to produce a summary page on which you will collect together all the important information which will be used in designing. This page should be called *Conclusions of research*. Bringing your research findings together will help you to formulate your design specification.

WHAT YOU NEED TO DO

Summarise your research results.

Write a detailed specification for the product.

The example in Fig. 10.3 is for a bike safety light. It uses a group of headings to focus thinking about what the product must do.

Automatic Bike Safety Lights

Here I will use 1 or 2 pages to specify what I may need to use for my project, to discuss and think about any problems that I may face in the course of the project and how I may conquer them. I will use my bubble diagram and take some of the ideas from this and discuss them and generally go into them in much more detail. I will do all this without coming to any final solutions, all I am trying to do is come up with a list of ideas and what I will probably need.

Functional requirements:
The lights should be brightly coloured and a colour which ensures maximum safety for the cyclist.
The lights must turn on automatically when the weather gets bad or the light deteriorates.
A pressure pad or light dependant resistor could be used or maybe both.
A pulse must be created within the circuit so the lights turn on automatically as well. This will make the lights easier to see for the driver.
There should be two lights, one at the front and one at the back for added safety and a connection between the front and back light so the lights come on at the same time and flash at the same time as well.
So, it's easy to see that I want the product to be as multi-functional as possible to make the product as valuable, as safe and as visually pleasing as bike lights can possibly be.

User:
The product should be aimed at teenagers aged between 12 and 17 who want to ride their bikes in the dark or in poor weather conditions. Although the product must be designed so it is suitable for other age ranges as well.

Ergonomics:
The product must be quite easy to attach to the bike and use. It must fit to any bike frame easily, so it can be bought, opened and used quickly. I want the product to be user friendly with easy to read instructions. The product must give a good impression to its customers, and it should look attractive at first sight.

Figure 10.3 Thinking about the problem and the first half of the specification

Maintenance
- The product must be easy to maintain
- The product may come with special screen wipes, if the screen needs cleaning
- The bulbs or LEDS may need changing
- The battery may need changing

Material Properties:
- It may be any colour
- It must not look too bulky
- It must be durable
- It needs to be suitable for outside use
- It must be reliable, i.e. not erode when wet

Constructional Requirements:
- It must not be too complicated to produce and manufacture
- The materials should not be too expensive or too hard to get hold of
- It must have a front and back light

Sizes
- It must not be too big
- It must be quite small and portable
- It needs to be a size that can fit onto almost any bike frame
- Must be smooth rounded design

Cost Constraints
- I don't believe this product will be too expensive to build but it should cost no more than £10 pounds to make as looking at my questionnaire I can see that people are only willing to spend around £10, and I would want to make a profit if I were selling this product.

Figure 10.4 Specification

Examiner's comments on Fig. 10.4
The specification is a good list but it lacks detail on construction and sizes. There is no evidence of the analysis of research. There is however sufficient information for a designer to start work generating ideas.

This example would fall in the middle mark band for Designing.

EXAMINER'S TIP

To think in a creative and imaginative way you may need to produce a thought shower or a rough ideas sheet. It is important for you to get all your thoughts onto paper very quickly. The system must be examined with clear sections about Input, Process, Output.

Basic ability	Demonstrates ability	Works competently with independence
• Demonstrate a limited response to a brief and produce a simple specification for a prototype product. • Produce one or two simple design ideas using a limited range of strategies. [0–4 marks]	• Demonstrate an appropriate response to a brief and produce a suitable specification for a prototype product as a result of analysis. • Produce creative ideas and communicate these by using appropriate strategies. [5–10 marks]	• Demonstrate an appropriate and considered response to a brief and produce a detailed specification for a prototype product as a result of analysis. (AO2) • Produce creative and original ideas by generating, developing and communicating designs using appropriate strategies. (AO2) [11–14 marks]

Table 10.2 Mark scheme – Designing

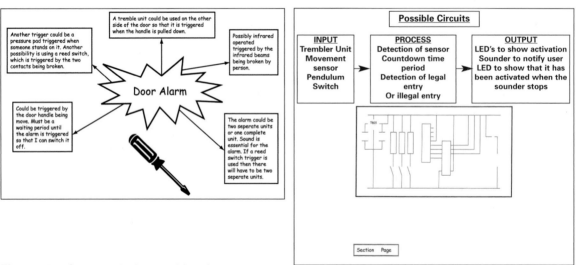

Figure 10.5 System blocks considered

The start of the design activity needs to show your thinking about solutions, almost like a research page giving possible solutions. You may have to find possible circuits to match the process blocks – these may be available in program libraries or textbooks. The systems approach allows you to be creative by listing the possible functions of the blocks.

The next stage is to start developing your thoughts using a range of graphic communication techniques. You can produce drawings by hand drawing or by the use of CAD programs. It is important to add annotation with notes and extra detail drawings to explain your design fully.

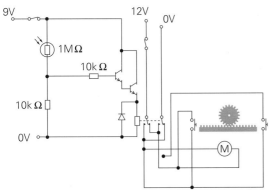

Figure 10.6 Concept modelling of curtain closer

Examiner's comments on Fig. 10.6
This page relates to the design of a curtain closing circuit which uses an LDR input and motor output with limit switches. In this form it is a concept drawing and not fully functioning. You could use this style of drawing to demonstrate the system, just putting parts together. You would add comments explaining the parts, including some appraisal of their function and stating how you would make improvements.

The next stage of design is to look at other designs which would perform similar functions; this method would show your creativity. Another approach is to develop one system where real improvements are made with a number of strategies. Input and Process stages could use PIC chips. If PIC chips are used, changes/development may relate to software programs.

Examiner's comments on Fig. 10.7
This page shows the flow chart for a PIC program with inputs from a target shooting game. The page shows the detail to be included when using PIC chips; the annotation tells you the design detail that has gone into developing the program. The problems that have been identified point to future development.

For an electronics project you should show the complete PCB with parts lists. For mechanisms or pneumatics, working drawings of all the parts to be made and components used in your making of the prototype system should be shown (Fig. 10.8).

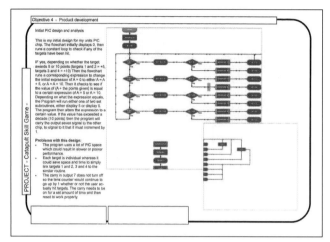

Figure 10.7 PIC design and modelling

Examiner's comments

The final PCB shows the component layout (Fig. 10.9). This circuit shows a problem with electronics – it is not a system, the circuit could be Input or Process but it is not a complete prototype.

 EXAMINER'S TIP

At the end of this section a final design must be clearly identified. This should have all the elements needed to produce a systems prototype that is capable of being tested. You should provide sufficient detail so the product could be made by another person.

The mark scheme is based upon levels of performance. To achieve the top level, the product must show complexity, for example a fully developed system with inputs. The process block may have multistages or chips with matching to input and output. When you look at the output it should fit the needs of the user.

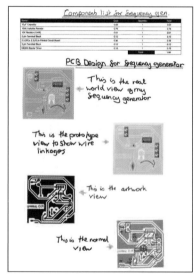

Figure 10.8 Developing the PCB

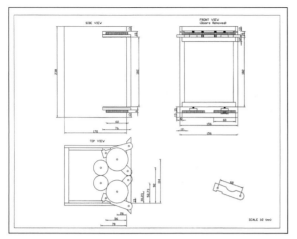

Figure 10.9 Detailed working drawing for the model

10.5 DEMONSTRATION OF GOOD MAKING SKILLS

Component Required	Symbol	Image	Description
Keyswitch	—		A metal switch operated by a key
Keypad	N/A		A keypad for inputting keycodes
4017 IC Chip			A decade counter
Wire - Singlecore	N/A		Wires used for soldering
Roll of Solder	N/A		A metal used to join components
PCB Holders	N/A		Hold the PCB in place
LED Holders	N/A		Hold LEDs in their holes
9V PP3 Battery	⊣⊢--⊣⊢		A 9V battery
LED			A small light
Buzzer	⊣		A sound emitting device
555 IC Chip			A timer integrated circuit
4011 NAND			Contains 4 NAND gates
Proximity Reed Switch	—o⁄o—		A switch operated by a magnet
Sheet of HIPs	N/A		High impact Polystyrene
PP3 Battery Holder	N/A		A lead connecting a PP3 battery
Sheet of PCB	N/A		A board which connects components
100µF, 100nF Capacitor	⊣⊢⁺		A component which stores a current
Resistors:			
10K, 100K, 270R, 330R, 4K7	⊣□⊢		A component which resists a current
MDF	N/A		A craft / custom wood
IC Holders	N/A		Used to hold ICs in place

Figure 10.10 Component lists

You need to plan and organise the making stage to make best use of your time, equipment, tools and materials. You need to consider each of the processes you will carry out and any associated health and safety issues. A little time thinking about the processes will avoid mistakes and problems.

You could use a Gantt chart to look at the order of working and when to start certain processes or perhaps you could carry them out at the same time (see Fig. 10.11). You could use the same chart to give feedback on how the making is progressing, recording actual time.

Once you have sorted out the stages of the making process, you can organise the order for materials and components (Fig. 10.10). The requirement list can be in a number of forms. Some PCB programs will produce the list for you but equally you can cut and paste your list.

Selection of the processes and tools will probably have been done during the final design stages. It is still good practice to produce a chart to show your thinking. You could widen the chart to include the quality checks you would use when checking the function.

Having selected tools and equipment, you will need to work carefully to produce an item

Basic ability	Demonstrates ability	Works competently with independence

• Plan and organise activities:
  – Select and use appropriate materials
  – Select and use hand and machine tools as appropriate to realise the product.
• Work safely to assemble, construct and finish materials and components as appropriate to generate a prototype product.
• Use workshop/design studio facilities as appropriate to realise the prototype product.
[0–6 marks]
	• Plan and organise activities:
	  – Select and use appropriate materials
	  – Select and use hand and machine tools as appropriate to realise the product.
	• Work effectively and safely to assemble, construct and finish materials and components as appropriate to achieve a good quality prototype product.
	• Choose and use workshop/design studio facilities as appropriate to realise the prototype product.
	[7–13 marks]
		• Plan and organise activities:
		  – Select and use appropriate materials. (AO1/AO2)
		  – Select and use hand and machine tools as appropriate to realise the product. (AO1/AO2)
		• Work skilfully and safely to assemble, construct and finish materials and components as appropriate to achieve a quality prototype product. (AO2)
		• Assess and apply knowledge of the workshop/design studio facilities as appropriate to realise the prototype product. (AO1/AO2)
		[14–20 marks]

Table 10.3 Mark scheme – Planning and making

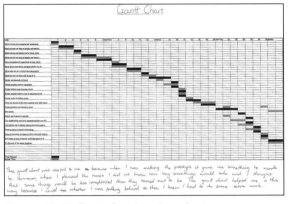

Figure 10.11 Part of a planning chart

of quality. Even with this prototype, you need to show you can make a product which demonstrates your abilities. Remember, it should be a functioning prototype which solves the design problem you identified.

Solving technical problems

It is inevitable that during your construction activity you will meet problems; in fact the best designs never stop evolving. It is important that you apply your knowledge and skills to think your way out of these problems and show your inventiveness. You must keep a record of the problems you encounter and the methods used to solve them. You could do this through the use of notes, photographs and diagrams in your Record of Production. Alternatively, you could 'mark up' your working drawings with the changes that you made.

Stage	Tools and materials	Processes
Cut circuit board out	PCB board PCB Design and Make (Milling machine used by technician)	Send PCB to be cut out – collect correct sized material for PCB, save PCB file in the correct folder, fill in the form for a PCB cut out and stick onto PCB material.
Cut acrylic out	Acrylic 2D Design and Make (Lasewr cutter used by technician)	Order acrylic to be cut out to a suitable size. Order acrylic to be cut out to shape on laser on laser machine.
Solder components into circuit board	Soldering iron (and sponge) Solder Components Wires Wire-strippers Wire-cutters	Solder components into circuit board
Prepare circuit and case to be connected	Drilling machine	Drill hole into circuit board 4mm diameter Drill 2 holes into case (for LDR) 1 mm diameter
Connect circuit to case	Soldering iron Solder 2 circuit board stand-offs Epoxy resin Clamp	Unsolder components that have to go through case Resolder these components once in place Mount circuit board Put components into their places in the case Stick battery pack
Stick case together	PKI	Stick sides of case together Leave to dry for 15 minutes remove plastic coating of acrylic

Figure 10.12 Selecting processes

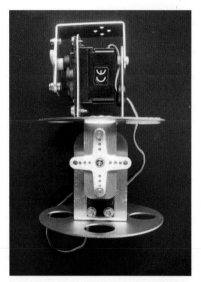

Figure 10.13 Detailed model of a steerable joint

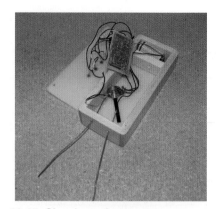

Figure 10.15 Simple moisture sensor

Figure 10.16 Traffic light model

Figure 10.14 Model vehicle suspension

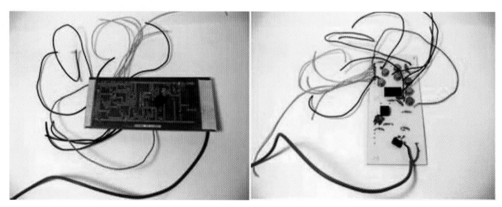

Figure 10.17 PCB to demonstrate circuit function of dice

Basic ability	Demonstrates ability	Works competently with independence
• Demonstrate a simple understanding of how to solve technical problems as they arise. [0–1 mark]	• Demonstrate a practical understanding and ability in solving some technical problems as they arise. [2–3 mark]	• Demonstrate a practical and thorough understanding and ability in solving technical problems effectively and efficiently as they arise. (AO2) [4 marks]

Table 10.4 Mark scheme – Solving technical problems

Recording the making

Basic ability	Demonstrates ability	Works competently with independence
• Simply record the making of the prototype product using notes and/or photographic evidence. [0–1 mark]	• Record key stages involved in the making of the prototype product; provide notes and photographic evidence. [2–3 marks]	• Record key stages involved in the making of the prototype product; provide comprehensive notes and photographic evidence. (AO2) [4 marks]

Table 10.5 Mark scheme – Record of making

Within your folio you need to provide a record of the key stages of making. The record should consist of photographs and notes. Your photographs and notes should show details of bench testing and safe working practices. Remember to record any problems you encounter and the solutions you have developed.

Examiner's comments on Fig. 10.18
The model is not a complete design, only an assembly of parts. It is possible to use a construction board; however more components would need to be added to make a realistic prototype. This example would only be marked at the 'basic ability' level of the mark scheme.

Figure 10.18 PowerPoint® video – working action of pneumatics modelling

Fig. 10.18 shows the testing of a pneumatics circuit for a can crushing machine. When viewed as a PowerPoint® presentation, this is seen as a video showing the moving cylinders and valves tripped by the action. If you produce your folio electronically, movies and sound can be embedded into your work.

To improve the quality of this prototype, parts should be added to show the can holding grips fixed to the construction board.

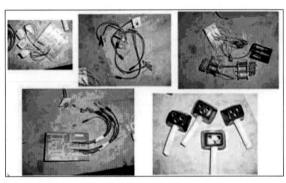

Figure 10.19 Student's record of making

Examiner's comments on Fig. 10.19
The evidence of manufacturing shown has good detail. The work would be improved if more information was presented with the pictures.

▶ Critical evaluation

You will need to carry out a critical evaluation of the processes involved in the designing and making of the prototype product.

The evaluation should start with your reflection on the making process for the prototype.

The comments show your problem-solving and how to work onwards and improve the circuit (see Fig. 10.20).

Basic ability	Demonstrates ability	Works competently with independence
• Give a limited evaluation of the modelling and prototyping process. • There will be little or no use of specialist terms. • Answers may be ambiguous or disorganised. • Errors of spelling, punctuation and grammar may be intrusive. **[0–2 marks]**	• Give an evaluation of the making process. • Reflect on how to improve the modelling and prototyping process. • There will be some use of specialist terms, although these may not always be used appropriately. • The information will be presented for the most part in a structured format. • There may be occasional errors in spelling, punctuation and grammar. **[3–5 marks]**	• Critically evaluate the processes involved in designing and making the prototype. (AO3) • Reflect and suggest modifications to improve the modelling and prototyping process. (AO3) • Specialist terms will be used appropriately and correctly. • The information will be presented in a structured format. • The candidate can demonstrate the accurate use of spelling, punctuation and grammar. **[6–8 marks]**

Table 10.6 Mark scheme – Critical evaluation

When testing the circuit, I came across a problem. Despite the circuit working both on Crocodile Technology and on my breadboard, as shown on previous slides, certain LED's did not work. It was the red LED's which were there to show when the door was opened, and when someone pressed the button. After investigation visually and with a multi meter, it became clear there was no negative lead to the AND gate. Despite later fixing this, the circuit still did not work properly and it was unknown what the problem was. To improve this, more time would need to be spent working out what the problem was, and if able, fix it to produce a working circuit. If unable to fix, the circuit would need to be done again, or maybe change the circuit a bit on PCB to make it work more effectively.

Figure 10.20 Comments for improvements when making

The first thing I did once my product was finished was test it using a real aluminium drinks can. This lead to a number of conclusions that I use to improve my product. These are shown on the diagram below.

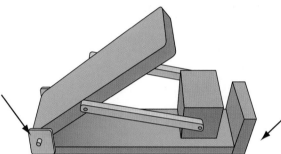

I noted that there were simply not enough screws in the pieces of mental holding the main arm to the base. This resulted in the main arm sliding backwards which made the crusher that is linked to the main arm unable to move. I simply solved this by adding one larger screw to each side of the existing screw.

These improvements meant that second time around my can crusher did crush the can efficiently. I have a higher chance of actually crushing the can but unfortunately I didn't because the leverage was not good enough to crush the can.

I noted that the resisting block that held the can in place while it was being crushed was coming loose where it was attached to the base. This meant the can could not be crushed which defeats the object of my crusher. I identified that the screws were not long enough or large enough. I solved this problem by using larger screws both in length and width.

	Can length after crushing attempt
Before modifications	112mm
After modifications	20mm

Figure 10.21 Proposals for modification

The can crusher is a simple mechanisms prototype. The information gained through testing has been used to suggest some good modifications (Fig. 10.21). Proposals for modification would be improved if these were extended to cover the making processes.

Within your evaluation it is important that you use the correct terms for the system parts. When recording your making you will need to state the problems you encountered. In the evaluation you can then reflect on the improvements to the making processes you introduced during making, as well as further improvements you would make.

CHAPTER 11

UNIT A512:
SUSTAINABLE DESIGN

By the end of this chapter you should have developed a knowledge and understanding of:

- the 6Rs
- social issues
- moral issues
- cultural issues
- environmental issues
- design issues.

This unit of the GCSE course aims to develop your knowledge and understanding of sustainability, environmental concerns, cultural, moral and social issues. You will need to consider how future designs and products will impact on the world in which we live.

By looking at old and new products, you will gain awareness and understanding of trends and innovations in design and manufacture, labelling, packaging and the impact that the design of such products is having on the environment, society and the economy.

Sustainable design is a whole new approach for product designers. With the Waste Electrical and Electronic Equipment (WEEE) Regulations on returning electrical goods to the manufacturer, everyone has to look at how a product can be disassembled allowing materials and components to be recycled or reused.

11.1 OVERVIEW OF THE UNIT

Moral, cultural, economic, environmental and sustainability issues are an important part of design and technology. Through this unit you will be able to answer some of the following questions:

- What is meant by a 'product life cycle'?

- Why were certain materials chosen and used?
- What is meant by 'planned obsolescence'?
- What do we mean by the 6Rs?
- What can we do to ensure that the eventual disposal of products/materials is as eco-friendly as possible?

The assessment of this unit is through an internally set and marked test:

- This assessment unit can be taken in either the January or June examination session.
- It represents 20 per cent of a full GCSE qualification or 40 per cent of a short course qualification.
- The maximum mark for the unit is 60.

- The paper is divided into two sections:
  - **Section A** consists of 15 questions covering generic issues associated with sustainability, society, the economy and the environment. Questions will be either multiple choice, short answer or true/false statements.
  - **Section B** consists of three questions which will require you to relate your knowledge and understanding of the '6Rs', materials, processes and the design of products. At least one part will involve extended writing so you can show your level of understanding and communication. Simple sketching may be required.

KEY SKILLS TO ACHIEVE HIGH MARKS IN THIS UNIT ARE:

- Think, with an 'open' mind about design; be aware of changes that are happening.
- Recall, select, use and communicate knowledge and understanding of concepts, issues and terminology within your material area.
- Record ideas showing design thinking, innovation and flair; this will involve detailed notes and where appropriate high quality sketches and annotated drawings.
- Seek out and use information from existing designers.
- Analyse and evaluate design and production skills and techniques.
- Understand materials, ingredients and components in the context of the chosen product.
- Consider how past and present design technology affects society.
- Demonstrate understanding of the wider effects of design and technology on issues including sustainability, society, the economy and the environment.

11.2 THE 6RS

RECYCLE	How easy is it to take apart? How can the parts be used again? How much energy to reprocess parts?
REUSE	Which parts can I use again? Has it another valuable use without processing it?
REDUCE	Which parts are not needed? Do we need as much material? Can we simplify the product?
REFUSE	Is it really necessary? Is it going to last? Is it fair trade? Is it too unfashionable to be trendy and too costly to be stylish?
RETHINK	How can it do the job better? Is it energy efficient? Has it been designed for disassembly?
REPAIR	Which parts can be replaced? Which parts are going to fail? How easy is it to replace parts?

Table 11.1 A visual flow diagram of the 6Rs

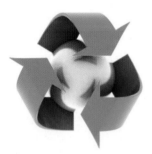

Figure 11.1 A recycling logo

Recycle

Recycling is what we do with the objects we use in our daily lives. Recycling is the conversion of waste products into new materials, to extend the life and usefulness of a product, item or object that seems to have no more purpose or use once it has been finished with or used for its initial purpose. Recycling means reusing a product or parts of a product, but sometimes before a product can be reused it will need to undergo processing or treatment.

There are three main types of recycling.

Primary recycling

The second-hand use of items, whether clothing, electronic or product based, is a form of primary recycling as the item is simply being used again. Charity shops stock a large selection of recycled products. Giving items to friends and relatives or selling them on using internet market sites, are all ways of primary recycling.

Figure 11.2 Primary recycling

Secondary or physical recycling

This is the process by which waste materials are recycled into different types of products.

The change the product will go through depends on the main fibre or material of the product. Some products can be left to biodegrade before being regenerated into something else. Packaging used for food is often difficult to recycle. However, biodegradable packaging such as 'potatopak' has been developed.

ACTIVITY

1. You can research packaging and look at the advantages and disadvantages of this type of packaging.

2. List the materials the packaging is made from and research alternative materials that would be able to be recycled.

Tertiary or chemical recycling

Products are broken down and reformulated, for instance, plastic bottles can be recycled into fibres and then re-spun into polyester to make fleece fabric used for coats and blankets. Car tyres can be re-used to make numerous products, for example, a computer mouse mat.

Figure 11.3 Old tyres

Recyclable materials

These include glass, paper, metals, wood, textiles, electronics, tyres, plastics and food wastes. Most, if not all things can be recycled in some way.

Figure 11.4 Paper being recycled at a waste collection plant

Why recycle?

Everything we dispose of goes somewhere, although once the container or bag of rubbish is out of our hands and out of our houses, we forget it instantly. Our consumer lifestyle is rapidly filling up rubbish dumps all over the world and as this happens, our concerns for the environment grow. When designing and making a new product, designers and manufacturers need to consider how their product can be recycled at the end of its life cycle.

You will need to know the following:

• materials that can be recycled

• products that use recycled materials

• disassembly – reprocessing materials for use in new products.

QUESTIONS

1. What does the term recycling mean?
2. List three products that can be recycled.
3. Name a material made from recycled products.

Figure 11.5 Recycling – plastic, metal, glass and paper

Products that can be reused for either the same purpose or a new purpose

Products that are designed to be re-used result in less waste; this leads to conservation of materials and resources. Many places around the UK collect unwanted products or repair them for redistribution for the same or a similar end use.

Products that can be adapted to suit an alternative use

Some local areas have set up their own websites and organisations for the re-use of unwanted items, and there are groups of people who actively aim to adapt existing products for alternative uses.

Reduce

When designing a new product, designers need to consider a number of questions to fit the reduce agenda:

- How can we simplify the product?
- How can we use less material or variety of materials?
- How can we reduce the number of parts in the product?
- Can the energy use, in getting the raw materials, manufacturing the product and using the product, be reduced?

Life cycle of a product

A new product progresses through a variety of stages from the original idea to its decline, where it might be discontinued or disposed of. You must consider the impact of a product on the environment and its impact on society as a whole. The main stages involved are:

- The raw materials – how are they harvested, made?
- The production process – how is the product made?
- Transport and distribution – you need to consider what, how, where and cost.
- Uses – what are the intended uses of the product? How will it be used by the client or the customer?
- Recycling – how can the product be recycled?
- Care and maintenance – what is needed, how much and is it environmentally friendly?
- Disposal – the waste from manufacturing or the product itself. Ask yourself the question: is it recyclable or biodegradable?

KEY TERM

LIFE CYCLE – the stages a new product goes through from conception to eventual decomposition

Eco footprint

This is the term used to refer to the measurement of our actions on the environment. You as a designer must consider the effect of your product on the environment from the first stages of your design ideas through to the final making and eventual disposal or recycling of your product. Your footprint involves showing that you have designed the product with the environment in mind and have tried to minimise the damage caused by the various stages throughout your product's life cycle.

Built-in obsolescence

This is where the product has been designed to last a set period of time. The functions of the product have been designed by the manufacturer to fail after a certain time limit. The consumer is then under pressure to purchase again. This built-in obsolescence is in many different products from vehicles to light bulbs, items of clothing to food use by or best before dates. Manufacturers can invest money to make the product obsolete faster, by making the product with cheaper components, which speeds up this planned obsolescence.

Energy and waste in the production process

The consumption of non-renewable energy resources such as coal and oil are causing an energy crisis. These resources will eventually run out. Using non-renewable resources adds to the pollution problem as products made from oil often take a long time to break down in the environment. Transportation of products is a high user of oil and petrol, which are refined fossil fuels.

'Green energy' is the leader of alternative energy sources which are considered environmentally friendly and non-polluting. Energy generated from natural sources include:

- wind power
- solar power
- geothermal
- hydro power
- tidal/wave power.

Figure 11.6 Wind turbines

Materials – waste

We often overlook how we waste as consumers, whether it be consumable products, or power sources such as electricity or packaging. Waste management is a growing problem, from chemicals that get into the water system, to paper and card used in packaging. Switching off our computers or not leaving the television on standby can help us to reduce the energy

EXAMINER'S TIPS

The questions below are open-ended questions and will require your answer to discuss relevant points in the context of your subject/material area.

Use of specialist terms and factual information used appropriately will allow you to score at the higher mark level.

1. Do methods of transportation harm the environment?
2. Are we using too much electricity or too many chemicals which could harm our environment?
3. What alternative sources of energy are available?

wasted. Reusing carrier bags or buying locally made products all helps reduce material waste and bring about a more eco-friendly footprint. Manufacturers now have to follow guidelines on how to get rid of their waste effluent. Research into effective management of pollution, energy and other material waste is constantly ongoing. You need to be aware of current changes within these areas.

▶ Refuse

Issues relating to sustainable design

Processing, manufacturing, packaging and transport of our products use huge amounts of energy and can create lots of waste. You need to look at the sustainability of a product from an environmental and social viewpoint. How is the product made and can we ensure that no or little harm is created to the

environment by this method of manufacture? Sometimes a choice between the performance of the product required and the impact on the environment by its manufacture has to be considered and debated.

Materials we should refuse to use

Why should you refuse to use some products? The answer includes a variety of reasons:

- It may be because the product is made unnecessarily from a man-made source instead of a natural source.

- It might be because of the toxic chemicals used on the product.

- What about the manufacturing process itself – has it been made under safety regulations?

- What about the rights of the workers and the conditions they have been working in?

- Packaging and transport distances and costs.

- It might not be good for you, for example, a high fat content.

- At the end of the product's life, recycling may be a problem. The product may end up as landfill with its breakdown causing chemical pollution.

You should think about these issues before you accept a product and above all do not buy it if you do not need it!

▶ Re-think

Within your own lifestyle and those of others close to you, you need to re-think the way in which you buy products and the energy required to use them. Society is constantly evolving and changing and you can evaluate how you could make a difference. The EEC has completed and launched a rethink on computers. One Laptop per Child (OLPC) aged between 6 and 12 is the aim for all children. Electric power is critical for Africa and South America so can solar cells be used? The computer is a very rugged machine able to use voltage from a number of sources.

Figure 11.7 One Laptop per Child at Khairat School with octagonal power connectors

How is it possible to approach design problems differently? What ideas can you develop to ensure sustainability is considered?

- Are you consuming more than your fair share? Is it possible you could live on less? What are your basic needs?

- Use of electricity is often given little thought. Can circuits work with less power? Solar cells can feed energy to a super capacitor. If a circuit has low current drain, such as CMOS chips, it will be able to run and be recharged when light levels are high.

- Can you use an existing product that has become waste? Can the materials or components be used for another purpose

without processing it? What can you design? What could be designed?

ACTIVITY

1. **In groups discuss what makes you want to buy a product?**

2. **Discuss and consider what you have bought recently and why. Did you really need it?**

▶ Repair

The throwaway society of today means it is quicker and easier to throw something away rather than repair it. You have looked at built-in obsolescence earlier in this chapter, where manufacturers encourage consumers to repurchase rather than repair. Consider the following points:

- Some products you can repair yourself; others can be taken to repair workshops.

- Some products are beyond repair or would cost too much to fix. Is this bad design?

- Unwanted electronic and electrical equipment is the fastest growing waste area. Why? The need to change our attitude to this is enormous. How can you do this?

Can products be designed for repair?

Leather shoes are hand stitched rather than being a glued construction. Soles can be added or reinforced at the local cobbler to resist wear.

If products are designed to be taken apart for recycling, the same approach can be adopted for repair. When common modules are assembled to make a product, the method improves the ability for repair. Global car companies are standardising designs to reduce the number of different parts in a range of vehicles. Engine management has become more computer based but modules have become cheaper as volumes have increased.

Products which have a lower technology input are, on the whole, easier to repair.

Products made by the local blacksmith can have parts replaced as they become damaged or rust.

Electronic products made with discrete components or plug-in chips are more easily repaired than circuit boards with directly mounted chips.

Mechanical and pneumatic assemblies are very easily rebuilt with new sub-assemblies.

11.3 SOCIAL ISSUES

Figure 11.8 Logo depicting global unity

Today we live in a global society. You need to be aware of the ways this can affect the designing of products. Products need to be designed for use by a range of different cultures and nationalities, all of whom may have different specific needs. Society today has become multicultural and diverse; some products may be designed for a specific section of society, others may be universal across all. Consider the following points:

- Social development through recognising the need to consider the views of others when designing and discussing designed products.
- Understanding the relationship between man and the general environment.
- Economic development cycle of a range of products and the impact on individuals, societies and countries.
- Issues associated with economic development and employment – where a product is made, costs of components, materials, manufacturing including labour and the transportation of the finished product.
- Values of society – why we wear clothes: protection, modesty, adornment. Clothing, for example, has become a way of reflecting our gender, culture and religion. Some items have become unisex and fit across all of society.

11.4 MORAL ISSUES

Moral issues are concerned with the way in which products are manufactured and the way in which they affect the safety, comfort and well-being of people who make them and those who come into contact with the designs/products. Many companies now try to ensure that products are made in the right conditions without exploiting workers and follow a code of practice. We need to consider the following issues:

- Moral development, reflecting on how technology affects the environment and the advantages and disadvantages of new technologies to local and national communities – GM foods, production automation, manufacture in developing economies.

- Conditions of working within a manufacturing environment, for example job satisfaction, wages, safety of work place and workers.

- The Ethical Trading Initiative (ETI) is an alliance of companies, non-governmental organisations (NGOs) and trade union organisations. Their aim is to promote and improve the implementation of regulated codes of practice that set out minimum working requirements. A useful website is: www.ethicaltrade.org. Ethical companies ensure that their employees have basic labour rights and also take care to protect the environment in the production, packaging and distribution of their goods. Ethical companies are often termed 'sweatshop free'. A sweatshop is a term used to describe a business with poor working conditions.

- The Fairtrade Foundation is the independent non-profit organisation that licenses the use of the 'FAIRTRADE Mark' on products in the UK, which meet internationally agreed Fairtrade standards set by Fairtrade Labelling Organisations International (FLO). The Foundation was established in 1992. (See www.fairtrade.org.uk for more information.)

Figure 11.9 FAIRTRADE Mark

11.5 CULTURAL ISSUES

Many cultures have important traditions that form part of their identity. How do products affect the quality of lives within different cultures? The use and maintenance of traditional skills and cultural knowledge can have an impact on modern products.

We need to consider the following issues:

- Look at, respond to and value the responses of others to design solutions.

- The impact of different cultures on modern products – the use and maintenance of traditional skills and knowledge.

Culture is about the way that people behave and relate to one another. It is about the way that people live, work and spend their leisure time. It is about people's beliefs and aspirations.

11.6 ENVIRONMENTAL ISSUES

In a modern, fast-changing society where products are continually being changed, it is important that you keep up to date with various issues. You will need to address the following key areas within your material area:

- Understand and be able to select materials that are both suitable and sustainable.

- Be aware of the disposal and recycling of materials and components and the appropriate methods of manufacture.

- Prepare materials economically, minimising waste and using pre-manufactured standard components.

- Have knowledge in the reduction of common use of environmentally unfriendly chemicals and materials dangerous to the environment, for example, bleaches, CFCs (chlorofluorocarbons), toxic materials. The pollution caused by manufacturing can be high and ways to reduce this are being investigated. It is sometimes necessary to use chemicals and man-made materials which are not the most ecologically sound if the specific performance characteristic of that chemical/material can only be obtained that way.

Chapter 2 gives more detailed information about these issues.

CFCs

CFCs are one of a group of synthetic substances containing chlorine and bromine, developed in the 1930s. Thought to be safe, non-flammable and non-toxic, they were widely used until the 1980s when it was discovered that they were the main source of harm to the ozone layer.

Carbon footprint

This is a measure of the impact human activities have on the environment in terms of the amount of greenhouse gasses produced through the outlet of carbon dioxide. This is having an impact on global warming. A carbon footprint is linked to the ecological footprint and can be measured through transportation of materials and goods, energy use in manufacture, the use of natural resources and renewable resources.

Figure 11.10 Carbon footprint logo

Carbon neutral

This means counteracting the carbon dioxide (CO_2), a greenhouse gas released when fossil fuels are burned and used. A company can become carbon neutral by looking at its current energy usage and reducing this use and then looking at the reduced energy use and counteracting it by other activities such as creating or using renewable power sources. Look at www.climatecare.org.

Carbon positive

After becoming carbon neutral you are not only counteracting the carbon dioxide you create but are now informing and encouraging others to change. You will start to produce more renewable energy than you need and therefore you have an excess of 'carbon offset' to sell to other companies.

Carbon offsetting

This is a method by which people and companies can undertake measures to offset the impact they have on the environment in terms of their carbon footprint. Carbon offsetting involves contributing to the development of more ecological methods of energy generation, such as the use of renewable sources.

Ecological footprint

This is the size of your footprint representing the area of the earth's surface necessary to sustain your resource consumption. If the whole world lived like the Americans, we would need five planets. Calculate your footprint at www.bestfootforward.com

Reforestation

This is the term used to describe the restocking of existing forests and woodlands. The advantage of this method is that the areas restocked can provide the ecosystem with resource benefits to soak up some of the negative effects of carbon dioxide.

Embodied energy

This covers all the energy needed to extract and process, transport and assemble a material or resource.

End-of-life disposal

This issue is linked to the need to dispose of redundant products and their packaging in a safe and environmentally friendly way. The use of labelling for specific packaging types is helpful to the consumer when buying products.

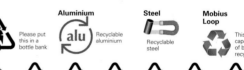

Figure 11.11 Symbols used in Electronics and Control Systems

11.7 DESIGN ISSUES

Buying a product can be expensive so you need to ensure that you have got what you want and that it will benefit you in some way. Research of the product beforehand and analysing the information gathered can help you draw a conclusion, ensuring your choice is successful.

QUESTIONS

1. How do you decide when to update your clothes or other products?

2. Why do you want to buy the latest mobile phone?

ACTIVITY

1. Identify how good design and product choice can improve the quality of life.

2. Look at the way that designers respond to changing styles, taste, technological advances and environmental pressures. What impact does this have?

Designers are constantly changing and evolving their work. Sources of inspiration come from all design and technology areas. In all products, new and constantly changing materials are being developed, Smart materials in all the subject areas have developed massively over the last few years. To help you keep up to date in these areas, it is useful to visit some of the websites shown below:

www.voltaicsystems.com – New fabrics made from recycled soda bottles for solar bags
www.ttf.co.uk – Timber Trade Federation to protect the interests of the wood industry
www.fsc-uk.org – Management of long-term timber supplies
www.bpf.co.uk – Leading trade association for the British plastics industry
www.c4s.info – Centre for Sustainability
www.wasteonline.org.uk – Recycling of many different materials
www.recyclemetals.org – BMRA: British Metals Recycling Association
www.design-technology.info/alevelsubsite – Smart materials and their uses
www.designinsite.dk – Click on the 'environment' link
www.practicalaction.org – Sustainable solutions for developing countries
www.stepin.org – Sustainable technology education project

Eco-design

This involves the whole system of looking at an end product from design to finished article, its use of materials and energy.

Eco-design is the process of designing a product from scratch with the environment in mind and trying to minimise the damage caused to the environment by the product's life cycle. A designer must think through the following main stages if the product is to be successful and acceptable as eco-designed:

- product planning
- product development
- design process
- functionality
- safety
- ergonomics
- technical issues and requirements
- design aesthetics.

The European Ecolabel is an official label awarded to a product guaranteeing it has fulfilled specific criteria. A product awarded the Ecolabel will have been found to have a smaller environmental impact than other similar products. The Ecolabel is the official sign of environmental quality. It is awarded by independent organisations and it is valid throughout Europe. The label's criteria aim to limit the environmental impacts of a product over its entire life cycle by looking at such issues as energy and water consumption, waste production and use of renewable resources.

The globalisation of products

The globalisation of products is the internationalisation of products, labour and

Figure 11.12 The European Ecolabel

skills throughout the world. Products are made in countries where specific traditions, skills and techniques, which are part of people's everyday lives, can give valuable income and jobs to a previously poor area. Manufacturers can take advantage of low labour wages. Different cultures have different needs and what is a requirement and need for one culture can be very different from that of another.

ACTIVITY

1. Working in a group, list the advantages and disadvantages you would need to be aware of by having products manufactured abroad. Remember to consider the different materials, the culture and working conditions.

2. Try and list six examples of products that you know have been manufactured abroad.

11.8 SUMMARY

Many areas in this chapter are also covered in specific subject detail in other chapters. Where possible these have been cross-referenced for you. Sustainable design is a world issue and a constantly changing one. You should want the world to be a great, sustainable place to live in, one that is for you, your friends and relatives and for future generations to come.

A sustainable way of designing can have an impact and positive effect on everyone. As a designer you need to remember and consider the social, economic and environmental implications of your decisions.

KEY TERMS

REFORESTATION – the term used to describe the restocking of existing forests and woodlands

SWEATSHOP – the term used to describe a business with poor working conditions

CULTURE – the way that people behave and relate to one another. It is about the way that people live, work and spend their leisure time. It is about people's beliefs and aspirations

CFCS – one of a group of synthetic substances containing chlorine and bromine, developed in the 1930s. Thought to be safe, non-flammable and non-toxic, they were widely used until the 1980s when it was discovered that they were the main source of harm to the ozone layer

CHAPTER 12

UNIT A513: MAKING QUALITY PRODUCTS

By the end of this chapter you should have developed a knowledge and understanding of:

- what you are required to do to satisfy the assessment criteria for this unit
- how to structure your work and folio evidence for this unit.

This unit will involve you in designing and making a quality product which is capable of being used by a customer or client. This unit represents 30 per cent of your full GCSE qualification.

12.1 SUBMISSION OF CONTROLLED ASSESSMENT WORK

Your work can be submitted on paper or in electronic format but not a mixture of both.

Work submitted on paper

A contents page with a numbering system should be included to aid organisation. All your work should be on the same size paper but it does not matter what size paper you use. You can produce your work by hand or by using ICT.

Work submitted electronically

Your work will need to be organised in folders so that the evidence can be accessed easily by a teacher or moderator. This structure is commonly known as a folder tree. There should be a top level folder detailing your centre number, candidate number, surname and forename, together with the unit code A513. The next folder down should be called 'Home page' which will be an index of all your work. The evidence for each section of the work should then be contained in a separate folder, containing appropriately named files. These files can be from the Microsoft Office® suite, movie, audio, graphics, animation, structured mark-up or text formats. PowerPoint® is an ideal platform for producing electronic portfolios.

12.2 RULES FOR CONTROLLED ASSESSMENT

The work associated with this unit must be completed under your teacher's supervision. However, some of your research work and testing of the product, by its very nature, may take place outside school under limited supervision. You must clearly reference the source of any information you use at the appropriate point in your portfolio.

12.3 ASSESSMENT

A maximum of 60 marks is available for this work. The 60 marks will be divided into five sections:

1. Designing – 16 marks
2. Planning and making your prototype product safely – 24 marks
3. Solving technical problems – 6 marks
4. Recording the making of your prototype product – 6 marks
5. Evaluation of the finished product against the specification including tests leading to modifications and improvements – 8 marks

KEY POINT

• You will need to think about how you use the time you have available and make sure that you spend longer on the sections which can be awarded more marks and less time on those sections with fewer marks.

12.4 STARTING POINTS

The examination board, OCR, will publish a list of themes which are to be used as the starting points for this controlled assessment task. The themes will change periodically so it is important that you check with your teacher that you are using the correct themes. You will choose one of the themes from the list provided. You will need to explore this theme to identify a design problem or situation that interests you and then develop a design brief.

A 'thought shower' could be used to explore the theme.

KEY POINT

• The theme you select for unit A513 must be different to the theme used in unit A511.

Designing

You will need to undertake **focused research** to gather just the information you need to help you design your product. The research may include investigation of the design brief, the gathering of relevant size and ergonomic data, establishing information relating to

Basic ability	Demonstrates ability	Works competently with independence
• Demonstrate a limited response to a brief and produce a simple specification for a product. [0–1 mark]	• Demonstrate an appropriate response to a brief and produce a suitable specification for a product as a result of analysis. [2–3 marks]	• Demonstrate an appropriate and considered response to a brief and produce a detailed specification for a product as a result of analysis. (AO2) [4 marks]

Table 12.1 Mark scheme – Research and specification

system operation and information relating to the environment where the product will be used. For example, if you were designing an alarm system for a mountain bike it would be necessary to research possible mounting positions for the alarm system, the size limitations of these possible mounting positions and the type of conditions that the alarm system will be exposed to, such as water, mud, sudden impact.

You will need to summarise the results of your focused research before writing a detailed specification for the product.

Remember that this section is worth a maximum of 4 marks. Be focused in your activity. Do not waste time with unnecessary research.

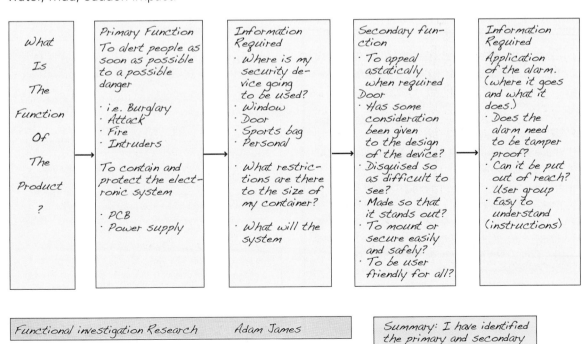

Figure 12.1 Map of research with primary and secondary information

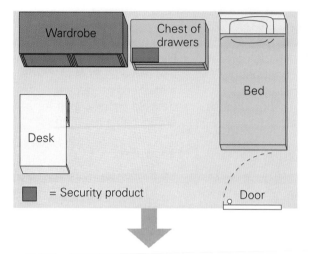

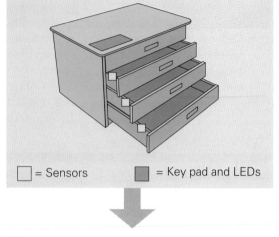

The diagram above shows the location for my security product in an aerial view. It will be positioned on a chest of drawers. The product will sound when one of the drawers is opened and one of the LEDs will stay on until the code is entered on the key pad. The keypad and LEDs will have to fit either on the front or the top of the drawers and the sensors will have to fit into the drawers.

The picture above shows the intended position of my security product on top of the chest of drawers. It shows the intended positions of the keypad and LEDs and sensors. The product is designed to alert you when your drawers have been opened and which drawer has been opened. It uses an audible and visual output (buzzers and LEDs).

Figure 12.2 Research information for the start of the project

Function: From my research I have found the following functions need:
- The system needs to alert a user
- It needs to be easy to mount.
- It can be of reasonable size because it is not portable.
- In this case the appearance needs to be a deterrent.
- The alarm system needs to be of a reasonable price.
- The alarm needs to be reliable so that people don't need to change the batteries all the time or take it back for repairs.
- The alarm needs to be user friendly so it must not have very sharp corners or wires hanging out

Function:
- The product must alert the user to a possible hazard
- The product must be user friendly
- The product must be reliable

The intended user:
- The product is intended to be used by a young adult aged 12-15
- The marketing of the product would be aimed at teenagers

Materials and finish:
- The materials used must be strong and durable
- The finish of the prototype must be smooth and shiny

Manufacturing:
- The product must be designed and manufactured in a school workshop environment, using appropriate techniques
- If the product were successful it is envisaged that it would be manufactured in quantity using the batch production method in a initial run of 100 units.

Life expectancy:
- As the product will be used by the intended user it will be expected to be durable for 5-10 years. I would therefore envisage that the products life span should be a minimum of 3 years

Ethical/Social/Moral Considerations:
- The manufacturing of the product should

Figure 12.3 Summary of research

Figure 12.4 A simple specification list: the specification is too general and could apply to almost any product

Basic ability	Demonstrates ability	Works competently with independence
• Produce one or two simple design ideas using a limited range of strategies. [0–5 marks]	• Produce creative ideas and communicate these by using appropriate strategies. [6–8 marks]	• Produce creative and original ideas by generating, developing and communicating designs using a range of appropriate strategies. (AO2) [9–12 marks]

Table 12.2 Mark scheme – ideas leading to final designs

Generating ideas

The lead for your designing activity should be the 'systems' function of the product. You should use systems diagrams to examine alternative methods of operation for the product. After consideration of each of the alternative methods, you will decide which method would be the most suitable for your product. You will need to use modelling and testing of your system to identify improvements and modifications. A final design should be developed based upon the outcomes of this modelling and testing.

You will need to develop a design for the casing or structure to hold the system. Use your graphic skills to present a number of creative ideas for the casing/structure. You should use annotation to explain your ideas in detail. You must show how parts will fit together and how components will be secured.

Modelling can be used to check the prototype and present a first solution to the user. Further modifications can be identified based upon the feedback you get from this modelling exercise. These modifications should then be incorporated in the production of final working drawings for the product.

The final working drawing should give details of the PCB or layout of the system and the sizes of the casing or structure. A cutting list of materials or components should be made at the end of this section.

EXAMINER'S TIPS

The 'Designing' section of work should take about 6 hours for 16 of the 60 marks which are available. You should aim to complete the design brief, research and specification in approximately 4 to 5 pages. The ideas should be in two parts, with function followed by casing/structure. Remember to add detailed notes to your design work to explain your decisions to the examiner.

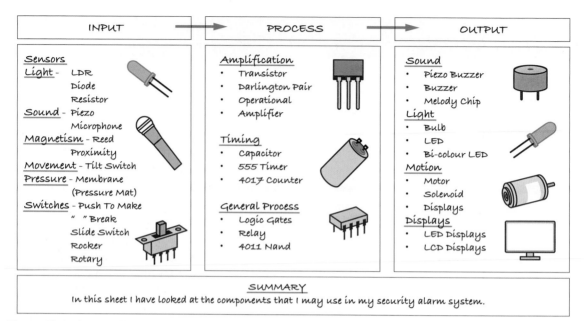

Figure 12.5 shows all the system parts – it would be better to focus on the parts needed for the particular solution

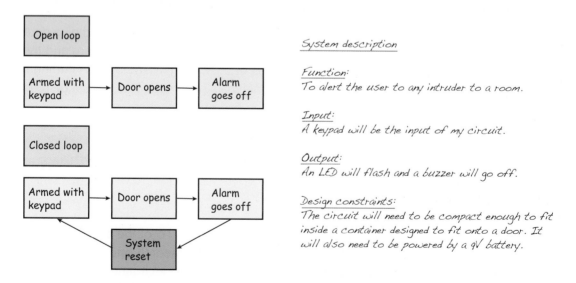

Figure 12.6 shows a block method of starting ideas – the next stage is to give detail for each system block

Basic ability	Demonstrates ability	Works competently with independence

• Plan and organise activities:
  – Select and use appropriate materials.
  – Select and use equipment as appropriate to the material area.
• Work safely to shape, form, assemble and finish materials or components as appropriate.
• Use workshop facilities as appropriate to the material area.
• The product will exhibit a low standard of outcome and may not be successfully completed.
[0–9 marks]
	• Plan and organise activities:
	  – Select and use appropriate materials.
	  – Select and use equipment as appropriate to the material area.
	• Work effectively and safely to shape, form, assemble and finish materials or components as appropriate.
	• Select and use workshop facilities as appropriate to the material area.
	• The product will be completed to a good standard and will meet most of the requirements of the final product specification.
	[10–17 marks]
		• Plan and organise activities:
		  – Select and use appropriate materials.
		  – Select and use equipment as appropriate to the material area.
		• Work skilfully and safely to shape, form, assemble and finish materials or components as appropriate.
		• Assess and apply knowledge in the workshop facilities as appropriate to the material area.
		• The product will be completed to a high standard and will fully meet the requirements of the final product specification.
		[18–24 marks]

Table 12.3 Mark scheme – Planning and making

▶ Demonstration of good making skills

You need to plan and organise the making stage of the controlled assessment task to make the best use of your time, equipment, tools and materials. You need to consider each of the processes you will carry out and any associated health and safety issues.

You could use a Gantt chart to look at the order of working and when to start certain processes or perhaps you could carry them out at the same time. You could use the same chart to give feedback on how the making is progressing, recording actual time taken.

You will need to look at your final design drawings:

- What materials do you need?
- What components and sub-assemblies are you going to use?
- What tools and equipment do you need?
- What health and safety issues need to be considered?
- How long will each process take?

Organise this information in a chart so you can read it easily and make modifications (See Fig. 12.7).

If you create a work programme using either Gantt charts or flow charts, you can show you have thought about the order to make the product. This level of planning is necessary to make sure you foresee problems and ensure the order of making and assembly is correct.

You are now ready to work on making your product, using your knowledge of materials and processes to work skilfully. Remember you are creating a good quality product that will function correctly, so you must use accuracy and skill when forming the product. Time is limited so you must make sure you do not have to remake any parts.

Examples of completed product projects are shown in Fig. 12.8, Fig. 12.9 and Fig. 12.10.

Solving technical problems

It is inevitable that during your construction activity you will encounter problems: few electronic systems work the first time. It is important that you apply your knowledge and skills to think your way out of these problems. You must keep a record of the

Operation	Description	Materials and equipment used	Risk assessment	Risk (Low/ Medium/High)
Input process and output sheet.	On this sheet I stated what my final what going to do.	To do this I used; a pencil, paper, a ruler and a rubber.	There is no risk creating this input process and output sheet.	Low
Research.	I researched how to create a fully funtional circuit that would do what I wanted.	To do this I used a computer.	There is no risk in doing this.	Low
Crocodile Clips .	I created a fully working circuit on Crocodile clips which did what I needed for my product.	To do this I used a computer and a programme called Crocodile Clips.	There is no risk in doing this.	Low
Building the circuit on a breadboard.	After creating a working cicuit on Crocodile Clips then I built the working circuit on a breadboard using rel components.	To do this I used; a breadboard, wire, wire cutters, wire strippers, a PP3 battery and various other electrical components.	Take care when using wire strippers and wire cutters. Keep your hands away from the cutting or stripping blade.	Medium
Circuit drawing.	After building the circuit on the breadboard I then drew the position if all the components and tracka into a circuit drawing.	To do this I used; the finished bread-board circuit, the circuit drawing on Crocodile Clips, a pencil, a rubber, a ruler and paper.	There is no risk in doing this.	Low
PCB wizard.	Once I had the circuit drawing I then drew the circuit on a computer using PCB wizard.	To do this I used the circuit drawing (hand drawn) and a computer.	There is no risk in doing this.	Low
Production of PCB.	From PCB wizard the drawing was then etched to a real PCB.			
Drilling of component holes.	Once the PCB was produced I then drilled all of the holes into the PCB that were needed to fix all of the components into the board.	To do this I used a 1mm drill.	Take care when using a drill. Make sure that your hands are nowhere near the drill while in the drilling process.	Medium
Sanding PCB tracks.	Once the PCB had been drilled and was ready for the components to be soldered to it, I lightly sanded the PCB so that there was none of the reacted material as to allow the best connection between tracks and components.	To do this I used and paper.	There is no risk in doing this.	Low
Soldering the components to the PCB.	Once there was a good connection between the tracks on the PCB and the components I placed the components in their correct pos-itions on the PCB and soldered them on to the board	To do this I used; solder, a soldering iron and a PCB stand	Take care when using a soldering iron. Make sure not to touch the solder and soldering iron while it is heated.	Medium
Testing and evaluating the finished PCB.	Once all of the components were correctly positioned and soldered into the board I then tested the circuit to ensure it worked.	To do this I did not need any materials or equipment.	There is no risk in doing this.	Low

Figure 12.7 Organisational chart for PCB production

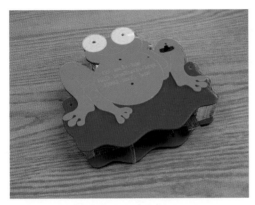

Figure 12.8 Bathwater temperature alarm

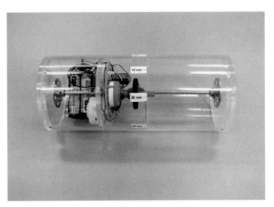

Figure 12.10 Cooking timer

Figure 12.9 Temperature sensor and fan

problems you encounter and the methods used to solve them. You could do this through the use of notes, photographs and diagrams in your record of production. Alternatively you could 'mark up' your working drawings with the changes that you made.

Record-keeping with photographs and notes explains what you were trying to do while manufacturing. It is important you write detailed information about the making activity alongside the photographs. The system part of the design does need care whilst recording to show the working parts or function.

Recording the making

Within your folio you need to provide a record of the key stages of making. The record should consist of photographs and comprehensive notes. Your photographs and notes should show details of the key stages in the making processes and safe working practices. Remember to record any problems you encounter and the solutions you have developed.

Basic ability	Demonstrates ability	Works competently with independence
• Demonstrate a simple understanding of how to solve technical problems as they arise. [0–2 marks]	• Demonstrate a practical understanding and ability in the solving of some technical problems as they arise. [3–4 marks]	• Demonstrate a practical and thorough understanding in the solving of technical problems effectively and efficiently as they arise. [5–6 marks]

Table 12.4 Mark scheme – Solving technical problems

Basic ability	Demonstrates ability	Works competently with independence
• Simply record the making of the product using notes and/or photographic evidence. [0–2 marks]	• Record key stages involved in the making of the product; provide notes and photographic evidence. [3–4 marks]	• Record key stages involved in the making of the product; provide comprehensive notes and photographic evidence. [5–6 marks]

Table 12.5 Mark scheme – Recording the making

Critical evaluation

You will need to critically evaluate your final product against each of the specification points that you developed at the start of this chapter. Has your design satisfied each point? Explain in detail how you met the point or, if you have not met a point, explain why this has happened. Try to avoid simple √/× responses or statements such as 'My product has met all my specification points'.

You should examine the function of your product in detail, and check the system operation. Bench testing of the input, process and output should lead to proposals for modifications and improvements:

• Do the inputs let the user operate the system?

• Is the process unit able to take the input information and take some action?

• Is the output behaviour suitable for the user?

• Do the parts and the sub-assemblies fit together successfully?

• Are the ergonomic needs of the user satisfied?

You should gather information from your testing that will allow you to identify further modifications or improvements to the design.

It is important you use the correct names and terms for the system and components. Your evaluation activity should be 'product' focused and should not use personal comments which are not based on tests or facts.

Basic ability	Demonstrates ability	Works competently with independence
• Gives a limited evaluation of the finished product with some reference to the specification. • There is no evidence of testing the product in use. • There will be little or no use of specialist terms. • Answers may be ambiguous or disorganised. • Errors of spelling, punctuation and grammar may be intrusive. **[0–2 marks]**	• Gives an evaluation of the finished product with reference to the specification. • Shows superficial testing and reflects on how to improve the product. • There will be some use of specialist terms, although these may not always be used appropriately. • The information will be presented for the most part in a structured format. • There may be occasional errors in spelling, punctuation and grammar. **[3–5 marks]**	• Critically evaluates the finished product against the specification. • Undertakes detailed testing; presents meaningful conclusions leading to proposals for modifications to improve the prototype product. • Specialist terms will be used appropriately and correctly. • The information will be presented in a structured format. • The candidate can demonstrate the accurate use of spelling, punctuation and grammar. **[6–8 marks]**

Table 12.6 Mark scheme – Critical evaluation

Examiner's comments

These three samples (Fig. 12.11, Fig 12.12 and Fig. 12.13) show a good level of detail when looking at the prototype. The initial evaluation is very concise with a chart of specification points. The later sections would be improved if section headings were used to order the work. The evaluation needs to focus more on function and ergonomics. This would lead to more detailed proposals for improvement.

 EXAMINER'S TIPS

The evaluation section is worth a maximum of 8 marks and it should be completed in 2 or 3 pages.

Specification	Method	Effectiveness
Function: 1. My product must securely protect the room. 2. My product must be tamperproof. 3. My product must be safe. 4. My product must satisfy the user.	User testing	The alarm fulfils its function well which is to protect the room that may have valuable goods in it. In my opinion the alarm is effective as a deterrent ande also can be concealed if need be. My circuit functions well because it has a latch which cannot be fooled by just closing the door once the output has been triggered it needs the reset button to be pressed and the keys to switch it off for it to reset. My product will also suit the niche market as my product is aesthetically pleasing and of a neutral colour. The product is also safe to use as there is no sharp dedges and wires are insulated so the the user cannot be harmed.
The intecede user: 1. My product must suit the intended age range. 2. The marketing of the product will be aimed at teenagers. 3. My product must be of a reasonable price.	Questionnaire User Test	I have found that my product is suitable for my intended age range. Also I have found through a series of questionnaires answered by people inside my intended age range that my product is reasonably priced.
Form: 1. The product must be attractive to the user. 2. The product must be aesthetically pleasing to the user. 3. The battery must be easy to reach and replace in the container. 4. The container must be small and compact.	Personal Opinion User testing	I have found the product is conpact because it is ( ) cm wide, ( ) cm long and ( ) cm high. Also my LED's, reset button and key switch are neat and in line with the container. The battery that powers the product is also easy to reach and can be easily replaced. The container of my product is also ergonomically and anthropometrically suitable for the intended user as I researched the suitable measurements.
Safety: 1. Corners must have no sharp edges. 2. The product must be 9V powered.	User Testing Visual Examination	The container has been designed in such a way that there are no sharp edges or sharp corners on any part of the container. Also any components and wires used are either secured into place or insulated with tape.
Materials and Finish: 1. My materials must be easy to access. 2. The materials used for the product must be non-toxic. 3. The product must be made of recyclable materials.	User Testing Visual Examination	The materials I have used were very easy to access. Also the materials used to produce my alarm system are non-toxic. The components I have used are also recyclable and could be re-used on another product which will bring no effect to the environment.
Manufacturing: 1. The product must have been manufactured and assembled in a workshop.	Personal/Expert Opinion	The design specification was completed and successful because the product was manufactured and assembled in a workshop.
Life expectancy: 1. The product will be used no more than 2-4 times a day so the product should ladt approx. 5-6 years.	Personal Opinion	If the product is of an overall high standard then the predicted life expectancy is accurate. HIPS is a very durable and flexible material which means that it can absorb a slight shock e.g. falling or knocking.
Ethical/Social/Moral Considerations: 1. The product must be biodegradable so that it does not pollute the environment also any excess material that is left during the manufacturing of the product should be recycled or reused if possible.	Expert Opinion	Most of the HIPS in used in the production of my container is unused but was re-used where possible. Chemicals that I used have been disposed off carefully and ecologically so that the environment was not affected. The specifications of my container were not met however they were the best materials to use.

Figure 12.11 Specification check evaluation

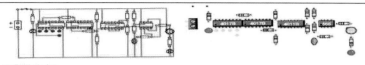

Final Evaluation

I am very pleased the outcome of my product. My final product meets and exceeds all my expectations. It is aesthetically pleasing and is a suitable colour for my chosen age range. The product has been formed very well with no webbing on any corners and the shape has been held very well. My product has been drilled well with no chips or marks visible and all holes are in line. The keypad fits perfectly into the container with no gaps between the edges of the container and the keypad. All components have been fitted securely and correctly. The soldering is of a high standard with all components being held securely in place on the PCB.

My product fulfilled my specification and this shows that I have designed and produced my product very well and it will be suitable for my intended user. My product is very easy to use as the input is a keypad and the outputs being LED's and a buzzer. The products keypad does not function fully as it does not reset the outputs when it should but the products 555 astable and 4011 flip flop do function fully. This means that when the key switch is enabled and the code is entered into the keypad the sensor can trigger the outputs. When the code is re-entered into the keypad the outputs should reset but do not. When the sensor is pushed back together the outputs turn off. This is the only fault with my product.

My product overall got a very good response from my third party testing. My questionnaire included 10 questions about my product which the consumer could answer 1-6, 1 being the best and 6 being the worst. All my response were in the first three sections, which means the consumer is happy with my prototype.

My favourite aspect of the product is the container. It is manufactured to a high standard and is aesthetically pleasing. The lid fits well and only needed slight modifications to fit securely into the container.

My least favourite aspect of the product is the circuit. The circuit does not work fully and there is some design issues were wires cross over the PCB in order to assemble the product. I have discussed this is "Proposals for Further Development".

Conclusion:

Figure 12.12 Evaluation of prototype function

Proposals For Further Development

Although my product has been a success, there are still some modifications that I could make to improve the production and manufacture of the product.

One modification in I could make to my product is the design and layout of my PCB. I have assembled my product but some wires cross over the PCB in order to reach the positions of the component they connect to. If more care had been taken to design the container and PCB so that wires and components are where they need to be. During final testing I found out that my circuit did not work as it should. To solve the problem I could refer back to my breadboard model that worked fully or my crocodile clips drawing. My resetting keypad does not reset my outputs. In order for my keypad to reset my outputs there needs to be as link to 4011. I think that the link between the second 4011 and my 4011 was damaged. I could fix this problem and another problems that arise with my product if I produced a second PCB.

These modifications should ensure that the production run of my product runs smoothly and problem free and produces a high quality product that is finished to a high standard.

Figure 12.13 Future development of the prototype

CHAPTER 13

UNIT A514: TECHNICAL ASPECTS OF DESIGNING AND MAKING

By the end of this chapter you should have developed a knowledge and understanding of:

- the content of unit A514
- areas for revision
- methods of revising effectively
- the type of questions that you can expect
- what the examiner is looking for in your responses
- equipment for the exam.

Unit A514 can be taken in either January or June of either year of your course. It consists of a written paper that will assess you on your knowledge, skills and understanding that have been gained during the course and also in Key Stage 3.

The areas that will be assessed are clearly laid out in the Examination Board's subject specification.

13.1 STRUCTURE OF THE QUESTION PAPER

Three papers will be available: one for each of the three specialist areas – electronics, mechanisms and pneumatics. Each paper will contain questions of comparable difficulty; they will allow you to show what you have learnt in the specialist area, as well as in the general areas of design. These general areas will be common to all three papers.

As a candidate you will only answer **one** of the papers. It is important that you only prepare for your chosen paper.

The question papers have two sections:

- Section One contains three questions based on knowledge of control systems.
- Section Two has two questions that will test your ability to show design thinking.

Each of the questions is worth 12 marks which gives a final total of 60 marks for the paper.

The unit will test the full range of ability from grade G up to A* level. This will mean that there may be parts of a question that you find hard to answer. It is important that you continue through the paper as the next question will contain easier parts that you can answer with confidence.

Answers will be in the form of short written statements, notes, sketches and calculations. Each type of response will need a slightly different approach, which should be practised before you take the paper.

The Specification requires a knowledge and understanding of the following areas:

Designing and making quality manufactured products

When you take this unit, it is expected that you will have carried out at least the first of the practical units. It is important that you have a clear understanding of the practical aspects of designing and making as the questions asked will draw on that practical experience.

The design process need not be a neat, clear process that you follow through in a linear way. It is more often the case that you will have to keep returning to an area in order to proceed with your ideas. For example, research will be carried out at all stages of design, from showing that there is a need for your proposed idea, through to finding out people's response to the finished product. There are certain parts of the process that have to be in place before you proceed to the

next stage but other areas can be worked on side by side. For planning it is useful to use a Gantt chart which can identify the key areas, such as a specification, which are needed before any serious work on ideas takes place.

When it comes to the manufacturing stage, it is a good idea to keep clear notes or photographs of processes as you cover them, particularly the ones that you may only see or use briefly during the course.

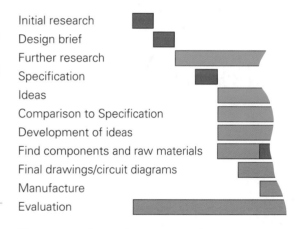

Figure 13.1 Gantt chart showing key areas that determine when the next stage can start

Planning production

This area of knowledge will come from your practical experience, not only in the exam course, but in Key Stage 3 as well. Practical projects always have a deadline put on them, matching the time allocated to the project. In early projects your teacher will have set the deadline and you will most likely have worked to a given schedule. In unit one and three of the GCSE course, the overall time available will have been given to you but detailing should have been carried out by yourself. The experience gained should enable you to answer any questions relating to time planning.

An aspect of planning that is often overlooked is that of obtaining resources ready for when you need them.

There are a few important rules for this:

- check availability before using in a design
- check on lead time – that is the time taken for delivery, once ordered
- check on any discounts for bulk purchase, e.g. five or more of an item
- check for materials or components already stocked by your school.

Once you have planned the practical work and arranged for materials to be ready, one other important item of planning is that of machine availability. It is no good planning to use a laser cutter on one particular day and then finding that 10 other members of your group also want to use it. Planning should include unforeseen circumstances, machines going wrong, materials not being there, etc. Build time into your plan for what is known as 'slippage' or getting behind with the work. When it comes to the exam you may be asked directly about planning or there may be a question on ordering materials or components. That area can be revised by using component catalogues or websites to remind you of the way that ordering codes are used and quantity discounts are provided.

▶ Performance characteristics of different materials

You will need to be aware of how materials react in different circumstances, for example, in extreme heat or extreme cold, or if they work as required in a damp atmosphere. Processes that will need to be known on materials will include cutting, shaping,

forming and finishing. Methods used for the common materials should be known or revised before the exam.

During the two years of a GCSE course, it is possible that some new or 'smart' materials will become available. It is important that these are considered in your own designing but it is not likely that you will come across them in your exam; the exam will be written toward the start of your course so will not include any really new materials. Concentrate on having a sound knowledge of the materials that you have used in your own practical work, as you will be able to write about these with more confidence. Research at least one specific example for each category of material; for example make sure that you can give the name of a ferrous metal, a non ferrous metal, a pure metal and an alloy.

Some examples of 'smart' materials are given in this book. You can use the internet to research current methods of using these materials. It often happens that a material is discovered with a special property but no particular use. On occasions like this when a new use is found, products using the 'smart' material will appear in the market very quickly.

▶ The impact of emerging technologies on designers and consumers

An example of technologies that fit into this category include flat screen displays: in a very short period of time, computer monitors and TVs using cathode ray tubes have been replaced by LCD and plasma screens. This has rendered the cathode ray tube almost obsolete as far as domestic use goes. The switch from analogue to digital TV broadcasting is another change that will have an impact on everybody. In some cases the change is brought about by consumer taste; in others it is forced by legislation.

When preparing for this exam try to think of a few examples of how design and the type of product available are being altered by outside events. Many of you will have designed printed circuit boards using specialist software for the task, later using the software to simulate the circuit in real use. This is a relatively new way of designing and, although it has been used commercially for some years, it is quite a recent development in schools. 3D scanning and rapid prototyping are areas that are advancing rapidly, having a big impact on the speed that new products get to market. When recording the progress

of your project it is quite likely that you will have used a digital camera. The move away from cameras using film has revolutionised the way that designers work in this respect. Images can be recorded at each stage of a project at little cost and shown instantly to an audience that could be on the other side of the world. In this way consultation between engineers can be carried out far more quickly than in the past.

Figure 13.2 Storage for computer files

EXAMINER'S TIPS

Revision for this aspect could include working with a small group and listing all products that you can think of that have gone out of use in the last five years through the introduction of new technologies, or of products that have been, or are being, developed using a new technology. If you think about the way that battery technology has improved, list the products that have benefited. By working in this way you can cover more than one aspect of revision at once; researching lithium batteries will lead not only to their application but also to the nature of the battery and technical points such as battery capacity in mAh.

The examples shown in Fig. 13.2 illustrate how storage for computer files has changed from the 1970s through to the present. Some of the disadvantages of early methods can clearly be seen. In the case of punched tape, it was very fragile and to find a particular area of code, the whole tape may have had to be run through the reader. This also applied to cassette tape. Floppy disks were originally quite floppy and prone to damage. The latest type, the memory stick, has the advantage of small size and high capacity but is easily lost.

▶ Tools and equipment used to make quality manufactured products

Preparing yourself for answering questions on tools and equipment can be quite straightforward if you have kept notes as you carry out practical work. If you have not, one of the best approaches is to use suppliers' catalogues that list the types and details of a range of tools. Tools can be put into categories for ease of remembering them: marking out tools, cutting tools, machine tools, joining tools, etc. They can be further divided by linking the tool to the type of material it will be used on. Examples of this being a hacksaw that could be used on metals or plastics but not normally on wood; a pop rivet gun that can be used for joining metals or plastics but not wood; a tenon saw that can be used on any timber product but not on metals.

In addition to hand tools, the range of machine tools that you have used should be revised. This will depend largely on what is available in your school – if you do not have a laser cutter it can still be researched by looking on manufacturers' websites via an internet search.

▶ Processes and techniques used to make quality manufactured products

In the written exam you will be expected to have some knowledge of the processes associated with your specialist area. For pneumatics, it may be the processes used to provide a constant supply of clean compressed air for operating the equipment.

For mechanisms, it could be the production of accurately spaced holes for gear shafts; for electronics, a knowledge of the soldering process. The type of question that can be expected is that which will require you to put the stages of a process into the correct sequence. Vacuum forming is a process that could be required in all three specialist areas; the sequence of events in the process should be remembered along with the reason for each stage in the process. If this is carried out for each major process, even if the question is not quite what you expected, it will be possible to think through how to answer using information from what you have revised.

A good way of remembering a process is to write a step-by-step account of how it is carried out. Either a block diagram or a flow diagram will make it easier to understand when you go back to revise the process. The soldering process is shown in this way in Fig. 13.3. Alternatively a quick sketch may be all that you need as a reminder of a process as shown in Fig. 13.4

For both this section and the previous one it is worth considering what exactly makes a 'quality' manufactured product. In many cases, it is the final appearance of the

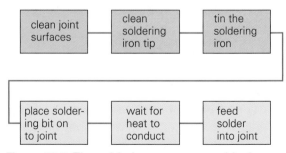

Figure 13.3 The soldering process as a block diagram

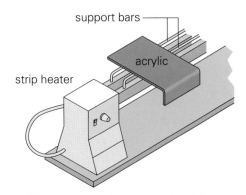

support bars

acrylic

strip heater

Figure 13.4 Bending plastics on the strip heater

product that will be the first indicator that it has quality. When viewed in more depth, though, the quality should be evident throughout the product. In an electronics project the wiring and circuit will normally be hidden; however, a well-made project will have had as much care taken over the hidden parts as with the exterior. Ease of opening for maintenance will have been considered and simple things like easy battery replacement will have been designed into the casing.

It is only when you use a product for the first time that the ergonomic qualities become clear. Positioning of controls or handle shapes cannot be judged visually. Mobile phones and calculators are a good product to analyse for ergonomic suitability. In many cases, the keys are too close for consistent operation or they do not give tactile feedback when they have been operated.

The exterior of a product is one of the first things that will be noticed so aesthetic qualities are important. Control systems projects will all be functional and as such they will fail if they do not function as intended. Thought can be given to the appearance, though, through simple things like the choice of vacuum-forming plastic used for a casing.

Many decorative sheet plastics are now available at a cost of little more than the standard polystyrene used in many school projects. ABS, which is an inherently stronger material that will not crack when stressed, is available in a variety of colours, textures and thicknesses. Use of a material like this can make a product immediately more attractive.

When cutting profiles out, particularly in acrylic or MDF, a laser cutter will give a vastly superior finish to hand cutting. It will also be far more accurate dimensionally.

The impact of the control system on the environment, including the need to consider sustainability

Impact on the environment can be considered in three distinct ways: during manufacture, during use and on final disposal of the product.

When preparing to answer questions on this aspect, you should be aware of the part played by your particular control system. Electronics manufacture will include the need for chemicals in production of a PCB. Individual components will have been produced using heat energy and heat will be needed for the soldering process that will connect the components together. The electronic product will require electrical energy during use; in most cases that will come from batteries or transformed mains power; it could though, come from photovoltaic cells, or solar cells to use the more recognisable term. What impact do the batteries have on the environment? Disposable batteries will often end up in landfill sites, with potentially dangerous chemicals able to escape into the ground.

Rechargeable batteries will require a means of charging, normally using mains power, though some will use power from a car charging system. Eventually though even rechargeable batteries need replacing, causing the same disposal problems as alkaline type batteries.

Mechanical systems when used may be human or animal powered, in which case they are quite sustainable. They could also be powered using chemical energy such as in a car engine. Increased sustainability can be provided by reducing the load on the engine and ensuring that all of the fuel is converted into usable energy. Since the mid-1970s, car manufacturers have been trying to reduce fuel consumption by a combination of reducing the weight and drag of the car body and by increasing the efficiency of the engine. Use of dual fuel cars, which use two types of fuel, and of hybrid cars, which use two types of power unit, is becoming more common. Mechanical systems have in the past made good use of sustainable resources, windmills and watermills being two good examples. Pneumatic systems require a method of compressing air to power the system; an electric motor being the usual means of driving the compressor. Once compressed, the air can be stored and easily transported around a building.

In terms of disposal after use, the most difficult to achieve environmental success with is probably the electronic circuit. Because of the relatively short lifespan of electronic goods, there are a lot that require disposal. Removing usable metals from a circuit board is time consuming and costly at present but legislation such as the Waste Electrical and Electronic Equipment Regulations (WEEE 2006) is forcing manufacturers into action.

The aim of this legislation is to encourage the re-use and recycling of electrical goods by making the manufacturers responsible for the final disposal of the goods that they make. The regulations also require the separate collection and environmentally sound disposal of electrical waste. The regulations came fully into force in July 2007 and affect anyone who is involved in the manufacture, sale, distribution or use of electrical equipment. One effect of this could be that the manufacturers pass on the cost to consumers in the initial price of the product.

The use of legislation such as this means that the manufacturers do not have a choice in the matter so a quicker result is obtained. Methods of ensuring that the regulations are complied with change quickly; this means that use of internet research is really essential if you are to have a clear appreciation of current practice.

Health and safety issues

In the exam you will be expected to be aware of any health and safety requirements for your chosen area. Those doing the pneumatics paper should have a clear understanding of how air pressure is reduced and regulated in a system. Any pressure vessels or receiver tanks require regular checking for evidence of rust or corrosion. Mechanisms could involve the use of heavy lifting equipment so an understanding of safe working load is needed. Electronics candidates should be aware of safety procedures with mains electricity, including the use of residual current devices (RCDs), which help to protect from severe shocks.

Figure 13.5 A consumer unit RCD that has a 30mA trip alongside a 13A socket with a 10mA trip

General areas of revision should cover the use of risk assessments for each piece of equipment used that is potentially hazardous. COSHH data for any chemicals or dangerous substances that are used should be reviewed. An awareness of how hand tools can be used safely with the minimum risk of injury to the user and any bystanders will be needed. For each piece of machinery used it is worth remembering one or two safety rules that are specific to that piece of equipment. The type of question that will be asked will often require safety precautions for a particular machine or process such as using a pillar drill.

13.2 EFFECTIVE REVISION

If you have completed your practical projects in a methodical way, recording information as you go, revision will be easy. There are a number of ways that you can improve your chance of success though by using a range of supplementary resources for revision. Websites from suppliers such as *Rapid Electronics* and *RS Components* will provide a ready source of component images. If you use a phrase such as 'vacuum forming process' in a search, a large number of useful sites will be returned. Using key words for your search is a good way of gaining additional knowledge to back up that gained from practical experience.

Simulation software is another good way of reminding yourself of how various circuits work or how mechanisms behave. If you have saved circuits earlier in the course, group them together in a single folder for revision.

Alongside the use of books and websites for reminding you of tools and their uses, a sketchbook can be used to quickly sketch the tools as they are researched. This will make it quicker if you have to sketch tools or equipment in the exam.

For each of the specialist areas there are likely to be calculations involved. Practise the type of calculations that can be expected and make sure that you are confident in the correct use of the units involved.

Product analysis will almost certainly appear somewhere in the exam. It can be one of the easiest areas to revise as it can be carried out anywhere on any product. Ask yourself why a particular material has been used or what the principles are behind the function; carry out ergonomic tests on a range of products – all of these will develop analytical skills.

Fig. 13.6 shows a re-chargeable drill, a good example for product analysis.

Figure 13.6

Along with the specific areas of revision, there is the language of each specialist area. Circuit symbols are used in pneumatics and electronics; revision of the symbols is an important area that should not be overlooked. Those doing the mechanisms paper should

be aware of the standard ways of showing gear teeth or other drive systems. Those who have specialised in electronics should be able to quickly work out resistor values using a colour code, or place components correctly in a breadboard. With the breadboard it is now possible to use simulation software to make up a breadboard circuit that can be tested; this is a relatively quick method that can also boost your knowledge of the basic circuits and components.

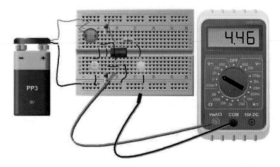

Figure 13.7 Light sensing circuit on a simulated breadboard

13.3 TYPES OF QUESTION THAT YOU CAN EXPECT

At the start of each question there are key words that will give you a clear indication of what the examiner is expecting as a response. The other indication is at the end of the question – the mark given in square brackets. A low mark for the question part will indicate that a short answer is expected. In many cases there are lines allowed for the answer; the number of lines is usually a good indication of how much writing is expected.

Key words such as 'State' or 'Give' will indicate a short response is required. For more detail the question may ask you to 'Describe', this is an indication that a description of a process or technique is

needed. If you find it easier to use sketches for your description do so, there is every chance that you will gain marks. There are also the questions where notes and sketches are needed; make sure that you include what is asked for in the question.

Questions that ask for an explanation will normally carry two or three marks. For these you will be expected to justify your answer; that means giving reasons for making a statement. Make sure that the instructions are followed; if two reasons are asked for in a question, that is all that you need to do. You will gain no extra marks for giving four reasons.

Questions requiring a sequence of events will often give boxes for you to put your response in. Think carefully before completing and if necessary use any blank areas on the paper for initial working.

Calculation questions require a particular technique. They will normally have two or three marks available and will include any formulae that you are expected to use. They should be tackled in the following way:

- Stage one should be to substitute correct values into the formula. Make sure that you are using the correct units before substituting. It may be that you will have to convert nF to µF before carrying out the calculation.

- The second stage is the arithmetic required for the calculation. A calculator should be used but it is a good idea to estimate the result as well so that you know roughly what the answer should be.

- The final stage is to present the answer in the correct units. Some questions will give credit for correct units being used so play safe and use the units.

13.4 WHAT THE EXAMINER IS LOOKING FOR

It may seem obvious but the main thing is legibility. If the examiner cannot read your answers they cannot award you marks.

If you have followed the instructions for each question there is far more chance of gaining marks.

Answers should be entered into the correct space on the paper; the examiner does not expect to have to search through the paper for an answer. If you do make a mistake and have to correct it, a clear line through the original answer is all that is required.

And finally:

EQUIPMENT FOR THE EXAMINATION

Make sure that you take enough pens and pencils into the exam. A ruler is needed for questions requiring sketching and particularly for the pneumatic or electronic circuit questions.

For calculation questions a calculator is required.

KEY POINTS

- Read the question carefully and only do what is required.
- Attempt all of the questions; if you miss one it is a guaranteed zero.
- Make sure that answers are legible.
- Try to use specialist terms when describing tools and components.
- Be familiar with how commercial products are manufactured – practise product analysis.
- Make sure that you can convert units and sub units.
- Practise rearranging formulae.
- Apply practical knowledge of processes to your answers.
- Split processes into stages.
- Use recognisable sketches and standard symbols where necessary.

INDEX